Chemistry of the iron group metallocenes:
ferrocene, ruthenocene, osmocene

Part One

This is a volume in the series
THE CHEMISTRY OF ORGANOMETALLIC COMPOUNDS

THE CHEMISTRY OF ORGANOMETALLIC COMPOUNDS
A Series of Monographs

Dietmar Seyferth, *editor*

Department of Chemistry
Massachusetts Institute of Technology
Cambridge, Massachusetts

Chemistry of the iron group metallocenes:

ferrocene, ruthenocene, osmocene

Part One

MYRON ROSENBLUM

Department of Chemistry
Brandeis University
Waltham, Massachusetts

Interscience Publishers
a division of
JOHN WILEY & SONS   New York · London · Sydney

To Rachel

Introduction to the Series

In 1937 all that was known about organometallic chemistry was summarized most excellently by E. Krause and A. von Grosse in their book, *Die Chemie der metallorganischen Verbindungen*. In the intervening years and, in particular, since about 1950, organometallic chemistry has undergone a tremendous growth in depth and in breadth. Not only have organosilicon, organotin, organoboron, organoaluminum, and organolithium chemistry grown almost explosively, but the whole new area of transition metal–organic chemistry has come into being and has grown to impressive proportions. Since the publication of Krause and von Grosse's book, no treatment of comparable scope has appeared. Books such as those by Coates and by Rochow, Hurd and Wilson serve as a good introduction to the subject but do not give the comprehensive treatment required by those who are active in organometallic chemistry.

It is the purpose of this series to bring Krause and von Grosse's description of organometallic chemistry up to date. It is not possible to cover organometallic chemistry as exhaustively as Krause and von Grosse did twenty-five years ago. Indeed, complete coverage, in the sense that all known organometallic compounds and all references concerning this subject are listed, is not desirable, now that the literature on organometallic chemistry has become so voluminous. But it is hoped that by selective use of this literature it is possible to cover as completely as possible all that is known about the chemistry of organometallic compounds: the methods used for their preparation, their physical properties, their structures, and their chemical reactions. Included in the subject of "chemical reactions" is the field of organofunctional organometallic chemistry: the effect of a metal–carbon bond on the reactivity of an organic functional group in the same molecule, as well as the effect of an organic functional group on the properties of the metal–carbon bond. However, a discussion of the organic chemistry of organofunctional organometallic compounds when nothing can be said about the effects of the metal–carbon bond on the reactivity of the functional group would not fall within the scope of this series. The emphasis is on the "metallic" part of organometallic chemistry.

A mere listing of the reactions of organometallic compounds as is given by Krause and von Grosse will be avoided. The reactions of organometallic compounds, as well as the reactions leading to their formation, will, wherever possible, be discussed in terms of what is known today about chemical bonding, structure, and reaction mechanisms. Physical properties in a similar manner will be related to our current knowledge of chemical bonding and structure. Organometallic chemistry is a borderline field, and for such a discussion it is necessary to make full use of what both inorganic and organic chemistry can offer in the way of theoretical and practical results. Correlations within periodic groups as well as between periodic groups will be stressed.

The following volumes, in addition to the present one, are in preparation: *Organolithium Chemistry* (G. L. Closs); *Organosodium and Organopotassium Chemistry* (R. A. Finnegan); *Organometallic Chemistry of the Group II Metals* (R. Dessy); *Organoaluminum Chemistry* (J. C. Snyder); *Organometallic Chemistry of Gallium, Indium and Thallium* (W. A. G. Graham); *Organogermanium Chemistry* (M. Lesbre, P. Mazerolles, and J. Satgé); *Organotin Chemistry* (D. Seyferth); *Organolead Chemistry* (H. Shapiro and F. Frey); *Organometallic Chemistry of Arsenic, Antimony, and Bismuth* (G. O. Doak and L. D. Freedman); and *Olefin and Acetylene Complexes of Transition Metals* (M. A. Bennett).

The authors, it will be noted, are all active in research in the areas about which they write.

DIETMAR SEYFERTH

Department of Chemistry
Massachusetts Institute of
Technology
Cambridge, Massachusetts

PREFACE

It is now barely thirteen years since the discovery of ferrocene, an event which marks the beginning of a period of unusual ferment and significant change in the field of organometallic chemistry.

The preparation of ferrocene, toward the end of 1951, was quickly followed by a recognition of its unique chemical structure and shortly thereafter by the discovery of its aromatic character. It was not long before cyclopentadienyl complexes of other transition elements as well as the lanthanides and actinides had been prepared, and to this growing number of progeny were soon added a multitude of new organometallic complexes in which cyclic and acyclic olefins as well as acetylenes were bound as ligands. The reformulation of Heine's long neglected and puzzling chromium compounds as arenechromium complexes, similar in structure to the biscyclopentadienyl metal complexes, brought even benzene within the purview of such metal coordinating groups. These developments have been accompanied by widespread interest in the chemistry and electronic structure of these substances, and by an increasing awareness of their potential use as intermediates in organic synthesis.

The present volume, the first of two, was written with the intent of providing a comprehensive and critical review of the chemistry of ferrocene and its congeners, ruthenocene and osmocene, the so-called iron-group metallocenes. The intensity of research activity in this field, largely generated by the discovery that ferrocene could be subjected to electrophilic substitution, may be judged by the fact that since 1952 almost 1000 papers have been published in this area alone. Although the task of providing an up-to-date review of these developments is therefore not a simple one, our knowledge of these substances has unquestionably matured to the point where such a review would appear to be both timely and useful. Every attempt has been made to provide as inclusive and up-to-date a bibliography as is possible. The literature references should be complete through 1962 and much of 1963. In addition, several literature citations in 1964 have been made possible through the cooperation of colleagues who were kind enough to provide me with preprints of their papers.

In general, the material is organized and treated according to metallocene derivative type. Although there are obvious shortcomings to such an arrangement, it nevertheless is one that lends itself readily to ordering a relatively large body of chemical information in a coherent and easily retrievable form. Each of the chapters dealing with acyl-, alkyl-, and arylmetallocenes is concluded by a table of these derivatives which, it is hoped, will supplement the more general treatment of material within each chapter with the specific kind of information and referencing that is often of great value.

In addition, one chapter has been devoted to a review of the physical properties of the metallocenes, and another to a summary, in largely descriptive form, of the electronic structures of these complexes. It is apparent that such information is useful, if not essential, for an understanding of much of the chemistry of these substances.

In Chapter 1 I have attempted to summarize, in historical form, those procedures developed for the synthesis of biscyclopentadienyl complexes, and also to provide a brief description of some of the reactions of mono-cyclopentadienyl iron complexes.

The work on this volume was begun in 1962 when I was on leave from Brandeis University, and it was supported in part by a grant from the National Institutes of Health. Grateful acknowledgement of this support and of assistance from Brandeis University is hereby made.

It is a pleasure to thank Professors R. H. Richards, K. L. Rinehart, and F. A. Cotton who read much of the early manuscript and made many valuable suggestions. I am particularly indebted to Professor P. L. Pauson and to Dr. G. R. Knox whose detailed and knowledgeable criticism of the entire manuscript was of the greatest assistance in removing many errors and in improving the treatment of the material.

In preparing the manuscript I was fortunate to have had the excellent secretarial services of Miss Ann Thompson and Mrs. Barbara MacDonald, and it is a pleasure to acknowledge my debt to them.

Finally, I owe a particular expression of gratitude to my wife Rachel whose encouragement and active help were so important in writing this book.

MYRON ROSENBLUM

Lexington, Massachusetts
February, 1965

CONTENTS

Part One

Part Two

1 CARBOXYLIC ACIDS AND DERIVATIVES

2 BRIDGED AND FUSED-RING METALLOCENES

1 Preparation of metallocenes

Two general methods, exemplified in the synthesis of ferrocene, have been used for the preparation of cyclopentadienyl metal complexes. In the first of these, the cyclopentadienide ion and either a ferrous or ferric salt are brought into reaction, while the second employs cyclopentadiene and either iron powder, iron oxides, or iron carbonyls. These latter reactions are generally carried out at elevated temperatures. While the cyclopentadienide method is more suited to laboratory use, certain of the high-temperature methods, particularly those employing iron penta-carbonyl, find special application.

CYCLOPENTADIENIDE METHOD

Grignard reagent

Ferrocene was first prepared by Kealy and Pauson by the reaction of cyclopentadienylmagnesium bromide and ferric chloride in ether-benzene solutions (39).* Subsequent attempts to extend the procedure to the synthesis of nickelocene and cobaltocene (13) were not satisfactory, largely due to the insolubility of the metal halides.

However, the more soluble tetrachlorides of titanium, zirconium, and vanadium were converted to their biscyclopentadienyl dihalide derivatives by this procedure (63). The metal acetylacetonates soon proved to be useful substitutes for the more insoluble metal halides, although an excess of the Grignard reagent is required since some is consumed by reaction with the β-diketone. Ruthenocene (61), nickelocene (63, 65, 66), and the cobalticenium ion (62) were first made in this manner.

* The use of high boiling ethers in this reaction has more recently been reported (58).

Alkali metal salts

The alkali metal salts of cyclopentadiene have been used with considerable success in the synthesis of a wide variety of cyclopentadienyl complexes. In one of the first variants of this procedure, cyclopentadiene in liquid ammonia is converted to the ion by treatment with an alkali metal (14).

$$\text{(cyclopentadiene)} + M \xrightarrow[\text{(M = Li, Na, K, Cs, Rb)}]{\text{liq. NH}_3} \text{(cyclopentadienide)} \; M^+ + \tfrac{1}{2}H_2$$

Subsequent addition of the anhydrous transition metal nitrate or thiocyanate salt, as for example $Ni(SCN)_2$, gives the insoluble complex metal ammine cyclopentadienide.

$$2C_5H_5^- + [Ni(NH_3)_6](SCN)_2 \rightarrow [Ni(NH_3)_6](C_5H_5)_2 + 2SCN^-$$

These, in turn, lose ammonia on heating *in vacuo* to give the corresponding metallocene.

$$[Ni(NH_3)_6](C_5H_5)_2 \xrightarrow{\Delta} Ni(C_5H_5)_2 + 6NH_3$$

Fischer's group has employed this technique for the preparation of cyclopentadienyl complexes of cobalt (15), nickel (14), chromium (15, 16), manganese (15), and iron (19). Of the alkali metals, sodium and lithium are to be preferred, since their cyclopentadienide salts are more soluble in liquid ammonia than the others (15).

The use of sodium or potassium cyclopentadienide in tetrahydrofuran, or ethylene glycol dimethyl ether in place of liquid ammonia, constituted an advantageous preparative modification. The procedure is the most generally applicable and, besides ferrocene (69, 70), many transition metal, lanthanide, and actinide cyclopentadienyl complexes have been synthesized by this method (6, 24, 25, 36, 64, 67, 68, 69). The patent literature abounds with variations of this technique for the synthesis of ferrocene in ether (74, 79, 80, 86), ethylene glycol dimethyl ether (83), tetrahydrofuran (88), benzene or toluene (79, 80), ethanol (87), and liquid paraffin (80, 81). Both ferric and ferrous salts have been used, although the latter give higher yields since part of the cyclopentadienide is not consumed in reduction of the metal salt (70). The cyclopentadienide may be generated either by exchange reactions with sodium acetylide, hydride (74, 80, 81, 86), or ethoxide (3, 35, 42, 87), or directly from the metal (69, 70, 80, 81).

Ammonium salts

A further simplification in procedure, which avoids the necessity of preparing the cyclopentadienide in a separate step, was first introduced by Birmingham, Seyferth, and Wilkinson in 1954 (3) and has since been greatly improved (69, 70). It is by far the most expeditious procedure for the synthesis of ferrocene. The method consists simply in treating a solution of cyclopentadiene in diethylamine* with either anhydrous ferric or ferrous chloride.† The acidity of cyclopentadiene is sufficiently great (pK_a 16) (10) that in the presence of excess amine a small but significant proportion is converted to the anion. The method has also been applied successfully in the synthesis of nickelocene (70), cobalticinium perbromide (60) and, on a microscale, in the preparation of iron isotopes of ferrocene (11). Several recent patents relating to the preparation of cyclopentadienyl complexes of nickel, zirconium, titanium, and cobalt, as well as iron, have been described (91–95).

A somewhat more direct and commercially applicable modification of this synthesis, which dispenses with the need for anhydrous ferric chloride, has recently been described by Pruett and Morehouse (53). In this procedure, ferrous chloride is prepared from diethylamine hydrochloride and iron powder in the melt,

$$Fe + 2(C_2H_5)_2NH \cdot HCl \xrightarrow{\Delta} FeCl_2 + H_2 + 2(C_2H_5)_2NH$$

so that the over-all reaction leading to ferrocene,

$$FeCl_2 + 2C_5H_6 + 2(C_2H_5)_2NH \rightarrow (C_5H_5)_2Fe + 2(C_2H_5)_2NH \cdot HCl$$

requires essentially only iron and cyclopentadiene as the raw materials, since the amine and its hydrochloride may be recycled.

Other cyclopentadienides

Cyclopentadienyl complexes, possessing a ferrocene-like molecular structure, but in which the metal-ring bonding is partially or largely ionic, may serve as a source of the anion. Thus, biscyclopentadienyl-magnesium, prepared directly from cyclopentadiene and magnesium at

---

* Other amines such as triethylamine and pyridine were found to be less effective.
† The use of solvents, other than tetrahydrofuran or dioxane (60), for the preparation of anhydrous ferrous chloride from iron powder and ferric chloride does not appear to offer any particular advantage (59). Anhydrous ferrous chloride may also be conveniently prepared by heating ferric chloride in chlorobenzene solution (40).

high temperatures (2), gives ferrocene quantitatively on treatment with ferrous chloride (41). Diffraction studies have shown that the magnesium compound possesses a sandwich type of structure as in ferrocene (72). Biscyclopentadienylmanganese, which also has a ferrocene-type structure (71), and like the magnesium compound is ionic in character, is converted instantaneously and quantitatively to ferrocene with ferrous chloride (69). The biscyclopentadienyl compounds of chromium and vanadium behave as metal cyclopentadienides yielding ferrocene in moderate yield on treatment with ferrous chloride (69). A discussion of the ionic character of bonding in several biscyclopentadienyl transition metal complexes based on these and other ligand displacement reactions has been given by Wilkinson, Cotton, and Birmingham (69). Tricyclopentadienyl complexes of the rare earths have likewise been shown to exchange rapidly with ferrous chloride (68), as has the monocyclopentadienyl complex of thalium (46), (C_5H_5Tl) and the mono- and biscyclopentadienyl complexes of titanium [$C_5H_5Ti(OC_2H_5)_3$ and $(C_5H_5)_2Ti(OCOCH_3)_2$] (45).*

Iron powder and a mixture of cyclopentadienylmercuric chloride and biscyclopentadienylmercury, prepared directly from the diene and mercuric chloride, have also been used in the synthesis of ferrocene (37). Unlike the cyclopentadienyl complexes previously described, the metal atom in the mercury compounds is σ-bonded to the diene ring (51).

METHODS EMPLOYING CYCLOPENTADIENE AT HIGH TEMPERATURES

With iron and its salts

The original preparation of ferrocene by these procedures was that of Miller, Tebboth, and Tremaine (43), who employed an iron catalyst in the presence of aluminum, potassium, or molybdenum oxides. Cyclopentadiene, passed through the mixture at 300°, is converted to ferrocene in moderate yield. Unfortunately, the catalyst soon becomes passive and must be reactivated. Several patents covering the use of iron and its oxides in both reducing and nonreducing atmospheres have since been given (75, 77, 81, 82, 84, 85, 89). The latter procedure has also been described in the chemical literature (56), and Riemschneider has presented some evidence that it is free iron rather than a lower oxide of the metal which is actually the effective component in these reactions (57).

* The preparation of cyclopentadienylmanganese tricarbonyl from tricyclopentadienyl-aluminum and manganous salts, followed by reaction with carbon monoxide, has recently been reported in a patent (96, 97).

With iron carbonyls

Iron pentacarbonyl may replace the free metal or its salts. Not only ferrocene, but nickelocene, cobaltocene, and chromocene as well have been prepared by passing a mixture of cyclopentadiene and the metal carbonyl through a heated tube (65, 75, 78, 87). This method has also been employed in the synthesis of the dinuclear metal carbonyls of chromium, molybdenum, and tungsten (18, 51, 66), and in the synthesis of cyclopentadienyl manganese tricarbonyl (98).

When the reaction with iron pentacarbonyl is carried out at temperatures between 100 and 180°, the dark purple dinuclear component (1) may be isolated (17, 33, 35, 49, 76).

$$C_5H_6 + Fe(CO)_5 \rightarrow [C_5H_5Fe(CO)_2]_2$$

(1)

Its infrared spectrum reveals the presence of bridging and nonbridging carbonyl groups (7, 47, 49), and an x-ray crystallographic study (33, 44) indicates that the molecule is centrosymmetric. In the crystal, the metal atoms and the two bridging carbonyl groups define a plane, with the remaining bonds from each iron atom to a ring and a terminal carbonyl group directed above and below this plane as shown in 1a. The presence

(1a)   (1b)

of a metal-metal bond in this substance is in accord with its diamagnetism and is further supported by the rather short distance between these centers (2.45 Å), which is near the Fe-Fe distance of 2.46 Å in iron enneacarbonyl (52).

The formation of 1 probably proceeds through successive replacement of carbonyl by olefinic ligands to give cyclopentadiene iron tricarbonyl (2) initially. This substance may then lose carbon monoxide and rearrange to cyclopentadienyliron dicarbonyl hydride (3), which can in turn lose hydrogen and dimerize to give 1. Both of these postulated intermediates have been prepared as shown in Fig. 1-1, and do in fact decompose spontaneously at room temperature to give the dinuclear complex (1) (9, 12, 22, 28).

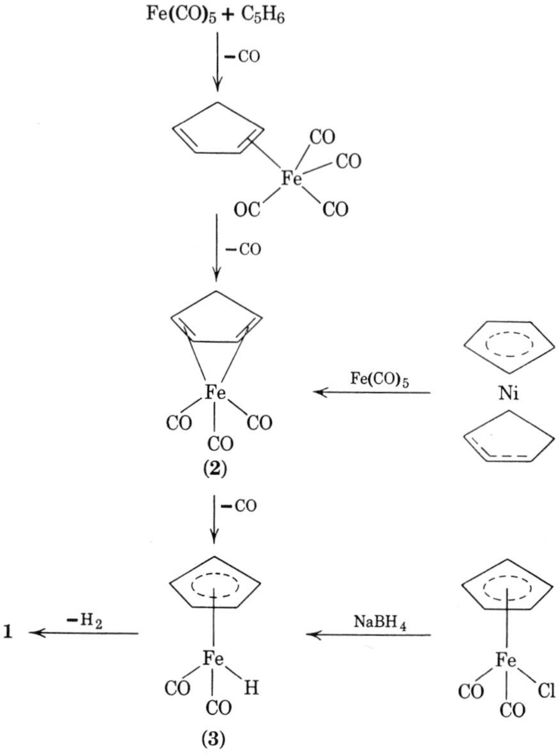

$$Fe(CO)_5 + C_5H_6$$

FIG. 1-1

The dinuclear compounds (1) is unique in that it does not appear to have the same structure in solution as in the crystal. The multiplicity of carbonyl bands in the infrared and Raman spectra,* and the presence of at least one infrared carbonyl band coincident with a Raman line are incompatible with a centrosymmetric structure (7, 8, 47, 49). The presence of equilibrating *cis* and *trans* forms in solution is rendered unlikely by the observation that the relative intensities of the several carbonyl absorptions do not change between room temperature and $-110°$ (47). It has recently been suggested (47) that the molecular structure in solution is best represented by **1b**.

Fischer has recently reported the preparation of $[C_5H_5Ru(CO)_2]_2$ and $[C_5H_5Os(CO)_2]_2$ (23, 26). These, like the iron derivative, are diamagnetic and their spectra exhibit absorption bands characteristic of π-bonded cyclopentadienyl rings. All three compounds possess appreciable and very similar dipole moments (26).† However, the crystal structure of the osmium compound differs significantly from the other two, and the infrared spectrum of the crystalline material, in contrast to that of the iron and ruthenium compounds, shows only the presence of terminal, nonbridging carbonyl groups.

* Some of these bands are apparently due to decomposition products (47).
† At 25° in benzene solution, the dipole moments of the Fe, Ru, and Os compounds are 3.08, 2.75, and 2.58 D, respectively (26).

On heating to 210°, the dinuclear iron compound loses carbon monoxide and ferrocene is formed (35, 49). As might be expected, the yield of ferrocene based on available iron in **1** is improved when this reaction is carried out in the presence of free cyclopentadiene (35). Decomposition of **1** in the presence of a substituted cyclopentadiene provides a potentially useful method for the synthesis of unsymmetrically substituted ferrocenes. Hallam and Pauson (35) have prepared benzyl- and 1,3-diphenylferrocene by this method.

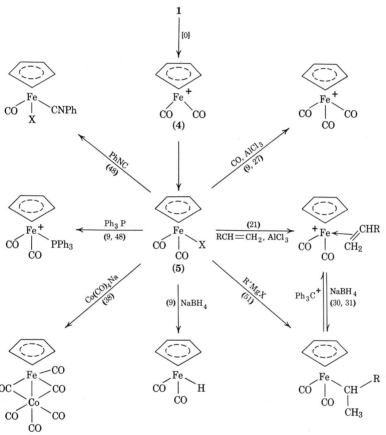

FIG. 1-2 The literature references are given in parentheses (lightface numbers).

The dinuclear compound (**1**) is the progenitor of many interesting monocyclopentadienyl derivatives. Oxidation by air in the presence of acid or with bromine or iodine furnishes the cation (**4**), from which neutral halogen compounds (**5**) are obtained (33, 34, 49, 51, 69). These, as well as the sodio derivative (**6**), prepared by direct reduction of **1** with sodium (17, 51), have been used in the synthesis of the derivatives shown in Figs. 1-2 and 1-3.

One of the more interesting of these latter compounds is obtained by treatment of **5** with sodium cyclopentadienide (34, 35, 50, 51). The

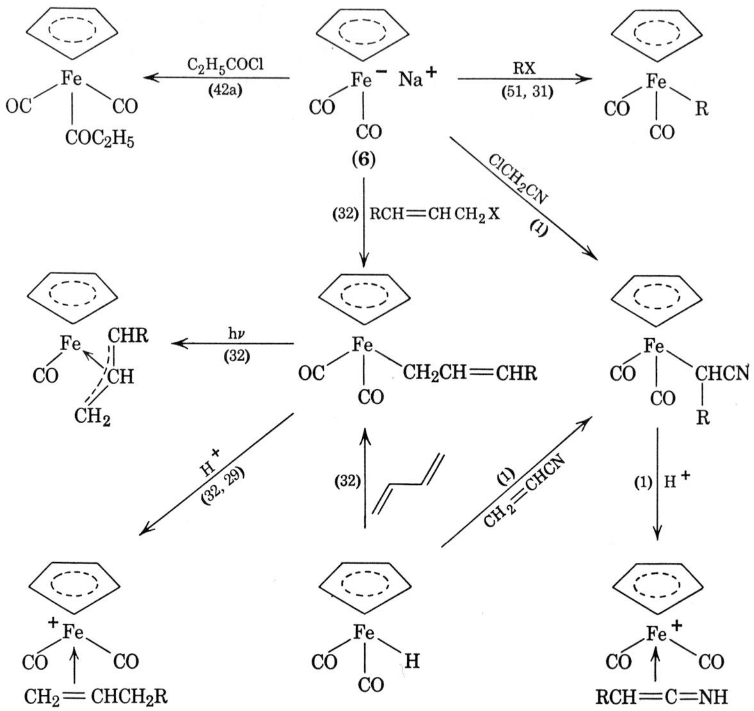

FIG. 1-3   The literature references are given in parentheses (lightface numbers).

substance (7) is unique in that the diene ring introduced in the displacement reaction is σ-bonded to the metal atom (73). It decomposes slowly at room temperature to give ferrocene, and at 90° to give the dinuclear tetracarbonyl (1) and only traces of ferrocene.

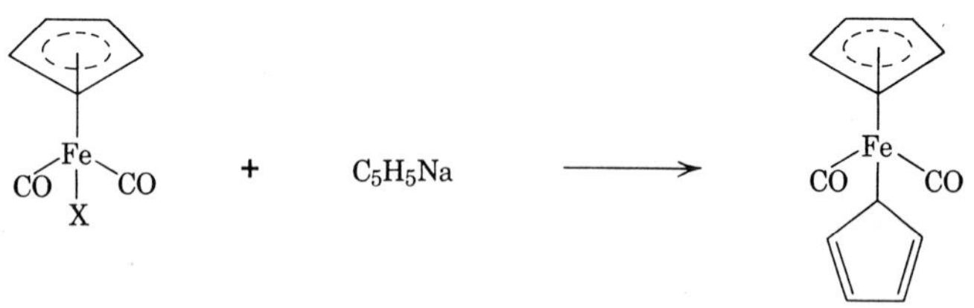

The presence of structurally distinct cyclopentadienyl fragments in **7** may be inferred from its infrared spectrum, which exhibits weak bands in the C—H and C=C stretching regions, as well as several at longer wavelengths not present in compounds having only π-bonded cyclopentadienyl.

rings (50, 51). However, the n.m.r. spectrum of the substance is not definitive (51).

Hallam and Pauson (35) have provided particularly convincing chemical evidence in support of structure **7** by demonstrating the existence of two isomeric monosubstituted derivatives of it (**8** and **9**). On treatment with

hydrobromic acid, each loses the cyclopentadienyl ring introduced in the last step and reverts to its precursor bromide. The thermal decomposition of **9** to give benzylferrocene illustrates a second potentially general method for the synthesis of unsymmetrically substituted ferrocenes.

RUTHENOCENE AND OSMOCENE

The methods used for the preparation of these substances represent no significant departure from those used in the synthesis of ferrocene.

Ruthenocene was first described by Wilkinson, who prepared it from ruthenium(III) acetylacetonate and excess cyclopentadienylmagnesium bromide (61). Fischer and co-workers have reported the synthesis of both ruthenocene and osmocene employing ruthenium trichloride and osmium tetrachloride with excess sodium cyclopentadienide in either tetrahydro- furan or ethylene glycol dimethyl ether. Yields are considerably lower than those achieved in the synthesis of ferrocene under comparable conditions of reaction (20, 54, 55). More recently, a detailed procedure for the synthesis of ruthenocene has been given by Bublitz, McEwen, and Kleinberg (4). The preparation of radioactive ruthenocene has been reported in the patent literature (90).

REFERENCES

1. Ariyaratne, J. K. P., and M. L. H. Green, *J. Chem. Soc.*, 2976 (1963).
2. Barber, W. A., *J. Inorg. Nucl. Chem.*, 4, 373 (1957).
3. Birmingham, J. M., D. Seyferth, and G. Wilkinson, *J. Am. Chem. Soc.*, 76, 4179 (1954).
4. Bublitz, D. E., W. E. McEwen, and J. Kleinberg, *Org. Syn.*, 41, 96 (1961).
5. Cotton, F. A., and L. T. Reynolds, *J. Am. Chem. Soc.*, 80, 269 (1958).
6. Cotton, F. A., and G. Wilkinson, *Z. Naturforsch.*, 9b, 417, 453 (1954).
7. Cotton, F. A., A. D. Liehr, and G. Wilkinson, *J. Inorg. Nucl. Chem.*, 1, 175 (1955).
8. Cotton, F. A., H. Stammereich, and G. Wilkinson, *J. Inorg. Nucl. Chem.*, 9, 3 (1959).
9. Davison, A., M. L. H. Green, and G. Wilkinson, *J. Chem. Soc.*, 3172 (1961).
10. Dessy, R. E., quoted by A. Streitwieser in *Molecular Orbital Theory*, Wiley, New York, 1961, p. 414.
11. Ekemark, A., and K. Skagius, *Acta Chem. Scand.*, 16, 1136 (1962).
12. Filbey, A. H., and J. C. Wollensak, Abstracts of papers, 138th Meeting of the American Chemical Society, New York, September 1960, p. 54-P.
13. Fischer, E. O., and R. Jira, *Z. Naturforsch.*, 8b, 1 (1953).
14. Fischer, E. O., and R. Jira, *Z. Naturforsch.*, 8b, 217 (1953).
15. Fischer, E. O., and R. Jira, *Z. Naturforsch.*, 8b, 327 (1953).
16. Fischer, E. O., and W. Hafner, *Z. Naturforsch.*, 8b, 444 (1953).
17. Fischer, E. O., and R. Böttcher, *Z. Naturforsch.*, 10b, 600 (1955).
18. Fischer, E. O., W. Hafner, and H. O. Stahl, *Z. Anorg. Allgem. Chem.*, 282, 47 (1955).
19. Fischer, E. O., and H. P. Fritz, *Advances in Inorganic Chemistry and Radiochemistry*, Vol. I, Academic Press, New York, 1959, p. 55.
20. Fischer, E. O., and H. Grubert, *Ber.*, 92, 2302 (1959).
21. Fischer, E. O., and K. Fichtel, *Ber.*, 94, 1200 (1961).
22. Fischer, E. O., and H. Werner, *Tetrahedron Letters*, 1, 17 (1961).
23. Fischer, E. O., and K. Bittler, *Z. Naturforsch.*, 17b, 274 (1962).
24. Fischer, E. O., and Y. Hristidu, *Z. Naturforsch.*, 17b, 275 (1962)
25. Fischer, E. O., and A. Treiber, *Z. Naturforsch.*, 17b, 276 (1962).
26. Fischer, E. O., and A. Vogler, *Z. Naturforsch.*, 17b, 421 (1962).
27. Fischer, E. O., K. Fichtel, and K. Öfele, *Ber.*, 95, 249 (1962).
28. Green, M. L. H., C. N. Street, and G. Wilkinson, *Z. Naturforsch.*, 14b, 738 (1959).
29. Green, M. L. H., and P. L. I. Nagy, *Proc. Chem. Soc.*, 378 (1961).
30. Green, M. L. H., and P. L. I. Nagy, *Proc. Chem. Soc.*, 74 (1962).
31. Green, M. L. H., and P. L. I. Nagy, *J. Am. Chem. Soc.*, 84, 1310 (1962).
32. Green, M. L. H., and P. L. I. Nagy, *J. Chem. Soc.*, 189 (1963).
33. Hallam, B. F., O. S. Mills, and P. L. Pauson, *J. Inorg. Nucl. Chem.*, 1, 313 (1955).

34. Hallam, B. F., and P. L. Pauson, *Chem. & Ind.* (*London*), 653 (1955).
35. Hallam, B. F., and P. L. Pauson, *J. Chem. Soc.*, 3030 (1956).
36. Huggins, D. K., and H. D. Kaesz, *J. Am. Chem. Soc.*, **83**, 4474 (1961).
37. Issleib, K., and A. Brack, *Z. Naturforsch.*, **11b**, 420 (1956).
38. Joshi, K. K., and P. L. Pauson, *Z. Naturforsch.*, **17b**, 565 (1962).
39. Kealy, T. J., and P. L. Pauson, *Nature*, **168**, 1039 (1951).
40. Kovacic, P., and N. O. Brace, *J. Am. Chem. Soc.*, **76**, 5491 (1954).
41. The ionic character of bonding in this substance (ref. 5) has been questioned. Lippincott, E. R., J. Xavier, and D. Steele, *J. Am. Chem. Soc.*, **83**, 2262 (1961).
42. Little, W. F., R. C. Koestler, and R. Eisenthal, *J. Org. Chem.*, **25**, 1435 (1960).
42a. McCleverty J. A., and G. Wilkinson, *J. Chem. Soc.*, 4096 (1963).
43. Miller, S. A., J. A. Tebboth, and J. F. Tremaine, *J. Chem. Soc.*, 632 (1952).
44. Mills, O. S., *Acta Cryst.*, **11**, 620 (1958).
45. Nesmeyanov, A. N., O. V. Nogina, and V. A. Dubonitsky, *Izvest. Akad. Nauk SSSR Otd. Khim. Nauk*, 1481 (1962).
46. Nesmeyanov, A. N., R. B. Materikova, and N. S. Kochetkova, *Izvest. Akad. Nauk SSSR Otd. Khim. Nauk.* 1334 (1963).
47. Noack, K., *J. Inorg. Nucl. Chem.*, **25**, 1383 (1963).
48. Pauson, P. L. and D. H. Stobbs, *Angew. Chem. Intern. Ed. Engl.*, **1**, 333 (1962).
49. Piper, T. S., F. A. Cotton, and G. Wilkinson, *J. Inorg. Nucl. Chem.*, **1**, 165 (1955).
50. Piper, T. S. and G. Wilkinson, *Chem. & Ind.* (*London*), 1296 (1955).
51. Piper, T. S., and G. Wilkinson, *J. Inorg. Nucl. Chem.*, **3**, 104 (1956).
52. Powell, H. M., and R. V. G. Ewens, *J. Chem. Soc.*, 286 (1939).
53. Pruett, R. L., and E. L. Morehouse, *Advan. Chem. Ser.*, **23**, 368 (1959).
54. Rausch, M. D., E. O. Fischer, and H. Grubert, *Chem. & Ind.*, (*London*), 756 (1958).
55. Rausch, M. D., E. O. Fischer, and H. Grubert, *J. Am. Chem. Soc.*, **82**, 76 (1960).
56. Riemschneider, R., and D. Helm, *Z. Naturforsch.*, **14b**, 811 (1959).
57. Riemschneider, R., and D. Helm, *Z. Naturforsch.*, **16b**, 234 (1961).
58. Sokolova, E. B., M. P. Shebanova, and V. A. Zhichkina, *Zh. Obshch. Khim.*, **30**, 2040 (1960).
59. Sokolova, E. B., M. P. Shebanova, and L. F. Nikolaeva, *Zh. Obshch. Khim.*, **31**, 332 (1961).
60. Titov, A. I., E. S. Lisitsyna, and M. R. Shemtova, *Dokl. Akad. Nauk SSSR*, **130**, 341 (1960).
61. Wilkinson, G., *J. Am. Chem. Soc.*, **74**, 6146 (1952).
62. Wilkinson, G., *J. Am. Chem. Soc.*, **74**, 6148 (1952).
63. Wilkinson, G., P. L. Pauson, J. M. Birmingham, and F. A. Cotton, *J. Am. Chem. Soc.*, **75**, 1011 (1953).
64. Wilkinson, G. and F. A. Cotton, *Chem. & Ind.* (*London*), 307 (1954).
65. Wilkinson, G., P. L. Pauson, and F. A. Cotton, *J. Am. Chem. Soc.*, **76**, 1970 (1954).
66. Wilkinson, G., *J. Am. Chem. Soc.*, **76**, 209 (1954).
67. Wilkinson, G., and J. M. Birmingham, *J. Am. Chem. Soc.*, **76**, 4281 (1954).
68. Wilkinson, G., and J. M. Birmingham, *J. Am. Chem. Soc.*, **76**, 6210 (1954).
69. Wilkinson, G., F. A. Cotton, and J. M. Birmingham, *J. Inorg. Nucl. Chem.*, **2**, 95 (1956).
70. Wilkinson, G., *Org. Syn.* **36**, 31 and 34 (1956).
71. Weiss, E., and E. O. Fischer, *Z. Naturforsch.*, **10b**, 58 (1955).
72. Weiss, E., and E. O. Fischer, *Z. Anorg. Allgem. Chem.*, **278**, 219 (1955).
73. Several transition metal complexes having σ-bound cyclopentadienyl units have since been reported. Among these are $(\pi\text{-}C_5H_5)_2M(\sigma\text{-}C_5H_5)_2$ [M = Nb, Ta; E. O. Fischer and A. Treiber, Ber., **94**, 2193 (1961)], $(C_5H_5)_4Mo$, apparently

$(\pi\text{-}C_5H_5)Mo(\sigma\text{-}C_5H_5)_3$, E. O. Fischer and Y. Hristidu, *Ber.*, **95**, 253 (1962), and $(\pi\text{-}C_5H_5)Cr(NO)_2(\sigma\text{-}C_5H_5)$ (ref. 51).

Patents

74. Hobbs, C. L. (to E. I. du Pont de Nemours & Co.), Brit. Pat. 733,129 (July 6, 1955), *C.A.*, **50.**, 7146 (1956).
75. Garner, P. J. (to Shell Refining and Marketing Co., Ltd.), Brit. Pat. 737,110 (Sept. 1, 1955), *C.A.*, **50**, 13086 (1956).
76. Leedham, K. (to Shell Refining and Marketing Co., Ltd.), Brit. Pat. 737,124 (Sept. 21, 1955), *C.A.*, **50**, 9010 (1956).
77. E. I. du Pont de Nemours & Co., Brit. Pat. 737,780 (Sept. 28, 1955), *C.A.*, **50**, 14000 (1956).
78. California Research Corp., Brit. Pat. 744,450 (Feb. 8, 1956), *C.A.*, **51**, 491 (1957).
79. Hartley, J., T. H. Ramsay, and J. D. Shimin (to Shell Refining and Marketing Co., Ltd.), Brit. Pat. 737,109 (Sept. 21, 1955), *C.A.*, **50**, 13086 (1956).
80. Clapp, D. B. (to Associated Ethyl Co., Ltd.), Brit. Pat. 763,047 (Dec. 5, 1956), *C.A.*, **51**, 10588 (1957).
81. E. I. du Pont de Nemours & Co., Brit. Pat. 764,058 (Dec. 19, 1956), *C.A.*, **52**, 5480 (1958).
82. California Research Corp., Brit. Pat. 767,298 (Jan. 30, 1957), *C.A.*, **51**, 13937 (1957).
83. Lynch, M. A., and J. C. Brantley (to Union Carbide Co.), Brit. Pat. 785,760 (Nov. 6, 1957), *C.A.*, **52**, 11126 (1958).
84. Sieg, R. P. (to California Research Corp.), U.S. Pat. 2,769,828 (Nov. 6, 1956), *C.A.*, **51**, 9707 (1957).
85. Arimoto, F. S. (to E. I. du Pont de Nemours & Co.), U.S. Pat. 2,804,468 (Aug. 27, 1957), *C.A.*, **52**, 2086 (1958).
86. Hobbs, C. L. (to E. I. du Pont de Nemours & Co.), U.S. Pat. 2,763,700 (Sept. 18, 1956), *C.A.*, **51**, 8806 (1957).
87. Barusch, M. R., and E. G. Lindstrom (to California Research Corp.), U.S. Pat. 2,834,796 (May 13, 1958), *C.A.*, **52**, 16366 (1958).
88. Breslow, D. S. (to Hercules Powder Co.), U.S. Pat. 2,848,506 (Aug. 19, 1958), *C.A.*, **53**, 2250 (1959).
89. Hogan, J. P., and L. E. Gardner (to Phillips Petroleum Co.), U.S. Pat. 2,898,360 (Aug. 4, 1959), *C.A.*, **54**, 569 (1960).
90. Götte, H., and M. Wenzel (to Farbwerke Hoechst Akt.-Ges.), Ger. Pat. 1,049,860 (Feb. 5, 1959), *C.A.*, **55**, 2685 (1961).
91. Morehouse, E. L. (to Union Carbide), U.S. Pat. 3,071,605 (Jan. 1, 1963), *C.A.*, **58**, 12602 (1963).
92. National Lead Co., Brit. Pat. 798,001 (July 9, 1958), *C.A.*, **53**, 2250 (1959).
93. Herman, D. F., and R. M. Weil (to National Lead Co.), U.S. Pat. 2,898,355 (Aug. 4, 1959), *C.A.*, **53**, 17926 (1959).
94. Morehouse, E. L. (to Union Carbide Corp.), Brit. Pat. 797,151 (June 25, 1958), *C.A.*, **53**, 4297 (1959).
95. National Lead Co., Brit. Pat. 800,528 (Aug. 27, 1958), *C.A.*, **53**, 4296 (1959).
96. Shapiro, H., E. DeWitt, and J. E. Brown (to Ethyl Corp.), U.S. Pat. 2,987,534 (June 6, 1961), *C.A.*, **55**, 22338 (1961).
97. Shapiro, H., E. DeWitt, and J. E. Brown (to Ethyl Corp.), U.S. Pat. 2,987,531 (June 6, 1961), *C.A.*, **55**, 22340 (1961).
98. Ethyl Corp., Brit. Pat. 782,738 (Sept. 11, 1957), *C.A.*, **52**, 3851 (1958).

2 Electronic structure and bonding

The discovery of ferrocene set the stage for the synthesis of a vast and continually growing array of structurally diverse complex organometallics containing not only cyclopentadienyl, but benzene, olefin, and acetylene ligands as well. These developments have been accompanied by a considerable interest in the bonding forces in these substances and, in particular, in the electronic structure of ferrocene. The special interest in ferrocene derives not only from the fact that it may be considered the prototype of all other biscyclopentadienyl metal complexes, and that its physical and chemical properties have been most thoroughly investigated, but also because its high degree of molecular symmetry renders it particularly well suited to theoretical treatment.

We shall not attempt here to present a complete and detailed account of all the many theoretical treatments of ferrocene and its congeners, but shall confine ourselves instead to a summary of the major conclusions of several of the molecular orbital analyses. These provide, in our view, a useful, if as yet inexact, description of the bonding forces in these substances in terms of which many of their chemical and physical properties can be understood.

Although the several molecular orbital treatments differ in some important details, especially with respect to the number and character of the assumptions made, the basic approach is necessarily the same in all such treatments. Since particular advantage is taken of the symmetry properties of ring and metal orbitals from which molecular orbitals are constructed, a qualitative account of these properties is given.

We consider first the five local molecular orbitals of each of the cyclopentadienyl rings formed from the five p_z atomic orbitals. These fall into three groups which differ in their symmetry properties with respect to rotation about the molecular axis perpendicular to each ring and passing through their centers. In order of increasing energy, these orbitals have the symmetry designations A_1, E_1, and E_2. These are pictured in simplified form in Fig. 2-1 in terms of their component p_z orbitals. The single molecular orbital of A_1 symmetry has no nodal plane perpendicular to the plane of the ring, while those of E_1 and E_2 symmetry are each doubly degenerate and have one and two such nodal planes respectively. More precisely, the transformation properties of these orbitals are such that the A_1 orbital remains invariant to rotation about the fivefold axis of symmetry, while the E_1 and E_2 orbitals are multiplied by factors of cos α and cos 2α, respectively, on rotation through an angle α.

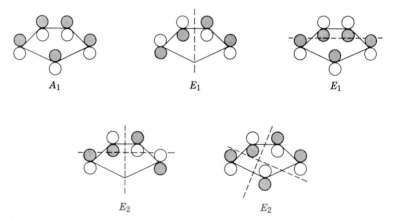

A_1 E_1 E_1

E_2 E_2

FIG. 2-1 Cyclopentadienyl molecular orbitals shown in terms of their component p_z atomic orbitals. Differences in the sign of the wave function are indicated by shaded and unshaded areas. The trace of a nodal plane on the plane of the ring is shown by the dashed line.

It is now possible to form linear combinations of these localized molecular orbitals, assuming no interaction between them, to give a set of ten new molecular orbitals which encompass both rings. These are designated as A_{1g}, A_{2u}, E_{1g}, E_{1u}, E_{2g}, and E_{2u} in the symmetry point group D_{5d} to which the pentagonal antiprismatic structure of ferrocene belongs. As before, the symbols E and A refer to degenerate and nondegenerate states with the nodal properties of the E-type orbitals defined again by the subscripts 1 and 2. The additional subscripts g and u are introduced to indicate the symmetry properties of the new molecular orbitals with respect to their inversion through the center of symmetry of the molecule, that is, whether such a transformation leaves the sign of the orbital unaltered (g) or results in its multiplication by -1 (u). These new molecular orbitals are depicted in simplified form in Fig. 2-2 in a manner which illustrates their symmetry properties. The z axis is taken as the fivefold axis of the molecule.

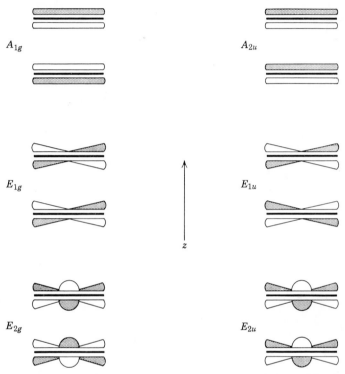

FIG. 2-2   Molecular orbitals for the two cyclopentadienyl rings of ferrocene. The σ-framework of each ring is formalized in terms of the heavy line, while shaded and unshaded areas above and below it distinguish segments of the molecular orbital which differ in sign. Only one member of a pair of degenerate orbitals is shown.

The $3d$, $4s$, and $4p$ metal orbitals may similarly be classified in the D_{5d} symmetry point group by the representations $A_{1g}(4s)$, $A_{2u}(4p_z)$, $E_{1g}(3d_{xz,yz})$, $E_{2g}(3d_{xy,x^2-y^2})$, and $E_{1u}(4p_{x,y})$ with the z axis defined as before. These orbitals are shown in Fig. 2-3.

The classification of metal and ring orbitals according to their symmetry properties is very useful for identifying those combinations which may give rise to bonding states. Since only those ring and metal orbitals which belong to the same representation can give rise to net overlap, only such combinations can be associated with ring-to-metal bonding, all other combinations being orthogonal. While, in principle, several such

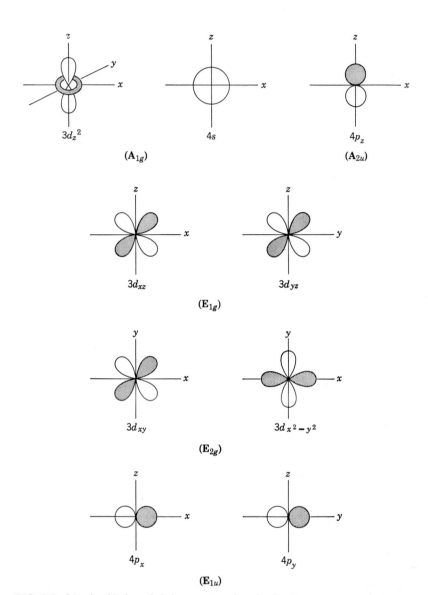

FIG. 2-3   Metal orbitals and their representations in the D_{5d} symmetry point group.

combinations are allowed by symmetry (Fig. 2-4), a determination of the relative contribution of each to the total ring-metal binding energy requires a calculation of overlap integrals and an estimation of the relative energies of the combining states.

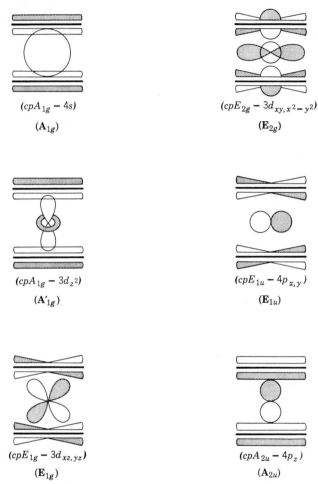

$(cpA_{1g} - 4s)$

$(\mathbf{A}_{1g})$

$(cpE_{2g} - 3d_{xy, x^2 - y^2})$

$(\mathbf{E}_{2g})$

$(cpA_{1g} - 3d_{z^2})$

$(\mathbf{A}'_{1g})$

$(cpE_{1u} - 4p_{x,y})$

$(\mathbf{E}_{1u})$

$(cpE_{1g} - 3d_{xz, yz})$

$(\mathbf{E}_{1g})$

$(cpA_{2u} - 4p_z)$

$(\mathbf{A}_{2u})$

FIG. 2-4 Symmetry allowed metal-ring molecular orbitals and their group representations. The combining ring orbital is indicated by the prefix cp, and only one member of a degenerate pair of molecular orbitals is shown.

In both the earlier qualitative treatments of Dunitz and Orgel (11) as well as that of Moffitt (29), almost all of the binding forces between the metal atom and the cyclopentadienyl rings were ascribed to covalent bonding derived from overlap of half-filled E_{1g} orbitals. The remaining orbitals were all fully occupied and essentially unmixed, so that the electronic configuration may be given as $(cpA_{1g})^2$, $(cpA_{2u})^2$, $(cpE_{1u})^4$, $(dA_{1g})^2$, $(dE_{2g})^4$, $b(cpE_{1g} - dE_{1g})^4$.

Moffitt's paper, which shortly followed that of Dunitz and Orgel, extended their treatment by calculating the relative energies of ring orbitals. He further estimated that the ring E_{1g} molecular orbitals and metal $3d$ orbitals were approximately equal in energy. Thus, the covalent bond formed by overlap of these orbitals would involve little charge displacement, and leave the metal and rings essentially neutral. The absence of

Table 2-1
Overlap Integrals and Binding Energies for Ferrocene Molecular Orbitals

MOLECULAR ORBITAL AND OCCUPANCY	OVERLAP INTEGRAL	BINDING ENERGY PER ELECTRON (e.v.)	TOTAL STABILIZATION ENERGY (e.v.)
$(cpA_{1g} - sA_{1g})^2$	0.50	1.4	2.8
$(cpA_{1g} - dA_{1g})^2$	0.01	—	—
$(cpE_{1g} - dE_{1g})^4$	0.37	2.0	8.0
$(cpE_{2g} - dE_{2g})^4$	0.29	0.4	1.6

appreciable charge separation in ferrocene is supported by the near identity in the acidity constants of ferrocenoic and benzoic acids (4, 26, 30, 53). In addition, Moffitt introduced a new element by assuming a mixing of $3d_{z^2}$ and $4s$ metal orbitals brought about by the electrostatic field of the rings. We shall return to this point later.

While Moffitt had explicitly discounted appreciable contributions to metal-ring bonding arising from any other symmetry allowed orbital overlaps, Dunitz and Orgel recognized that small secondary binding forces might have their origin in such interactions. In their second, more detailed analysis (12), overlap integrals were calculated for metal $3d$ and $4s$ orbitals with ring orbitals, using Slater orbitals and a value of 1.6 for the Slater radial parameter α for both iron $3d$ and $4s$ orbitals. As in Moffitt's treatment, these metal levels were taken to be degenerate and approximately equal in energy to the ring E_{1g} levels. The energy levels of the remaining ring orbitals were calculated by the simple LCAO method with a value of 60 kcal. taken for the resonance integral β. With the binding energy provided by the E_{1g} orbitals assumed to be 2 e.v. per electron and off diagonal matrix elements taken to be proportional to overlap integrals, the stabilization energies summarized in Table 2-1 were calculated.

As can be seen from the table, about 20% of the total metal-ring binding energy is derived from A_{1g} interactions and about 10% from E_{2g} interactions. These figures must, however, be regarded with considerable reserve, since the overlap integrals are strong functions of the radial parameter α near the value taken by Dunitz and Orgel. Nevertheless it is apparent that contributions to metal-ring bonding from other than E_{1g} interactions cannot be wholly neglected except perhaps for that involving the metal $3d_{z^2}(dA_{1g})$ orbital.

The self-consistent field (SCF) analysis of Yamazaki (54) and that of Ruch (37), which appeared shortly afterward, both explicitly included $4p$ orbital interactions. In addition, the values taken by Yamazaki for the Slater radial parameter α for metal $3d$ and $4s$ orbitals differ considerably from those used by Dunitz and Orgel. The brevity of this work, especially its ambiguities and the lack of definition in the form of the molecular orbitals used, detracts somewhat from its value. Furthermore, Yamazaki's conclusion that the over-all Fe—C bonding is appreciably ionic in character is certainly not in accord with the observation that the ionization constant of ferrocenoic acid is quite close to that of benzoic acid. Ruch's treatment fails to include an explicit account of some of the fundamental assumptions made in his calculations, and has been criticized on these and other grounds by Wilkinson and Cotton (52).* These authors have given a critical account of these theoretical analyses as well as the earliest treatment of Jaffe (20).

Two additional molecular orbital treatments, which are much more elaborate than any of the previous ones, have since been given by Shustorovich and Dyatkina (40, 43) and by Dahl and Ballhausen (10, 2). The Russian treatment, which employs Roothaan's SCF-LCAO-MO method (33) and Slater orbitals, preserves many of the features of the earlier analyses and, qualitatively, the results are similar to those of Yamazaki. The values of the radial parameter, α, taken by these authors are 1.0 for $4s$ and $4p$ metal orbitals, and 2.0 for $3d$ orbitals (Yamazaki had taken $\alpha_{4sp} = 0.878$ and $\alpha_{3d} = 2.200$). The normally accepted values for α_{2p} (1.6) and for the resonance integral, β_{cc} (2.39 e.v.) were used in their calculations. Brown (5) has recently carried out calculations of stabilization energies derived from metal $4p$ interactions as a function of the radial parameter α, which indicate that the values taken by Yamazaki and by Shustorovich and Dyatkina for α_{4p} are reasonable.

Dahl and Ballhausen's treatment also employs the LCAO-SCF method, but differs from that of Shustorovich and Dyatkina principally in the use of Watson's Hartree-Fock orbitals for iron rather than Slater functions

---

* Ruch has further amplified his views (35) in response to criticism by Schwab and Voitlander (38, 48).

(49). The forms of the molecular orbitals, their overlap integrals and energies derived by these calculations, are summarized in Table 2-2. The energy-level diagram for each of these treatments is shown in Fig. 2-5.

Table 2-2
Molecular Orbitals of Ferrocene

SYMMETRY	FILLED MO			EMPTY MO
	Form[a]	Overlap integral	Energy (e.v.)	Energy (e.v.)
After Shustorovich and Dyatkins (40, 43)				
A_{1g}	$0.87(A_{1g}) + 0.49(4s)$	0.359	−16.05	−1.50
A_{1g}'	$3d_z{}^2$	0.023	−8.44	—
A_{2u}	$0.99(A_{2u}) + 0.10(4p_z)$	0.063	−13.74	+0.54
E_{1g}	$0.93(E_{1g}) + 0.37(3d_{xz,yz})$	0.339	−11.02	+6.20
E_{1u}	$0.81(E_{1u}) + 0.59(4p_{x,y})$	0.380	−12.62	+1.52
E_{2g}	$0.52(E_{2g}) + 0.85(3d_{xy,x^2-y^2})$	0.192	−6.39	+4.92
E_{2u}	—	—	—	+2.23
After Dahl and Ballhausen (10, 2)				
A_{1g}	$0.774(A_{1g}) + 0.633(4s)$	0.527	−20.15	+27.51
A_{1g}'	$3d_z{}^2$	0.030	−14.03	—
A_{2u}	$0.882(A_{2u}) + 0.471(4p_z)$	0.236	−17.77	+12.39
E_{1g}	$0.891(E_{1g}) + 0.454(3d_{xz,yz})$	0.148	−12.48	+8.96
E_{1u}	$0.807(E_{1u}) + 0.591(4p_{x,y})$	0.468	−14.74	+24.64
E_{2g}	$0.440(E_{2g}) + 0.898(3d_{xy,x^2-y^2})$	0.079	−10.92	+3.98
E_{2u}	—	—	—	+1.43

[a] The two sets of orbitals, those associated with the rings and those associated with the metal atom, have been transformed so as to render them mutually orthogonal (10)

Neglecting for the moment the differences between the analyses in the ordering of bonding and particularly of the antibonding levels, they do concur substantially in assigning 12 electrons to strongly bonding metal-ring hybridized orbitals. Of the remaining six electrons, four occupy the weakly bonding E_{2g} levels, while two are placed in a nonbonding $3d_{z^2}$ orbital. Both treatments are likewise in accord in ascribing little net overlap between this latter metal orbital and the A_{1g} ring orbital. This general picture of the bonding in ferrocene is quite close to that which may be derived from the earlier analyses of Ruch and Yamazaki.

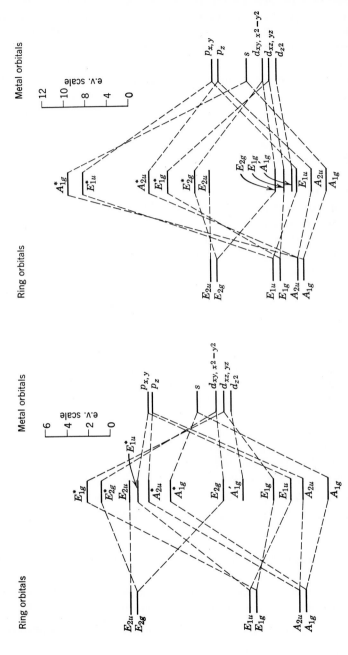

FIG. 2-5 Energy-level diagrams for ferrocene. *Left.* After Shustorovich and Dyatkina (40, 43). *Right.* After Dahl and Ballhausen (10, 2).

Of the six bonding orbitals, the A_{1g}, A_{2u}, and E_{1u} levels, containing eight electrons, are of the donor-acceptor type, since they are formed by overlap of filled ring orbitals with vacant metal orbitals. A portion of the electronic charge transferred to the metal by these interactions is returned to the rings through the polar covalent bond formed by overlap of the half filled metal and ring E_{1g} orbitals. Some additional charge is also transferred from the metal to the rings by the E_{2g} dative bond but, as has been pointed out by Wilkinson and Cotton (52), any weakening of bonding within the rings due to A_{1g}, A_{2u}, and A_{1u} overlaps cannot be compensated by this interaction, since the electrons are returned to the E_{2g} levels, which are antibonding with respect to the rings.

To the extent that the qualitative aspects of these several analyses may be accepted, the earlier conclusions of Dunitz and Orgel and of Moffitt, which assigned preeminence to the E_{1g} orbital electrons as a source of bonding must be rejected. On the other hand, Fischer's view, based on valence bond treatment, that all π electrons of the rings are equally involved in bonding (13–16, 36), while perhaps a better approximation to the true state of affairs, is certainly an oversimplification.

The collateral argument, which attributes the stability of ferrocene to the metal attaining an 18 electron krypton configuration through such π-electron transfer, has also been criticized on similar grounds (1, 2, 8). Unquestionably, special importance attaches to this array of electrons, as is evident from the relatively great stability of the iron group metallocenes, and from the wide occurrence of cyclopentadienyl, arene, olefin, and acetylene metal complexes in which the metal atom formally possesses this number of valence shell electrons. However, the significance of this "magic number" of electrons is more accurately assigned, in terms of the molecular orbital theory, to the filling of all strongly and weakly bonding molecular levels in these complexes than to the formal attainment by the metal atom of an inert gas configuration. On the other hand, Fischer's early suggestion that the metallocenes may be regarded as octahedral-type complexes is not fundamentally at variance with the molecular orbital picture, and from a structural point of view is a useful concept.* Linnett (25) has shown that by a suitable combination of A_{1g}, A_{2u}, E_{1g} and E_{1u} molecular orbitals two new sets of three more highly localized orbitals, directed pyramidally from the metal atom to each of the rings, may be obtained.

While the general agreement between the theoretical analyses is noteworthy, their several points of divergence are no less so. The Russian

* The preference for octahedrally directed rather than more highly delocalized bonding is in fact evident in certain diene-metal complexes whose molecular structures have been determined (see ref. 7 and leading references therein).

authors' calculated distribution of electron density in ferrocene places 0.68 units of positive charge on the metal atom, while Dahl and Ballhausen's treatment gives almost exactly the same figure, but reverses the sign, owing in large measure to the use of more highly contracted Watson orbitals in their calculations.* Dahl and Ballhausen have argued that their calculated charge distribution is more in accord with certain substitution reactions of ferrocene, referring perhaps to protonation of the metal atom by strong acids (9). However, such arguments may be in large measure extraneous to the question of charge distribution, since in each of the analyses the energetically most accessible electrons occupy the E_{2g} orbitals which are largely $3d$ in character. Moreover, the interaction of such electrons with an electrophile would not greatly reduce the over-all bonding in the molecule, since these are essentially nonbonding in character. Shustorovich and Dyatkina have also cited the results of x-ray absorption measurements in support of their charge assignment (3, 21, 47).

Dahl and Ballhausen's calculations place the E_{2g} orbital electrons at an energy of -10.92 e.v. However, the ionization potential of ferrocene as determined by mass spectroscopic measurements (17), by electron impact studies on the solid (6), and by oxidation reactions with iodine (46) may be estimated to be 6 to 8 e.v. The experimental estimate of this potential is thus considerably closer to the value calculated by the Russian authors (6.39 e.v.) and by Yamazaki (7.68 e.v.) than it is to that of Dahl and Ballhausen.

Shustorovich and Dyatkina (45) have also raised objection to their placement of the A_{1g}' level at -14.03 e.v. Such an assignment represents a stabilization of this level by about 7 e.v. over that in the free metal. Since the A_{1g}' level is essentially an unmixed $3d_{z^2}$ orbital, and since excess negative charge is placed on the metal atom in the Dahl and Ballhausen treatment, such a result is hardly credible.

On the other hand, the arrangement of antibonding levels pictured by Shustorovich and Dyatkina is not wholly satisfactory in terms of accounting for the metal to ring charge transfer characteristics of the u.v. spectrum of ferrocene and its aryl derivatives (34). Dahl and Ballhausen's arrangement of these levels would appear to give a better account of these absorptions.

---

* The Russian authors' calculations also suggest that in the transformation of ferrocene to the ferricenium ion the effective positive charge on the metal atom remains virtually unchanged (43). They are thereby led to conclude that the electron removed is withdrawn from a ring orbital rather than from the metal. This hardly seems plausible on energetic grounds, and is moreover not in accord with conclusions based on Mossbauer-effect studies of ferrocene and the ferricenium ion (Chapter 3, p. 55).

Regardless of the precise placement of E_{2g} and A_{1g}' levels in ferrocene, there is little doubt that they are quite close in energy. The bulk magnetic susceptibility of ferricenium picrate is sufficiently different from its spin only value (2.26 B.M.) (50) to indicate that the ground electronic state of the cation is $^2E_{2g}$ $[(A_{1g})^2(E_{2g})^3]$ rather than $^2A_{1g}$ $[(E_{2g})^4(A_{1g})^1]$ (22). The absence of electron paramagnetic resonance absorption in the solid salt has also been interpreted as evidence for this electronic configuration in the cation (19).

The analogy between these levels in ferrocene and the nonbonding t_{2g} levels in the ligand field or molecular orbital treatments of octahedral complexes is apparent. As Orgel has pointed out (31), the analogy is even closer if we consider the effect on these levels of flattening an octahedral complex along its threefold symmetry axis. Under this distortion, the degeneracy of t_{2g} levels is removed, and an arrangement of these orbitals identical with that found in ferrocene is attained (Fig. 2-6).

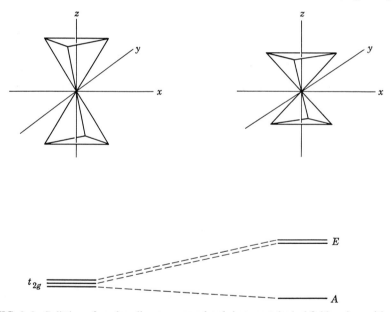

FIG. 2-6 Splitting of nonbonding t_{2g} energy levels in an octahedral field on imposition of a flattening distortion along the threefold symmetry axis (z axis). The forms of t_{2g} orbitals defined in terms of the coordinate system shown are d_{z^2}, $\sqrt{\frac{2}{3}}d_{x^2-y^2} + \sqrt{\frac{1}{3}}d_{xz}$, $\sqrt{\frac{2}{3}}d_{xy} - \sqrt{\frac{1}{3}}d_{yz}$ (31).

The proximity of E_{2g} and A_{1g}' levels is probably not greatly altered in the remaining metallocenes, although the relative energies of these orbitals may vary to some extent. This conclusion finds some support in the number of unpaired spins in these compounds determined by bulk magnetic susceptibility measurements. These data are summarized in Table 2-3.

In titanocene, with a total of fourteen electrons, the two in excess of those involved in ring-metal bonding must be placed in the A_{1g}' level. The presence of three rather than one unpaired electron, as anticipated, in vanadocene has been attributed by Orgel (31) to a larger loss of exchange-energy in spin pairing the d^3 configuration of vanadocene compared with spin pairing the d^2 configuration in titanocene. It is also quite possible

Table 2-3
Number of Unpaired Electrons in Biscyclopentadienyl Complexes

COMPLEX	NUMBER OF UNPAIRED ELECTRONS
$TiCp_2$	0
VCp_2	3
$CrCp_2$	2
$MnCp_2$	5
$FeCp_2$	0
$CoCp_2$	1
$NiCp_2$	2

that in vanadocene the A_{1g}' and E_{2g} orbitals are much closer in energy than they are in ferrocene. Thus the electronic configuration of this complex may be written as $(A_{1g}')^1(E_{2g})^2$. The small V^{51} hyperfine splittings observed by McConnell, Porterfield and Robertson in the e.p.r. spectrum of this substance has been interpreted as implying little mixing of either A_{1g}' or E_{2g} levels with the $4s$ orbital (28).

Chromocene with four nonbonding electrons may be assigned either the electronic configuration $(A_{1g}')^2(E_{2g})^2$ (42) or $(E_{2g})^3(A_{1g}')^1$ (10, 23). The presence of five unpaired electrons rather than one in the manganese complex, and its consequent ionic character must be attributed to the large exchange energy associated with the high spin ^6S state.

The observed paramagnetism of nickelocene was initially accounted for by Moffitt (29) in terms of mixing of $4s$ and $3d_{z^2}$ levels of the metal atoms which raised the energy of the higher state to that of the $4p$ metal orbitals. As we have noted, such mixings has been largely discounted by subsequent analyses and is not in accord with e.p.r. spectral data of vanadocene. Dunitz and Orgel (12) associated the paramagnetism of nickelocene with a half filling of the antibonding $E_{2g}*$ levels which they placed below the metal $4s$ and $4p$ orbitals. Ruch's analysis (37) would also assign these electrons to $E_{2g}*$ orbitals, while Yamazaki's energy level ordering (54), in which the lowest unfilled orbital is nondegenerate, would appear to be incapable of accounting for the observed paramagnetism of nickelocene. The more recent treatment of Dahl and Ballhausen (10) places these electrons in the degenerate E_{2u} orbitals, and although this assignment accommodates the magnetic properties of nickelocene, it is somewhat less satisfactory in that these electrons occupy an orbital which is primarily antibonding with respect to the rings alone. The observed increase in metal-ring bond length in nickelocene compared with ferrocene, together with a decrease in its thermodynamic stability (24, 51), would argue for placing these electrons into an antibonding molecular orbital.

While the analysis of Shustorovich and Dyatkina (40) is more nearly in accord with the lower stability of nickelocene, the ordering of energy levels is incapable of accounting for the observed paramagnetism of this substance unless the $A_{1g}*$ and $A_{2u}*$ orbitals are considerably closer in nickelocene than they are pictured to be in ferrocene.†

It is important to emphasize at this point that the foregoing discussion is predicated on the assumption that the arrangement of energy levels in these metallocenes is essentially the same as in ferrocene. Since the relative energies of metal and cyclopentadienyl orbitals and their overlaps may be expected to vary with the metallocene, such comparisons are not necessarily valid. This reservation is an especially important one not only in considering the arrangement of bonding and nonbonding orbitals, but in particular for the order and relative energies of antibonding levels.

The magnetic resonance properties of first-row transition metal cyclopentadienyl complexes have been discussed by Robertson and McConnell (32). They also present a ligand field analysis of $3d$ orbital splitting in these substances, based on an ionic model and a molecular orbital treatment, which follows closely along the lines laid down by Moffitt and by Dunitz and Orgel. Matsen (27) as well as Liehr and Ballhausen (23) have also presented a ligand field treatment. The latter author's analysis incorporates many of the earlier assumptions of Moffitt, especially the neglect of bonding interactions other than that derived from E_{1g} overlap. From the point of view of the later molecular orbital treatments, such an approximation is not entirely satisfactory.

A detailed valence-bond treatment of all of the first-row transition element metallocenes and of several derived from the second- and third-row metals has been given by Shustorovich and Dyatkina (39, 41).

---

† In a subsequent paper (44) the Russian authors have suggested that the odd electron in the nickelicenium ion occupies an antibonding orbital of E_{1g} symmetry, unlike the isoelectronic cobaltocene molecule in which this electron is placed in an $A_{1g}*$ orbital. A similar ordering of antibonding energy levels in the neutral nickelocene molecule would better accommodate its magnetic properties.

The valency state of the metal in these compounds is assumed to be one having half filled d_{xz} and d_{yz} orbitals for formation of two covalent bonds with ring orbitals of the same symmetry, and vacant s, p_x, p_y, and p_z orbitals for formation of donor-acceptor bonds with filled ring orbitals. In addition, weak interaction of filled d_{xy} and $d_{x^2-y^2}$ orbitals with vacant ring orbitals is assumed.

Although there remain some fundamental differences between several of the analyses, the common areas of agreement justify the following conclusions regarding the electronic structure of ferrocene. (1) Bonding interactions other than those involving E_{1g} orbitals are quite extensive, with a total of twelve electrons, as in the molecular orbital treatments of octahedral complexes, involved in ring to metal binding. (2) There is little if any mixing of $3d_{z^2}$ and $4s$ metal orbitals. (3) Both the d_{z^2} and d_{xy,x^2-y^2} metal levels are essentially non-bonding, with the latter orbitals slightly above the d_{z^2} energy level but close to it.

As for a choice between the various theoretical analyses, we may well feel justified in regarding them as the ancient Roman commoner, philosopher, and magistrate are said to have tolerantly regarded the diversity of religious belief, as either "all equally true, all equally false or all equally useful" (18).

REFERENCES

1. Ballhausen, C. J., "Theories of Bonding in Coordination Compounds," in S. Kirschner, ed., *Advances in the Chemistry of Coordination Compounds*, Macmillan, New York, 1961, p. 3.
2. Ballhausen, C. J., *Introduction to Ligand Field Theory*, McGraw Hill, New York, 1962, p. 218.
3. Barinsky, R. P., *Zh. Strukt. Khim.*, **1**, 200 (1960).
4. Benkeser, R. A., D. Groggin, and G. Schroll, *J. Am. Chem. Soc.*, **76**, 4025 (1954).
5. Brown, D. A., *J. Chem. Phys.*, **29**, 1086 (1958).
6. Brand, J. D. C., and W. Snedden, *Trans. Faraday Soc.*, **53**, 894 (1957). Quoted by these authors as a private communication from Reed; their ref. 16 and append. ix.
7. Churchill, M. R., and R. Mason, *Proc. Chem. Soc.*, 365 (1963).
8. Cotton, F. A., and G. Wilkinson, *Z. Naturforsch.*, **9b**, 453 (1954).
9. Curphey, R. J., J. O. Santer, M. Rosenblum, and J. H. Richards, *J. Am. Chem. Soc.*, **82**, 5249 (1960).
10. Dahl, J. P., and C. J. Ballhausen, *Kgl. Danske Videnskab. Selskab, Mat-fys. Medd.*, No. 5, **33** (1961).
11. Dunitz, J. D., and L. E. Orgel, *Nature*, **171**, 121 (1953).
12. Dunitz, J. D., and L. E. Orgel, *J. Chem. Phys.*, **23**, 954 (1955).
13. Fischer, E. O., and W. Pfab, *Z. Naturforsch.*, **7b**, 377 (1952).
14. Fischer, E. O., and H. Leipfinger, *Z. Naturforsch.*, **10b**, 353 (1955).
15. Fischer, E. O., *Rec. Trav. Chim.*, **75**, 629 (1956).
16. Fischer, E. O., and H. P. Fritz, "Compounds of Aromatic Ring Systems and Metals," in *Advances in Inorganic and Radiochemistry*, Vol. I, 1959, Academic Press, New York.

28   Chemistry of the Iron Group Metallocenes

17. Friedman, L., A. P. Irsa, and G. Wilkinson, *J. Am. Chem. Soc.*, **77**, 3689 (1955).
18. Gibbon, Edward, *The Decline and Fall of the Roman Empire*, Random House, Modern Library, p. 25.
19. Goldberg, R. M., and L. E. Orgel, *J. Chem. Soc.*, 363 (1962).
20. Jaffe, H. H., *J. Chem. Phys.*, **21**, 156 (1953).
21. Kauer, E., *Z. Physik Chem.* (*Frankfurt*), **6**, 105 (1956).
22. Levy, D. A., and L. E. Orgel, *Mol. Phys.*, **4**, 93 (1961).
23. Liehr, A. D., and C. J. Ballhausen, *Acta Chem. Scand.*, **11**, 207 (1957).
24. Lippincott, E. R., and R. D. Nelson, *J. Am. Chem. Soc.*, **77**, 4990 (1955).
25. Linnett, J. W., *Trans. Faraday Soc.*, **52**, 904 (1956).
26. Little, W. F. and R. Eisenthal, *J. Org. Chem.*, **26**, 3509 (1961).
27. Matsen, F. A., *J. Am. Chem. Soc.*, **81**, 2023 (1959).
28. McConnell, H. M., W. W. Porterfield, and R. E. Robertson, *J. Chem. Phys.*, **30**, 442 (1959).
29. Moffitt, W., *J. Am. Chem. Soc.*, **76**, 3386 (1954).
30. Nesmeyanov, A. N., and D. A. Reutov, *Doklady Akad. Nauk SSSR*, **115**, 518 (1957).
31. Orgel, L. E., *An Introduction to Transition-Metal Chemistry: Ligand Field Theory*, Wiley, New York, 1960, p. 166.
32. Robertson, R. E., and H. M. McConnell, *J. Phys. Chem.*, **64**, 70 (1960).
33. Roothaan, C. C. J., *Rev. Mod. Phys.*, **23**, 69 (1951).
34. Rosenblum, M., J. O. Santer, and W. G. Howells, *J. Am. Chem. Soc.*, **85**, 1450 (1963).
35. Ruch, E., *Z. Physik Chem.* (*Frankfurt*), **6**, 356 (1956).
36. Ruch, E., and E. O. Fischer, *Z. Naturforsch.*, **7b**, 767 (1952).
37. Ruch, E., *Rec. Trav. Chim.*, **75**, 638 (1956).
38. Schwab, G. M., and J. Völtlander, *Z. Physik. Chem.* (*Frankfurt*), **3**, 341 (1955).
39. Shustorovich, E. M., and M. E. Dyatkina, *Zh. Neorgan. Khim.*, **3**, 2721 (1958).
40. Shustorovich, E. M., and M. E. Dyatkina, *Doklady Akad. Nauk SSSR*, **128**, 1234 (1959).
41. Shustorovich, E. M., and M. E. Dyatkina, *Zh. Neorgan. Khim.*, **4**, 553 (1959).
42. Shustorovich, E. M., and M. E. Dyatkina, *Doklady Akad. Nauk SSSR*, **131**, 113 (1960).
43. Shustorovich, E. M., and M. E. Dyatkina, *Doklady Akad. Nauk SSSR*, **133**, 141 (1960).
44. Shustorovich, E. M., and M. E. Dyatkina, *Zh. Neorgan. Khim.*, **6**, 1247 (1961).
45. Shustorovich, E. M., and M. E. Dyatkina, *Zh. Strukt. Khim.*, **3**, 345 (1962).
46. Savitsky, A. V., and Y. K. Syrkin, *Trudy Po Khim. Khimicheskoi i Tekhnologii*, **1**, 165 (1961).
47. Vainshtein, E. E., Yu F. Kopelev, and B. T. Kotlyer, *Doklady Akad. Nauk SSSR*, **137**, 1117 (1961).
48. Völtlander, J., *Z. Physik Chem.* (*Frankfurt*), **6**, 371 (1956).
49. Watson, R. E., "Tech. Rep. No. 12, Solid State and Molecular Theory Group, M.I.T.," (1959), in *Phys. Rev.*, **119**, 1934 (1960).
50. Wilkinson, G., M. Rosenblum, M. C. Whiting, and R. B. Woodward, *J. Am. Chem. Soc.*, **74**, 2125 (1952).
51. Wilkinson, G., P. L. Pauson, and F. A. Cotton, *J. Am. Chem. Soc.*, **76**, 1970 (1954).
52. Wilkinson, G., and F. A. Cotton, "Cyclopentadienyl and Diene Metal Compounds," in *Progress in Inorganic Chemistry*, Vol. I, 1959, Interscience, New York.
53. Woodward, R. B., M. Rosenblum, and M. C. Whiting, *J. Am. Chem. Soc.*, **74**, 3458 (1952).
54. Yamazaki, M., *J. Chem. Phys.*, **24**, 1260 (1956).

3 Physical properties

MOLECULAR STRUCTURE

A number of partial and complete crystallographic structure determinations of the iron group metallocenes and several of their derivatives have been reported. These data are summarized in Tables 3-1 and 3-2 (pages 30 and 31).

Of the parent substances, ferrocene alone has the staggered or antiprismatic conformation (1a), in which nonbonded interactions between heteroannular carbon atoms are minimized. Lattice forces may likewise contribute to the stabilization of this conformation, but there is evidence which suggests that the lattice energies for the antiprismatic and prismatic forms (1a and 1b) are not significantly different (36). The antiprismatic conformation persists in all ferrocene derivatives that have been studied, with the exception of certain bridged ferrocenes in which the rigidity of the bridge forces the rings to adopt a more nearly prismatic orientation and causes considerable ring splaying (21, 83, 137).

(1a)

(1b)

In both ruthenocene and osmocene the distance separating the rings is significantly greater than in ferrocene. Interannular repulsive forces are consequently greatly reduced, and in the crystal these molecules exist in the eclipsed or prismatic conformation (1b).

Electron diffraction studies of ferrocene in the vapor phase have provided evidence for the absence of an appreciable barrier to rotation of the rings about their common fivefold axis (163), and the x-ray data suggests that even in the crystalline state considerable torsional vibration of the rings may persist (35).

Low-temperature crystallographic studies of ferrocene have been carried out by Edwards, Kington, and Mason (36) in an attempt to account for a λ point transition at 163.9°K in the heat capacity curve of ferrocene. However, no drastic change in unit cell constants was observed from 95° to 290°K, and an explanation for the change in heat capacity was sought in terms of partial disorder of intra- and intermolecular ring orientations above the λ point. The range of the λ transition (125 to 200°K) has been shown by Mulay and Attalla (113) to correspond roughly to the region of anomalous narrowing (115 to 225°K) in the line width of the proton magnetic resonance of solid ferrocene.

Although the preferred relative orientation of heteroannular dipolar substituents in metallocene derivatives might be expected to be transoid, this is by no means always true in the crystal. Thus, ferrocenedisulfonyl chloride does have the transoid structure (2) (168), but dibenzoylferrocene has the 1,3′ configuration (3) and diacetylruthenocene the cisoid structure

Table 3-1
Crystallographic Data

COMPOUND	SPACE GROUP	a, Å	b, Å	c, Å	β	REFERENCE
Ferrocene	$P2_1/a$	10.561	7.597	5.952	121.02°	35[a], 43, 34, 39, 129
1,1′-Dibenzoyl-	$P2_1/n$	11.69	25.36	6.27	90	173[a], 175
1,1′-Diacetyl-	$P2_1/a$	14.89	13.03	5.90	90	175
1,1′-Dipropionyl-	$Pbca$	13.40	5.8	37.92	—	175
1,1′-Dibutyryl-	Aba	11.84	14.02	9.74	—	175
1,1′-Dibenzo-	$P2_1/a$	11.32	7.85	8.09	115.3	185[a]
1,1′-Dichlorosulfonyl-	$P2_1/c$	7.95	7.85	10.95	97	168[a]
1,1′-(Tetramethylethylene)-	$P2_1/c$	7.756	10.97	15.41	92.63	21[a]
α-Keto-1,1′-trimethylene-	$P2_1/c$	22.98	7.381	5.833	93.38	83[a]
Biferrocenyl	$P2_1/c$	10.17	7.86	12.62	132.0	85
1′,1′-Dichloro-	$P2_1/c$	10.94	8.65	10.60	121.5	85
1′,1′-Diethyl-	$C2/c$	19.14	7.52	16.29	127.5	85
1′,1′-Diacetyl-	$P2_1/c$	5.74	18.89	9.09	113.0	85
1′,1′-Diacetoxy-	$P2_1/c$	8.04	10.51	11.61	95.5	85
1,1′-Triferrocenyl-	$C2/c$	13.23	6.16	27.38	98	85
Ruthenocene	$Pnma$	7.134	8.993	12.783	—	70[a], 71
1,1′-Diacetyl-	$P\bar{1}$	5.73	8.15	13.70	α-77.8 β-85.1 γ-69.4	186
Osmocene	$Pnma$	7.159	8.988	12.800	—	82

[a] Full structure determination.

Table 3-2
Interatomic Distances

COMPOUND	M—C (Å)	C—C (Å)	OTHER DISTANCES (Å)	REFERENCE
Ferrocene	2.045 ± 0.01	1.403 ± 0.02	Inter-ring 3.32	35
Ferrocene[a]	2.03 ± 0.02	1.43 ± 0.03	Inter-ring 3.25	163
Ferrocene[a]	2.07 ± 0.01	1.42 ± 0.01	C—H 1.12 ± 0.02	1
1,1'-Dibenzoylferrocene	2.05 ± 0.02	1.41 ± 0.03	C—C (Ph) 1.39 ± 0.03 C=O 1.21 ± 0.01	175
Ferrocene-1,1'-disulfonyl chloride	1.99 ± 0.02	1.38 ± 0.06	S—O 1.55 S—Cl 2.06 S—C 1.64	168
1,1'(Tetramethylethylene)-ferrocene	1.97 ± 0.02 (min.) 2.11 ± 0.02 (max.)	1.45 ± 0.03	Angle between ring planes, 23°	21
α-Keto-1,1'-trimethylene ferrocene	2.008 (min.) 2.072 (max.)	1.428	Angle between ring planes, 9.8°	83
Ruthenocene	2.21 ± 0.02	1.43 ± 0.03	Inter-ring 3.68 ± 0.01	70, 71
Osmocene	2.22		Inter-ring 3.71	82

[a] By electron diffraction.

(4) in the crystal* (173, 186). The 1,3′ configuration has also been suggested for diacetyl- and dipropionylferrocene on the basis of less detailed crystallographic data (175).

(2)   (3)   (4)

Dibenzoferrocene has the gauche conformation (5), which may be stabilized by dispersion forces between the benzenoid rings (185). This substance is of some theoretical interest since it is not clear how much of the initial benzenoid character of the six-membered ring is retained in the complex. Unfortunately, the x-ray study does not provide sufficiently precise values of the atomic coordinates to settle this point. However, the ease with which this ring is hydrogenated (44, 148) suggests that it may have lost much of its delocalization energy.

(5)

PHYSICAL PROPERTIES AND THERMODYNAMIC QUANTITIES

These data are summarized in Table 3-3. Literature references are given in parentheses and, where conflicting data exist, the reference selected provides the best source of comparative data for the three metallocenes. Additional references are provided in the footnotes.

MAGNETIC SUSCEPTIBILITY

The magnetic properties of the iron group metallocenes and some of their derivatives are summarized in Table 3-4. Molar susceptibilities of

* Since the rings are relatively free to rotate in these and probably in all biscyclopentadienyl complexes in all but the crystalline state, only one heteroannular disubstituted derivative exists in these states. These derivatives are generally designated as 1,1′ derivatives without prejudice as to the relative orientation of substituents.

Table 3-3
Physical and Thermodynamic Properties

	FERROCENE	RUTHENOCENE	OSMOCENE
Color	*Orange*	*Pale Yellow*	*Colorless*
M.P. (°C)	174°	199°	229°
B.P.$_{760}$ (°C)	249° (86)[a,b]	278[a]	311[a]
Triple point (°C)	183° (86)[c]	—	—
Density, γ_{25} (g./cm.^{3})	1.49 (52)	1.86 (52)	2.60 (52)
Molecular vol. (cm.^{3}/g.)	124.7 (52)	124.6 (52)	123.4 (52)
Decomp. temp. (°C)	470° (52)	610° (52)	540° (52)
Vapor pressure constants: log $P_{mm} = A - B/T$ (52)			
Solid A	10.0335[d]	10.1869[f]	10.0186
B	3565.1[d]	3860.8[f]	3955.8
Liquid A	7.5407[d]	8.0073	7.0015
B	2432.8[d]	2821.2	2404.3
Heat of sublimation, solid (kcal./mole)[a]			
	16.29[d]	17.64	18.00
Heat of vaporization, liquid (kcal./mole)[a]			
	11.12[e]	12.89	10.99
Heat of fusion (kcal./mole)[a]			
	5.17[e]	4.75	7.01
Heat of formation from: $M(g) + 2C_5H_5 (g) \rightarrow M(C_5H_5)_2 (g)$			
ΔH°_{298}(kcal./mole)	−147 (195)	−187 (52)	−187 (52)
Standard heat of formation from elements of $C_{10}H_{10}M$ (s) by combustion			
ΔHf°_{298} (kcal./mole)	33.8 (26, 195)[g]		
Data derived from spectroscopic measurements for $C_{10}H_{10}M$ (g) (96)			
$\Delta Hf^{\circ}_{298.16}$ (kcal./mole)	50.61		
$\Delta Ff^{\circ}_{298.16}$ (kcal./mole)	75.97		
$\Delta Sf^{\circ}_{298.16}$ (kcal./mole)	−85.07		
$\Delta Hf^{\circ}f^{\circ}$ (kcal./mole)	57.5		

For thermodynamic quantities, C_p°, $(H^{\circ} - E_0^{\circ})/T$, $-(F^{\circ} - E_0^{\circ})/T$ and S° for ferrocene from 0°–300°K, see refs. 36 and 38; from 298.16°–1500°K, see ref. 96.

[a] Calculated from data given by ref. 52.
[b] See ref. 197 for additional comments.
[c] At a pressure of 162 mm.
[d] For other values, see refs. 25, 37, and 86.
[e] For other values, see ref. 86.
[f] For other values, see ref. 25.
[g] Calculated from data given by ref. 86. A more accurate value, based on the spectroscopically determined thermodynamic quantities (96) and the heat of sublimation of ferrocene measured by Edwards and Kington (37) is 33.08 kcal./mole.

33

diamagnetic substances are given directly in cgs units where these data are available from bulk susceptibility measurements. For paramagnetic compounds, susceptibilities are given in Bohr magnetons, corrected for diamagnetic contributions. All measurements were determined on the solids.

Table 3-4
Molar Susceptibilities

COMPOUND	SUSCEPTIBILITY	TEMPERATURE ($^\circ$K)	REFERENCE
$Fe(C_5H_5)_2$	$-125 \cdot 10^{-6}$	298	40, 49, 119, 159, 192
$Fe(C_5H_5)_2^+ I_{2.25}^-$	2.34 ± 0.12	90, room temp.	40
$Fe(C_5H_5)_2^+ BF_4^-$	2.49	90, 190, 294	170
$Fe(C_5H_5)_2^+$ picrate	2.26	298	192
[a]$Fe(C_9H_7)_2$	$-175 \pm 5 \times 10^{-6}$	90, 292, 297	46, 127, 159
[b]$Fe(C_9H_{11})_2$	Diamagnetic	90, 293	46
$Fe(C_{10}H_9)-Fe(C_{10}H_9)$	$-92.5 \cdot 10^{-6}$	293	119
[a]$Ru(C_9H_7)_2$	Diamagnetic	90, 289	46, 49
[b]$Ru(C_9H_{11})_2$	Diamagnetic	90,291	48
$Os(C_5H_5)_2$	$-193 \cdot 10^{-6}$	293	52, 49
	$-181 \cdot 10^{-6}$	90	52

[a] C_9H_7 = indenyl
[b] C_9H_{11} = tetrahydroindenyl.

The fact that the ferricenium cation has a susceptibility significantly greater than its spin-only value (1.73 B.M.) has been cited as evidence that its ground state is $^2E_{2g}[(12)(a_{1g})^2(e_{2g})^3]$ rather than $^2A_{1g}[(12)(e_{2g})^4(a_{1g})^1]$ (94).

The principal susceptibilities of ferrocene have recently been determined by Mulay and Fox (110, 112) from single crystal anisotropy measurements and crystallographic data (35). These results are shown in Fig. 3-1(*a*).

Mulay and Fox (112) have attempted to account for the anisotropy difference, $\Delta K_\perp$, between K_3 and the average of K_1 and K_2 in terms of a π-orbital ring current (125). The particular model adopted is that derived from the molecular orbital treatment of Moffitt, in which each of the rings is bonded to the metal atom by a single $d\pi$—$p\pi$ bond, leaving four electrons to circulate in each ring. Although the agreement between the calculated and observed values of $\Delta K_\perp$ is good, the model adopted is hardly admissible in the light of the later, more detailed theoretical treatments. Furthermore, it is not clear how much of a contribution to the ring currents is to be associated with the electron pair of the metal-ring bond. Pauling has given a valence bond treatment of ferrocene in which somewhat less than five electrons are said to circulate in each ring (126), assuming no contribution from metal-to-ring bonds. On this basis Mulay and Fox (112) have argued that the Fischer picture of octahedral type bonding in ferrocene is unacceptable.

It is nevertheless interesting to note that the molecular susceptibilities, including the anisotropy in the equatorial plane (K_1 and K_2), can be

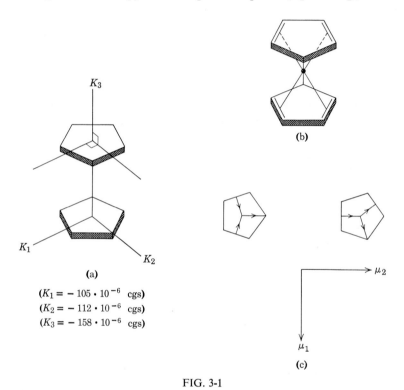

K_3

(b)

K_1

K_2

(a)

($K_1 = -105 \cdot 10^{-6}$ cgs)
($K_2 = -112 \cdot 10^{-6}$ cgs)
($K_3 = -158 \cdot 10^{-6}$ cgs)

μ_2

μ_1

(c)

FIG. 3-1

accounted for in terms of just such bonding. In this approach, each of the approximately octahedral type bonds shown in Fig. 3-1(b) is assigned an equivalent diamagnetic susceptibility directed along the metal-ring bond. If these susceptibilities are now formalized in terms of point magnetic dipoles, it is possible to calculate the relative magnitudes of the two resultant orthogonal magnetic dipoles in a plane parallel to the two rings by averaging over the five equivalent resonance forms for each ring. Two of these forms are shown in Fig. 3-1(c).

From the directions assigned to μ_1 and μ_2, these must be associated with K_1 and K_2 respectively. If now μ_1 is assigned a value of -105×10^{-6} cgs, the calculated value of μ_2 is -111×10^{-6} cgs in excellent agreement with the measurements. Furthermore, if each of the three equivalent metal-to-ring bonds is pictured as being directed from the metal atom to a point in space somewhat below the ring plane (~ 0.7 Å), as would be expected for $d\pi$—$p\pi$ type bonding, then the observed value of K_3 can likewise be reproduced.

Nesmeyanov has recently reported the magnetic properties of several polyferrocenylene and ferrocene alkane polymers (119, 120). In the solid state some of the polymers obtained by condensing ferrocene with alkylene dihalides are claimed to be paramagnetic. Furthermore, the para-magnetism is said to increase rather than decrease, as would be expected, with increasing temperature. No field dependence suggestive of ferro-magnetism was observed.

MASS SPECTRA

The mass spectra of a series of biscyclopentadienyl derivatives of V, Cr, Mn, Fe, Co, Ni, Ru, and Mg, as well as biscyclopentadienylrhenium hydride, have been given by Friedman, Irsa, and Wilkinson (55). With the exception of the last compound, the major fragments observed were the parent molecule ion, $C_{10}H_{10}M^+$, and those formed by dissociation of C_5H_5 fragments, $C_5H_5M^+$ and M^+. The comparatively weak, metal-ring bond in the magnesium and manganese compounds is manifested by a signifi-cantly lower relative yield of the parent molecule ion for these substances compared with the remaining more nearly covalent compounds (196). Smaller variations in the relative proportions of the three ions for the covalent derivatives are not easily interpreted. Nevertheless, the increasing stabilities of molecule ions $C_{10}H_{10}Ni^+$, $C_{10}H_{10}Fe^+$, and $C_{10}H_{10}Ru^+$ does accurately parallel the increasing metal-ring bond strengths in these substances (95–97, 195).

Since biscyclopentadienyl metal derivatives are in general fairly volatile, they serve as useful vehicles for the determination of isotopic abundances and masses of the metal nuclei. In this manner the ratios of V^{50}/V^{51} and Re^{185}/Re^{187} were checked (55) and more accurate isotope abundance measurements for ruthenium were obtained (54).

Some use has recently been made of the mass spectra of substituted ferrocenes for the determination of their molecular weights and purity (23). As with the parent substance, the preponderant peak is that due to the molecule ion.

Reed and Tabrizi (132) have also examined the spectra of a number of ferrocene derivatives and tentatively conclude that those possessing aliphatic side chains do not exhibit the tendency toward facile "benzylic" type C—C or C—H cleavage so characteristic of similarly constituted benzene derivatives. Instead, side-chain fragmentation follows the pattern anticipated of the aliphatic system.

INFRARED AND RAMAN SPECTRA

General aspects

A detailed analysis of the infrared and Raman spectra of ferrocene, decadeuteroferrocene, and ruthenocene has been given by Lippincott and Nelson (97), following two earlier preliminary reports (95, 96). A similar treatment has also been provided for ferrocene by Mayants, Lokshin, and Shaltuper (103). Table 3-5 summarizes the assignments made for the infrared bands of ferrocene and ruthenocene from these analyses. Also included in the table are spectral data for osmocene recently reported by Rausch, Fischer and, Grubert (52, 130, 131) and some of the far infrared data of Fritz and Schneider for ruthenocene and osmocene (57). The assignments by these latter authors are based largely on a comparison with the data of Lippincott and Nelson and, with the possible exception of the peaks beyond 800 cm.$^{-1}$, appear reasonably secure. In addition to the peaks listed in Table 3-5, each of the metallocenes exhibits a series of five closely spaced weak absorptions in the region of 1700 cm.$^{-1}$, which may represent combination and overtone bands involving C—H bending modes (97).

Lippincott and Nelson have also included in their paper the results of a normal coordinate analysis of the cyclopentadienyl rings in ferrocene (97). The calculated valence force symmetry constants were shown to be quite comparable to those calculated for benzene and the tropylium ion.

Based on a comparison of the peak positions and estimated force constants for metal-ring symmetric and antisymmetric stretching frequencies in ferrocene and ruthenocene, it has been concluded that the rings are more tightly bound in the ruthenium compound (57, 97). Similar arguments suggest that the metal ring-bond in nickelocene is relatively weak in agreement with thermochemical (195) and mass spectral data (55).

Fritz has discussed the variation in infrared spectral bands for a series of mono-, bis-, and triscyclopentadienyl metal compounds (56). While the first four absorptions in Table 3-5 do not exhibit any pronounced or regular variation,* the C—H ($\perp$) bending mode shows a progressive shift to lower frequency as the metal-ring bond becomes more ionic. Thus,

---

* See, however, ref. 131.

this vibration occurs in the region of 800 cm.$^{-1}$ for the covalent Fe, Ru, and Os metallocenes but is at 701 cm.$^{-1}$ for potassium cyclopentadienide. Other biscyclopentadienyl compounds of intermediate bond type such as those of V and Cr exhibit absorption in the region between these extremes.

Table 3-5
Infrared Frequency Assignments for Ferrocene, Ruthenocene, and Osmocene

	FREQUENCIES (cm.$^{-1}$)		
ASSIGNMENT	Ferrocene[e]	Ruthenocene[e]	Osmocene[f]
C—H stretch	3085	3100	3095
Antisymmetric C—C stretch	1411	1413	1405
Antisymmetric ring breath	1108	1103	1096
C—H bend (‖)[a]	1002	1002	995
C—H bend (⊥)[b]	811	806	819
Antisymmetric ring tilt	492	528[h](446)[g]	428[g]
Antisymmetric ring-M stretch	478	446 (379)[g]	353[g]
Ring-M bend	170[c]	185[d]	

[a] Parallel to the plane of the cyclopentadienyl ring.
[b] Perpendicular to the plane of the cyclopentadienyl ring.
[c] Reported to have been observed by E. D. Palik, Ohio State University, by Lippincott and Nelson (97), their reference 15.
[d] Calculated by Lippincott and Nelson (97).
[e] Determined as a nujol mull (97).
[f] Determined in KBr (131).
[g] Determined as a nujol mull (57).
[h] Not observed by Fritz and Schneider (57), who found instead a band at 379 cm.$^{-1}$ not reported by Lippincott and Nelson (97).

In addition, the intensity of the band near 1100 cm.$^{-1}$, which is strong in the covalent compounds, was observed to decrease preceptibly in the more ionic derivatives.

Structurally significant bands

The two absorption peaks exhibited by ferrocene near 9 and 10 μ (1100 and 1000 cm.$^{-1}$), have proved invaluable in assigning structures to polysubstituted ferrocenes. The spectral generalization, often referred to in the literature as the 9–10 rule, may be stated as follows. *Ferrocene derivatives, in which one ring is unsubstituted, exhibit absorption near*

9 and 10 μ, while those having both rings substituted lack such absorption.* Since this rule was first proposed for ferrocene derivatives (141), the number of compounds which have been shown to conform to it has grown enormously (117, 131, 143).† In certain cases, however, substituents in a heteroannular derivative may themselves exhibit absorption at these wavelengths, so that the absence of bands at 9 and 10 μ is generally a more reliable guide to structure than is their presence. However, the number of instances of such complications is apparently rather small (60, 101, 123, 136).

The spectral region near 11 μ has been shown to be of value in distinguishing between 1,2 and 1,3 disubstituted acetyl-alkyl-, acetyl-aryl-, and diarylferrocenes. Those derivatives having a 1,2 grouping of substituents exhibit a single peak in this region, while those with 1,3 disposed groups show two peaks (143–146). These points are discussed at greater length in Chapters 4 and 6.‡

The additivity principle

To a very good first approximation there appears to be little coupling between the vibrational modes associated with substituents in one ferrocene ring with modes associated with substitutents in the second ring.§ Thus, with the exception of the bands at 9 and 10 μ, the infrared spectra of such derivatives closely approximate the sum of the spectra of the constituent unsymmetrically substituted ferrocenes (Fig. 3-2). There is little

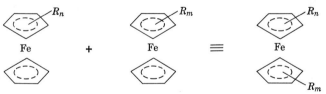

FIG. 3-2   Spectral additivity principle. R_n and R_m represent substituent(s) on the ring indicated.

* There is little reason to expect that ruthenocene and osmocene derivatives would not likewise conform to this generalization. The limited data for derivatives of these metallocenes support this conclusion.
† Quantitative applications of the 9–10 rule have also been discussed (141, 61).
‡ Nesmeyanov and Kazitsym have (118) suggested that 1,3-substitution in dialkyl-ferrocenes is characterized by absorption at 7.8 μ, but the validity of the correlation is doubtful since the structures of the compounds used in deriving the rule were shown subsequently to be incorrect (137a).
§ Kazitsyna, Lokshin and Nesmeyanov (89) have noted some displacements in the position of carbonyl absorption in heteroannularly disubstituted ferrocenoic acids and their methyl esters, but these are rather small.

reason to believe that this generalization will not hold for ruthenocene and osmocene derivatives as well.

ELECTRONIC SPECTRA

The ultraviolet and visible absorption spectra of the metallocenes and of the ferricenium and ruthenicenium cations are reproduced in Figs. 3-3 and 3-4.

Scott and Becker (160, 161) have presented a detailed discussion of band assignments for the absorption and emission spectra of ferrocene and

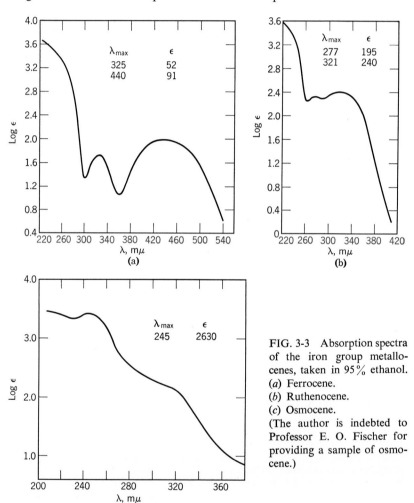

FIG. 3-3   Absorption spectra of the iron group metallocenes, taken in 95% ethanol.
(a) Ferrocene.
(b) Ruthenocene.
(c) Osmocene.
(The author is indebted to Professor E. O. Fischer for providing a sample of osmocene.)

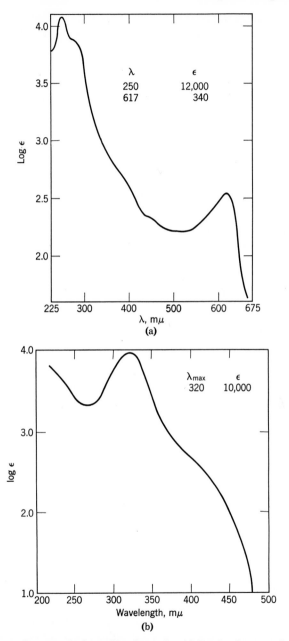

FIG. 3-4 Absorption spectra of metallicenium salts. (*a*) Ferricenium tetrafluoroborate, taken in water. (*b*) Ruthenicenium perchlorate in 0.01 *N* perchloric acid. (Reprinted with permission from Wilkinson, ref. 193.)

nickelocene within the framework of the several theoretical treatments of ferrocene published through 1960. The two long wavelength bands at 440 and 325 mμ in the spectrum of ferrocene can be assigned with some certainty to (d-d) type transitions within the ligand field formalism. The upper level is apparently mixed to a greater extent with ring orbitals than is the ground state, judging from the moderate sensitivity of the position of these bands to ring substitution (160, 161). Since these absorptions exhibit a bathochromic shift when electron acceptor substituents are placed on the rings, the charge-transfer excitation is from the metal to the rings (100, 147, 160). The shorter wavelength ferrocene bands (between 200 and 300 mμ) may not be assigned with equal certainty, but possibly involve either similar charge-transfer type transitions, ring localized transitions, or combinations of these.

A comparison of the spectra of a variety of mono- and disubstituted arylferrocenes has led to the suggestion that the separate ring chromophores do not interact appreciably (100, 147).

Yamada, Nakahara, and Tsuchida (202, 203) have reported studies of the dichroism of ferrocene crystals and suggest that for the bands at 324 and 440 mμ polarization of the electric vector is principally in the direction perpendicular to the rings. The intensity of the lower wavelength band near 250 mμ was reported to be independent of crystal orientation.

Brand and Snedden (17) examined the spectrum of ferrocene in a series of halogenated alkane solvents and have concluded that the weak absorption near 307 mμ, which is observed in these solutions and which had previously been attributed to a solvent shift of the 325 mμ absorption (86, 196), is a charge-transfer excitation from the metallocene to the alkyl halide. The qualitative correlation observed between the wavelength of this band and the half wave potential of the alkyl halide, which is a measure of its tendency to act as an electron acceptor, is in agreement with this interpretation (17). The decomposition of carbon tetrachloride solutions of ferrocene on irradiation is doubtless due to such an electron transfer process.

$$Fe(C_5H_5)_2 + RX \rightarrow Fe(C_5H_5)_2^+ + R\cdot + X^-$$
$$\downarrow$$
$$Fe^{+3}$$

X-RAY ABSORPTION EDGE

Several measurements of x-ray absorption of ferrocene, ferricenium chloride, dibenzoferrocene, octahydrodibenzoferrocene, and ferrocene polymers have been reported (5, 14, 15, 50, 84, 88, 187, 188). In general, absorption peaks on the low energy side of such spectra are believed to correspond to excitation of a $1s$ electron to the lowest unoccupied metal p or f shell. The principal maximum for these compounds is near 20 e.v. with a weak shoulder at 10 e.v. The high energy peak has been assigned to a $1s \rightarrow 5p$ transition and is claimed to support the view that biscyclopentadienyl complexes may be regarded as so-called "penetration complexes" in which metal $3d$, $4s$, and $4p$ levels are filled. This interpretation has been challenged by Wilkinson and Cotton (197). The weak shoulder at 10 e.v. has been attributed to excitation of a $1s$ electron to an antibonding molecular orbital of $4p$-type symmetry (50).

NUCLEAR MAGNETIC RESONANCE SPECTRA

Solution spectra

Ring proton chemical shifts for the iron group metallocenes are summarized in Table 3-6.

Table 3-6
Chemical Shifts of Metallocene Protons[a]

METALLOCENE	CHEMICAL SHIFT (τ)
Ferrocene	5.96
Ruthenocene	5.58
Osmocene	5.29

[a] Five per cent solutions in carbon tetrachloride.

Viewed as aromatic systems, the chemical shifts in these substances are anomalous since they lie at much higher field than would be anticipated, assuming a π-orbital ring current, typical of aromatic systems, to be associated with each cyclopentadienyl ring. Proton resonances in these compounds appear at approximately 3 p.p.m. to higher field than in benzenoid compounds. While a drift of electrons from the metal atom might provide some additional shielding, its magnitude would hardly be large enough to account for the observed chemical shifts (53, 93).

The effect of the metal atom itself may, of course, not be neglected, and is apparent in the inequivalence of α and β protons in (**6**) (64) and of ring protons in the highly splayed bridged ferrocene (**7**) (137).*

* Some other examples of the shielding effect of the metal atom on olefinic protons in metal olefin complexes are to be found in references 9, 22, 58, and 65. A recent review of these compounds has been given by Bennett (10).

(6)   (7)

(M = Co, Rh)

The proton magnetic resonance spectra of substituted ferrocenes are of considerable value in assigning structures to these derivatives. More detailed discussions of these are given for each type of derivative, but several of their common features may be noted here. In general, electron withdrawing substituents lead to pronounced chemical shift differences, in some cases as much as 0.3 p.p.m., between protons in the 2 and 3 positions with respect to the substituent. Protons in the 2 position of these compounds lie at lower field and may be displaced by as much as 0.75 p.p.m. from the protons of the parent compound. For cyclopentadienyl rings which are singly substituted by electron withdrawing groups, $H_{2,5}$ and $H_{3,4}$ generally give rise to an unsymmetrical pair of triplets corresponding to the spectrum of an A_2B_2 case with $J_{adj} \cong J_{cross}$ and small compared with the chemical shift difference between $H_{2,5}$ and $H_{3,4}$. Derivatives bearing electron donor groups such as alkyl substituents do not generally exhibit a chemical shift difference between H_2 and H_3, although protons on the substituted ring may be shifted slightly to higher field.

The C^{13} magnetic resonance spectrum of ferrocene has been determined by Lauterbur (92). Although the C^{13} resonance in ferrocene occurs at significantly higher field than in benzene, and corresponds roughly to that calculated for the cyclopentadienide ion, these results do not necessarily require a similar charge distribution in the metallocene since, as pointed out by Lauterbur, ring-metal bonding may have an important effect on the chemical shift. The magnitude of the C—H spin coupling constant was found to be close to that observed for benzene. Thus, the C—H bond is essentially an sp^2 hybrid, although about 50% s character would be calculated for this bond on the basis of the internal ring angles (108°) and orthogonality principles (27). Similar anomalous C—H coupling constants have, however, been observed by Lauterbur in pyrrole, furan, and thiophene.

The proton resonance spectrum of the ferricenium ion is not observed due to line broadening. By extrapolating the chemical shifts observed for known mixtures of ferrocene and ferricenium ion, to zero ferrocene concentration, an approximate chemical shift of $-10\,\tau$ may be estimated for ring protons in the cation (148). This represents a considerably smaller displacement in the position of proton resonance than has been observed in the paramagnetic species nickelocene, titanocene, and vanadocene (104, 105).

Broad line spectra—ring rotational barrier

Proton magnetic resonance spectra of crystalline ferrocene and ruthenocene have been reported (79, 80, 106), as have data for derivatives of these compounds (107–109, 111, 113). In general, line widths and second moments increase with increasing ring substitution and with decreasing temperature. The potential barrier to ring rotation has been measured for a number of these compounds by determination of line widths as a function of temperature. In general, the activation energy associated with re-orientation of the rings is rather low and ranges from 2 to 5 kcal/mole.* The energy barrier in ruthenocene and its derivatives appears to be about 1 kcal. greater than in the corresponding ferrocenes (111). These data are completely in accord with earlier chemical experience on the basis of which the essential free rotation of the rings in ferrocene was inferred (141, 142). Thus, no isomeric heteroannularly disubstituted ferrocenes have been shown to exist, and the number of isomeric di- and poly-substituted ferrocenes formed in any reaction is never greater than the number predicted on the basis of the free rotating model.

ELECTRON SPIN RESONANCE SPECTRA

No electron spin resonance is observed for the ferricenium ion either in the solid state or in solution, due to the fact that the ground state of the ion is orbitally degenerate (62, 94, 138). The paramagnetic resonance absorption reported to be observed by Nöth, Voitlander, and Nussbaum (114) with solutions of ferricenium ions in acetone has been shown by Golding and Orgel to arise from ferric ions formed by decomposition of the salt (62).†

DIPOLE MOMENTS

Data of dipole moments for the iron group metallocenes and several of their derivatives are collected in Table 3-7. As expected, all of the parent

* Struchkov (174) had earlier discussed the problem of the rotational barrier in ferrocene and had suggested a value of 3–10 kcal./mole.
† Nesmeyanov and co-workers (120) have also reported observing resonance absorption with ferricenium salt solutions, which is possibly due to such decomposition. They also claim to have observed absorption by the solid salt (not specified) in contradistinc-tion to the results of Golding and Orgel (62).

substances have a zero dipole moment. While this is apparently true for biscyclopentadienyl compounds of Ni, Co, Cr, and V in benzene (51, 172), Strohmeier and von Hobe (172) have shown that those complexes in which the metal-ring bond is partially ionic as in Cp_2Cr and Cp_2V exhibit measurable moments (~ 0.6 D) in dioxane solution. The effect is attributed to donor interaction of the solvent with the metal atom. The

Table 3-7
Dipole Moments of Metallocenes and Their Derivatives

COMPOUND	μ (DEBYES)	REFERENCE
Ferrocene	0	(141, 190, 192)
Ruthenocene	0	(45, 51)
Osmocene	0	(51)
Acetylferrocene	3.02	(134)
1,1′-Diacetylferrocene	4.23	(134)
p-Chlorophenylferrocene	2.06	(139)
1,1′-Bis-p-chlorophenylferrocene	3.12 ± 0.03	(164)
Dibenzoferrocene	0	(51)
Dibenzoruthenocene	0	(190)

implication that the metal atom bears a partial positive charge finds support in the theoretical treatment of Shustorovich and Dyatkina (165) and in the dipole moments of several π-cyclopentadienyl metal carbonyl and nitrosyl complexes in which the ring-metal moment ($M^+ - C_p^-$) is estimated to be $2 - 2.5$ D (76). This is opposite to the sense of the ring-metal bond dipole in arenechromium tricarbonyl complexes (76).*

The dipole moments of acetylferrocene and p-chlorophenylferrocene are considerably greater than those of their benzenoid analogs (aceto-phenone 2.90 D, p-chlorobiphenyl 1.57 D), reflecting the pronounced electron releasing capacity of the ferrocene rings.

The dipole moment of 1,1′-diacetylferrocene is quite close to the value predicted for a free rotation of the cyclopentadienyl rings. However, the dipole moment for bis-p-chlorophenylferrocene is about 0.2 D greater than is predicted from theory, and may reflect a slight stabilization of conformations in which, as a result of dispersion forces, the benzene rings are partially eclipsed.

The zero dipole moments reported for dibenzoferrocene and dibenzo-ruthenocene require that no dipole be associated with the 6-5 ring system of each of these compounds.

* An excellent review of dipole moment data for π-cyclopentadienyl and π-arene metal complexes has been given by Fichtel (42).

BASICITY

In strong acid media both ferrocene and ruthenocene undergo extensive protonation on the metal atom (28). The evidence for this is derived principally from the n.m.r. spectra of the cations in boron trifluoride hydrate solution. These exhibit high field resonance characteristic of metal bound protons (66, 198). The high field absorption in the spectrum of the ferrocene cation at 12.09 τ is a broad, unresolved multiplet, due to spin coupling of this proton with all the ring protons. Ring protons, in turn, given rise to the expected doublet absorption at 5.03 τ ($J = 1.3$ cps). Apparently proton exchange between the solvent and the ruthenocene cation is sufficiently rapid to lead to exchange collapse of this spin coupling. Both the high and low field absorptions (17.2 and 4.67 τ) appear as sharp singlets. Osmocene must be a considerably weaker base than the other metallocenes. The absence of high field absorption in boron trifluoride hydrate is attributable to either a much smaller extent of protonation or to rapid proton exchange between solvent and the metal.

Although the existence of a ring protonated σ-complex is not demonstrated by these experiments, such a species must nevertheless be in equilibrium with the more stable cation (at least for ferrocene), since ring proton exchange takes place in strongly acidic media (28, 121).

Protonation of the metal atom has been suggested to account for the failure of the metallocene nucleus to migrate in the acid catalyzed rearrangement of metallocenylphenylcarbinyl azides (12, 13, 19, 20) and for the relatively low basicity of p-ferrocenylazobenzenes (98).

Metal protonation seems to be the rule in cyclopentadienyl complexes of the transition elements as well as in their carbonyls (29, 31, 63, 67), but in those complexes of conjugated olefins in which one or more of the olefinic groups are not employed in metal bonding such as, for example, cycloheptatriene, cyclooctatriene, and cyclooctatetraene iron tricarbonyls protonation occurs on the ring to give a stabilized pentadienylic cation (22, 30, 32).

Ballhausen and Dahl (4) have suggested that in the protonated metallocenes the cyclopentadienyl rings are no longer parallel but are somewhat tilted so that the angle ω, defined by perpendiculars to each ring from the metal atom, lies between 135 and 180° [Fig. 3-5(a)]. On the basis of their molecular orbital treatment, they conclude that the overlap integral for metal-ring bonds is relatively insensitive to the value of ω, and hence considerable splaying of the rings is in principle allowed without significant loss in bond energy. Moreover, the altered geometry brings about a hydridization of the nonbonding metal $3d_{z^2}$ and $3d_{xy,x^2-y^2}$ orbitals to give three mutually orthogonal orbitals which lie in the xy plane and are very strongly space oriented in the direction of the ring opening, as shown in Figure 3-5(*b*).

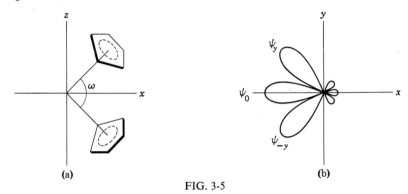

(a)   (b)

FIG. 3-5

In the protonated iron group metallocenes and in the neutral hydride Cp_2ReH (63),* the additional ligand probably makes use of the ψ_0 orbital, since repulsion of electrons in the remaining filled orbitals is thereby minimized. The n.m.r. spectrum of the cation $Cp_2ReH_2^+$ (63), formed by protonation of the hydride, indicates that the protons are equivalent and suggests that each is bound by one of the equivalent ψ_y and ψ_{-y} orbitals.

The theory very nicely accounts for the existence of such metal hydrides as Cp_2MoH_2, Cp_2WH_2, and Cp_2TaH_3, for the related cations $Cp_2MoH_3^+$ and $Cp_2WH_3^+$ (67) and for the complex $Cp_2WH_2 \cdot BF_3$ (162). As expected, the tantalum compound does not form any stable cation. The n.m.r. spectra of these compounds provide additional evidence for the spatial distinctions between the ψ orbitals (67). Both protons in Cp_2MoH_2 and Cp_2WH_2 are equivalent as in the isoelectronic cation $Cp_2ReH_2^+$, but in $Cp_2WH_3^+$ and Cp_2TaH_3 the protons give rise to a resonance absorption pattern compatible with that expected for an A_2B set.

Further confirmation of these suggestions has recently been provided by x-ray analysis of Cp_2MoH_2 (11). The rings in the molecule are in fact splayed, with an angle of $25° \pm 3°$ between them, and the hydrogen atoms located by difference Fourier methods were found to make an HMoH angle of $90° \pm 10°$, in excellent agreement with theory.

ELECTRON TRANSFER REACTIONS

General aspects

One of the simplest and most characteristic reactions of the metallocenes is their oxidation to cationic species through loss of one or more electrons

* The prefix Cp designates the cyclopentadienyl ring.

from the metal atom. Oxidation may be effected electrolytically (124) and photolytically (17), as well as by a variety of organic and inorganic oxidants, and the resulting cations are referred to as ferricenium, ruthenicenium, and osmicenium ions.*

While chemical or anodic oxidation of ferrocene and ruthenocene apparently involves a one electron-transfer process (124, 141, 192, 193), osmocene loses two electrons on oxidation with silver sulfate or ferric chloride (52). Under conditions of chronopotentiometric oxidation in acetonitrile, both ruthenocene and osmocene undergo two electron-transfer processes, the latter compound exhibiting two well-defined waves (18, 91). Thus, in a general way, the behavior of these substances reflects the typical increased stabilization of higher oxidation states of the second- and third-row transition elements.

Ferricenium salt solutions exhibit a characteristic dichroism. Dilute solutions appear blue or green, while more concentrated solutions are blood red (141). Ruthenicenium salt solutions are generally pale yellow (193), while those formed by oxidation of osmocene are orange or red brown in color (52).

Generally, the cations can be reduced by a number of chemical reagents such as stannous chloride, sodium bisulfite, or ascorbic acid.

While both ferricenium and ruthenicenium salts are moderately stable in aqueous acid solution, they decompose rapidly in neutral and basic solutions, giving in part the neutral metallocene and hydroxides of the metal (62, 141, 167, 193). Osmocene behaves quite differently. Oxidation with ferric ammonium sulfate gives the cation $[(C_5H_5)OsOH]^+$ isolated as the hexafluoro phosphate. With iodine in aqueous sulfuric acid, the corresponding iodo cation $[(C_5H_5)_2OsI]^+$ is formed. The anion is apparently bound covalently in these ions, since the salts are diamagnetic and iodide is not replaced in the latter cation on titration with silver sulfate (52).

Little is known of the physical and chemical properties of substituted metallicenium cations, although the effect of substituents on the redox potentials of the parent nuclei has been extensively probed. 1,1'-Diethylferrocene is reported to give liquid ferricenium salts when oxidized with iodine or ferric chloride (141) and Nesmeyanov and Vol'kenau (115) have briefly mentioned the oxidation of several alkylferrocenes, but give no details. Acylferricenium salts appear to be relatively unstable (141). However, the blue amorphous ferricenium salts derived from benzoylferrocene and from diferrocenyl ketone are reported to be stable in aqueous acid solution (141).

---

* The oxidation of ferrocene in the presence of triphenylmethyl chloride in nitromethane solution has also been reported (75).

The polarographic behavior of ferrocene and ruthenocene has been studied by Page and Wilkinson (124). In a 90% ethanol, sodium perchlorate, perchloric acid electrolyte, a thermodynamically reversible potential of −0.56 v *versus* the NHE (Latimer scale) was determined. Under the same conditions, ruthenocene did not exhibit identical anodic and cathodic half-wave potentials, but the average value (−0.63 ± 0.02 v) suggests that ruthenocene is less readily oxidized than ferrocene. Chronopotentiometric studies of the iron group metallocenes in acetonitrile likewise suggest an increase in oxidation potential from ferrocene to osmocene (91). However, Savitsky and Syrkin (152) have determined the equilibrium constants for the reactions of ferrocene and ruthenocene with iodine in benzene solution and report a value of −1.5 kcal/mole for the enthalpy of the reaction:

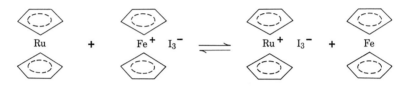

$$Ru \quad + \quad Fe^+ \ I_3^- \ \rightleftharpoons \ Ru^+ \ I_3^- \ + \ Fe$$

These results may, in large measure, be due to a change in the relative solvation energies of the two cations.

Metallocene derivatives

A number of studies concerned with the effect of substituents on the oxidation potential of ferrocene have been reported. Oxidation potentials of *p*-substituted monoarylferrocenes have been determined both titrimetrically in acetic acid (102) and by chronopotentiometry in acetonitrile (78). These show an excellent correlation with the Hammett σ_p constants with a value of −2.41 for the reaction constant in 75% acetic acid.

Little and co-workers (99) have recently extended these observations through chronopotentiometric determination of the potentials of a considerably larger number of *m*- and *p*-substituted phenylferrocenes, as well as several *o*-derivatives. Quarter-wave potentials were in general reversible and found to correlate well with Hammett σ constants for the *m*- and *p*-derivatives and with Tafts *o*-substituent constants (σ_0*) for the latter derivatives. The method is a useful one for the determination of secondary substituent constants, especially for σ_0*, since it is more convenient and more general than the procedure given by Taft (177).

Chronopotentiometric measurement of oxidation potentials of a variety of substituted ferrocenes, as well as some derivatives of ruthenocene and osmocene have been reported by Kuwana, Bublitz, and Hoh (18, 91), and by Hoh, McEwen, and Kleinberg (78). These potentials were found to exhibit a fair correlation with Taft's σ^* constants, but only for those substituents whose resonance interactions with the ring would be expected to be small.* A more general correlation could be made with σ_m or σ_p constants, but the latter was distinctly better (78).

Little (99a) has carried out further chronopotentiometric studies of mono- and 1,1'-disubstituted ferrocenes in acetonitrile solution which further demonstrate the correlation of potentials for these compounds with Hammett σ_p constants, but not with either σ^* or σ_I. The value of the reaction constant ρ was found to be -7.61. For the latter derivatives, quarter wave potentials were correlated with a summation of σ_p constants for a considerable diversity in the electronic nature and combination of substituents.

Polarographic half-wave potentials of various ferrocene derivatives have also been determined (16, 133, 179–182, 189), and Komenda and Tirouflet (90) have recently reported oscillopolarographic measurements on several ferrocene derivatives bearing electron donor or acceptor groups.† An excellent correlation was observed between the parameter ΔQ (related to the difference between the redox potential of ferrocene and the substituted compound) and σ_p, but not with σ_m or σ^*. The effect of the two substituents in heteroannularly disubstituted derivatives was found to be additive, and all of the reactions were reversible. As pointed out by these authors, the method constitutes a useful one for the determination of σ_p constants and is probably to be preferred over polarographic or chronopotentiometric measurements, since these may exhibit irreversible characteristics for some compounds (18, 73, 90, 91).‡

Gubin and Perevalova (68) have recently determined formal oxidation potentials for a number of monosubstituted ferrocenes by potentiometric titration in acetic acid-perchloric acid solution. In contrast to the results of others, they found that a correlation of oxidation potentials with σ_p could be obtained only if the data were divided into two sets, one for OMe, OAc, H, Me, Et, i-Pr substituents ($\rho = -4.23$) and the other including Ph, p-NO$_2$Ph, CO$_2$H, CO$_2$Me, I, Cl, Br substituents ($\rho = -7.94$). The results were rationalized by assuming that the second group of

---

* See also ref. 128 for a similar conclusion based on a somewhat greater diversity of —CH$_2$X-substituted ferrocenes.
† Three studies concerned with polarographic reduction of functional groups in several ferrocene and cyclopentadienylmanganese tricarbonyl derivatives have recently appeared (73, 74, 183).
‡ Komenda and Tirouflet (90) have calculated a value of $+0.48$ for σ_p -CHO by this method.

substituents interact directly with the metal atom, thereby abnormally increasing the oxidation potential of the derivative. While there appears to be some evidence for this type of interaction in solvolysis reactions, it is somewhat surprising to find the halogens included in the second substituent set, since their direct interaction with the metal atom might be expected to be opposite in effect to that of the remaining substituents in this set.*

In a subsequent paper (122), Nesmeyanov, Perevalova, and Gubin have modified their original conclusions and have suggested that their data for both mono- and 1,1'-disubstituted ferrocenes exhibit a good linear correlation with Taft's $\sigma_p{}^0$ constants (178).

Nesmeyanov, Perevalova, and Gubin (122, 128) have also determined the redox potentials of diferrocenyl and of a number of compounds with two ferrocenyl radicals separated by one or more atoms such as $-CH_2-$, $-Hg-$, $-CH_2CH_2-$, $-CH_2OCH_2-$, $-CN_2\overset{+}{N}(CH_3)_2CH_2-$. Virtual conjugation between the ferrocenyl nuclei in diferrocenyl is apparently not an important feature in determining the redox potential of this substance, since its potential (-0.189 v),† although lower than that of ferrocene (-0.245 v), is not greatly different from that of methylferrocene (-0.198 v) and is identical with the first potential of diferrocenylmethane (-0.189 v). By contrast, the difference between the first and second potentials of diferrocenylmethane ($\Delta = 0.119$ v) and of diferrocenyl-mercury ($\Delta = 0.372$ v) is appreciable. This difference falls off markedly as the saturated chain separating the ferrocene nuclei is lengthened, indicating that the effect on the second potential is primarily due to the electrostatic field of the ferricenium ion in the singly oxidized species.

In terms of the electronic structure of ferrocene, the variations observed in the oxidation potentials of its derivatives are by no means unexpected, since resonance or inductive effects of the substituent on the electron density of the rings would be expected to be transmitted effectively through the easily polarizable $d\pi$-$p\pi$ metal-ring bonds. The fact that the oxidation potentials correlate with σ_p but not with σ^+ substituent constants reflects the efficient transmission of these electronic effects to the rings, and suggests the absence of any appreciable resonance-type interactions between the rings and the metal atom.

---

* Based upon his observation that the quarter-wave chronopotentiometric potentials for acetoxy- and phenoxyferrocene showed irreversible characteristics, Little has suggested that the formal oxidation potentials reported by Gubin and Perevelova for acetoxy- and methoxyferrocenes, which were of particular importance in defining one of their linear plots, may be in error (99).

† Potentials measured vs. S.C.E.; sign convention that of Latimer.

Solvation and chelation of the ions

The solvation energy of ferricenium triiodide in ethanol has been estimated by Savitsky and is found to be close to that of cesium triiodide (154). From the relation between solvation energy for a series of triiodides and the ionic radii of their cations, it is concluded that the positive charge in the ferricenium ion is primarily concentrated on the metal atom. A number of studies of the association of the ferricenium cation with various anions and chelating reagents such as triiodide (17), chloride (72), thiocyanate, cyclohexanetetraacetic acid, citric acid, oxalic acid, and tartaric acid (166) have been reported. Not unexpectedly, chelation appears to stabilize the higher oxidation state of the metallocene (166).

Kinetics of electron transfer

The kinetics of the oxidation of ferrocene by iodine in aqueous ethanol have been studied by Savitsky and Syrkin (151). They calculated an activation energy and entropy of 14.6 kcal./mole and -5.85 cal./mole deg. for the reaction:

$$C_{10}H_{10}Fe + \tfrac{3}{2}I_2 \rightleftharpoons C_{10}H_{10}Fe^+ + I_3^-$$

Electron transfer between 10^{-4} molar solutions of ferrocene and the ferricenium ion has been studied by Stranks (171), by isotopic exchange, and by Dietrich and Wahl (33) by n.m.r. line broadening measurements. The approximate second order rate constants ($k > 7 \times 10^6$ at $25°$), determined by Stranks, are not significantly less than would be predicted for a diffusion controlled process, and the half time for exchange, even at $-75°$, was found to be of the order of a few milliseconds. Similar rapid exchange has been observed between cobaltocene and the cobalticenium cation (87, 194).

Analytical methods

A colorimetric procedure for the quantitative determination of ferric ion by titration of a standard solution of ferrocene has recently been described by Wolf, Franz, and Hennig (199, 200). The end point is indicated by a color change from red to blue, and an accuracy of 0.5% is claimed with no interference by a variety of other metal ions.

Simple methods for the detection of ferrocene in complex reaction mixtures by either destructive oxidation to ferric salts (8, 59) or complexation with potassium ferricyanide (7) have been described. Rosenberg and Riber (140) have recently reported a colorimetric procedure for the microanalytical determination of iron in ferrocene derivatives by destructive oxidation with nitric acid and hydrogen peroxide, followed by spectrophotometric determination of the ferric thiocyanate complex.

RADIOCHEMICAL STUDIES

The Szilard-Chalmers reaction in neutron irradiated ferrocene has been studied by Sutin and Dodson (176). They found that the yield of Fe^{59} ferrocene was about 12% after irradiation, but could be increased to about 20% by either allowing the samples to stand at room temperature for several weeks or by annealing at higher temperatures. During this postirradiation treatment, the yield of inorganic radioactive iron decreased by less than 1%. While the inorganic yield showed some dependence on the conditions of irradiation, being greatest when the proportion of fast neutrons in the flux was reduced, the yield of radioactive ferrocene was found to be far less dependent on the conditions of irradiation.

Neutron irradiation studies of ferricenium picrate have also been carried out by Jach and Sutin (81), who found that the yield of radioactive ferricenium salt was only 2.4% and that it was not significantly increased by heating the sample after irradiation.

A model for these reactions was suggested in which almost all neutron capture results in molecular decomposition. The radioactive organometallics are then formed by recombination of the recoil species $C_5H_5Fe\cdot$ or $C_5H_5Fe^+$ with cyclopentadienyl radicals.

Neutron irradiation of ruthenocene has been shown to yield radioactive biscyclopentadienylrhodium by neutron capture and β-decay (6).

$$C_{10}H_{10}Ru^{104}(n,\ \gamma)C_{10}H_{10}Ru^{105} \xrightarrow{\beta^-,\ \gamma} C_{10}H_{10}Rh^{105} \xrightarrow{\beta^-}$$

The efficiency of ferrocene as a scavenger of radicals formed on irradiation of carbon tetrachloride has been studied by Collinson, Dainton, and Gillis (24). A G_R value (number of radicals formed per 100 e.v. of energy absorbed) of 2.34 ± 0.07 was determined.

REDUCTION

Ferrocene is quite resistant to catalytic hydrogenation and indeed this aspect of its chemistry constituted one of the early pieces of evidence for its aromaticity (201). Although no comparable studies have been carried carried out with ruthenocene and osmocene, there is little reason to believe that their reactivity would be significantly different. The remarkable inertness of ferrocene may be judged by the observation that it is not hydrogenated in the presence of a rhodium catalyst over a period of several weeks while benzene is fully reduced under these conditions in five minutes (184). Quite similar observations have been recorded by Fischer (47) and by Balandin, Khidekel, and Patrikeev (3). Ferrocene can be reduced catalytically in the presence of a nickel catalyst but pressures of 280 atm. and temperatures of 300 to 340° are required (116). Even then, more than 50% of the substance is recovered unchanged after nine hours of such treatment. The products of reduction are cyclopentane and pyrophoric iron.

By contrast, reduction of ferrocene may be readily achieved with alkali metals in amine solutions. Trifan and Nicholas found the most efficacious of these systems to be lithium in ethylamine (184). Under these conditions, ferrocene is completely reduced within several minutes to iron and the cyclopentadienide anion. The mechanism of the reaction probably involves a stepwise addition of two electrons either at the metal atom or directly to the rings.

(11)

CHROMATOGRAPHIC ANALYSIS

Owing to their color, ferrocene derivatives are particularly well suited to chromatographic methods of purification and identification. Column chromatography, generally employing alumina, has been most widely used, and for various isomeric derivatives the order of elution has been shown to follow a regular pattern and hence constitute a useful primary indication of structure (69, 77, 135, 142, 144–146). Schlögl and co-workers have successfully employed paper chromatography with ferrocenecarboxylic acids and amino acids (155) and thin layer chromatography with a large variety of ferrocene derivatives (156–158). Vapor phase chromatography has not as yet found extensive use, but the separation of several isomeric acetyl-alkylferrocenes has been carried out (149), and even the relatively high melting diphenylferrocene isomers may be resolved by this means (150).

OTHER PHYSICAL MEASUREMENTS

Several studies of the Fe^{57} Mossbauer effect in ferrocene, ferricenium salts, and various ferrocene derivatives have recently been reported (41, 191, 204). Wertheim and Herber (191) found that ring substitution had little effect on either the quadrupole splitting (2.37 mm./sec.) or isomer shift (0.68 mm./sec., $T = 78°$ K) of ferrocene. For ferricenium tetrafluoroborate, room temperature values of 0.80 mm./sec. and 0.28 mm./sec. were determined by Zahn, Kienle, and Eicher (204) for the quadrupole splitting and isomer shift respectively. These authors have argued that the lower quadrupole splitting observed in the cation results from cancellation of negative quadrupole interactions due to bonding σ and π orbital electrons by positive quadrupole interactions associated with δ orbital electrons, and that therefore the electron involved in the oxidation of ferrocene must be removed from a $3d\delta$ metal orbital.

The ionization potential of ferrocene has been estimated by Friedman, Irsa, and Wilkinson to be 7.05 ± 0.1 e.v. from appearance potential measurements of the molecular ion (55). Brand and Snedden (17) cite an unpublished value of 8.33 ± 0.2 e.v., determined by Reed for the process

$$C_{10}H_{10}Fe(s) \rightarrow C_{10}H_{10}Fe(g) \rightarrow C_{10}H_{10}Fe^+(g)$$

by electron impact studies on crystalline ferrocene. When corrected for the heat of sublimation of ferrocene (37), this gives a value of 7.57 ± 0.2 e.v. for the ionization potential. Savitsky and Syrkin have estimated a value near 6 e.v. from oxidation studies of ferrocene by iodine (153).

Aroney, LeFevre, and Somasundaram have measured the molar Kerr constant and the total dielectric polarization of ferrocene (2). The latter quantity (52.4_6 cc) is just about 5% greater than the molecular refraction (50.4 cc, Na—D line), confirming the nonpolarity of the molecule. The measured value of 19.9×10^{-12} for the molar Kerr constant agrees quite well with that calculated by assuming that the molecule is equivalent to a Krypton atom sandwiched between two parallel pentagonal rings in each of which the carbon–carbon bond elipsoids have the same semiaxes as those of the C_{Ar}—C_{Ar} bonds in benzene. The polarizeability of the iron atom is very nearly isotropic, but the molecule is apparently somewhat more polarizable in planes parallel to the rings than perpendicular to them.

REFERENCES

1. Akishin, P. A., N. G. Rambidi, and T. N. Bredikhina, Z. Strukt. Khim., 2, 476 (1961).
2. Aroney, M., LeFevre, and K. M. Somasundaram, J. Chem. Soc., 1812 (1960).
3. Balandin, A. A., M. L. Khidekel, and V. V. Patrikeev, Zh. Obshch. Khim., 31, 1876 (1961).
4. Ballhausen, C. J., and J. P. Dahl, Acta Chem. Scand., 15, 1333 (1961).
5. Barinsky, R. P., Zh. Stukt. Khim., 1, 200 (1960).
6. Baumgartner, F., E. O. Fischer, and U. Zahn, Ber., 91, 2336 (1958).
7. Behun, J. D., Talanta, 9, 83 (1962).
8. Belder, A. N., E. J. Bourne, and J. B. Pridham, Chem.& Ind. (London), 996 (1959).
9. Bennett, M. A., L. Pratt, and G. Wilkinson, J. Chem. Soc., 2037 (1961).

10. Bennett, M. A., *Chem. Rev.*, **62**, 611 (1962).
11. Bennett, M. J., M. Gerloch, J. A. McCleverty, and R. Mason, *Proc. Chem. Soc.*, 357 (1962).
12. Berger, A., J. Kleinberg, and W. E. McEwen, *Chem. & Ind. (London)*, 204 (1960).
13. Berger, A., W. E. McEwen, and J. Kleinberg, *J. Am. Chem. Soc.*, **83**, 2274 (1961).
14. Boke, K., *Z. Physik. Chem. (Frankfurt)*, **10**, 59 (1957).
15. Boke, K., *Z. Physik. Chem. (Frankfurt)*, **11**, 326 (1957).
16. Boichard, J., and J. Tirouflet, *Compt. Rend.*, **251**, 1394 (1960).
17. Brand, J. C. D., and W. Snedden, *Trans. Faraday Soc.*, **53**, 894 (1957).
18. Bublitz, D. E., G. Hoh, and J. Kuwana, *Chem. & Ind. (London)*, 635 (1959).
19. Bublitz, D. E., W. E. McEwen, and J. Kleinberg, *J. Am. Chem. Soc.*, **84**, 1845 (1962).
20. Bublitz, D. E., J. Kleinberg, and W. E. McEwen, *Chem. & Ind. (London)*, 936 (1960).
21. Burke, Mary, Univ. of California, Los Angeles, private communication.
22. Burton, R., L. Pratt, and G. Wilkinson, *J. Chem. Soc.*, 594 (1961).
23. Clancy, D. J., and I. J. Spilners, *Anal. Chem.*, **34**, 1839 (1962).
24. Collinson, E., F. S. Dainton, and H. Gillis, *J. Phys. Chem.*, **65**, 695 (1961).
25. Cordes, J. F., and S. Schreiner, *Z. Anorg. Chem.*, **299**, 87 (1959).
26. Cotton, F. A., and G. Wilkinson, *J. Am. Chem. Soc.*, **74**, 5764 (1952).
27. Coulson, C. A., *Valence* (2nd ed.) Oxford Univ. Press, Amen House, London, p. 193.
28. Curphey, T. J., J. O. Santer, M. Rosenblum, and J. H. Richards, *J. Am. Chem. Soc.*, **82**, 5249 (1960).
29. Davison, A., and G. Wilkinson, *Proc. Chem. Soc.*, 356 (1960).
30. Davison, A., W. McFarlane, L. Pratt, and G. Wilkinson, *J. Chem. Soc.*, 4821 (1962).
31. Davison, A., W. McFarlane, L. Pratt, and G. Wilkinson, *J. Chem. Soc.*, 3653 (1962).
32. Dauben, H. J., and D. J. Bertelli, *J. Am. Chem. Soc.*, **83**, 497 (1961).
33. Dietrich, M. W., and A. C. Wahl, *J. Chem. Phys.*, **38**, 159 (1963).
34. Dunitz, J. D., and L. E. Orgel, *Nature*, **171**, 121 (1953).
35. Dunitz, J. D., L. E. Orgel, and A. Rich, *Acta Cryst.*, **9**, 373 (1956).
36. Edwards, J. W., G. L. Kington, and R. Mason, *Trans. Faraday Soc.*, **56**, 660 (1960).
37. Edwards, J. W., and G. L. Kington, *Trans. Faraday Soc.*, **58**, 1323 (1962).
38. Edwards, J. W., and G. L. Kington, *Trans. Faraday Soc.*, **58**, 1334 (1962).
39. Eiland, P. F., and R. Pepinsky, *J. Am. Chem. Soc.*, **74**, 4971 (1952).
40. Englemann, F., *Z. Naturforsch.*, **8b**, 775 (1953).
41. Epstein, L. M., *J. Chem. Phys.*, **36**, 2731 (1962).
42. Fichtel, C., Dissertation, Univ. of Munich, 1961.
43. Fischer, E. O., and W. Pfab, *Z. Naturforsch.*, **7b**, 377 (1952).
44. Fischer, E. O., and D. Seus, *Z. Naturforsch.*, **9b**, 386 (1954).
45. Fischer, E. O., *Angew. Chem.*, **67**, 475 (1955).
46. Fischer, E. O., and H. Leipfinger, *Z. Naturforsch.*, **10b**, 353 (1955).
47. Fischer, E. O., *Rec. Trav. Chim.*, **75**, 629 (1956).
48. Fischer, E. O., and U. Piesbergen, *Z. Naturforsch.*, **11b**, 758 (1956).
49. Fischer, E. O., G. Joos, and W. Meer, *Z. Naturforsch.*, **13b**, 456 (1958).
50. Fischer, E. O., G. Joos, and E. Vogg, *Z. Physik. Chem.*, **18**, 80 (1958).
51. Fischer, E. O., and S. Schreiner, *Ber.*, **92**, 938 (1959).

52. Fischer, E. O., and H. Grubert, *Ber.*, **92**, 2302 (1959).
53. Fraenkel, G., R. Carter, A. McLachlan, and J. H. Richards, *J. Am. Chem. Soc.*, **82**, 5846 (1960).
54. Friedman, L., and A. P. Irsa, *J. Am. Chem. Soc.*, **75**, 5741 (1953).
55. Friedman, L., A. P. Irsa, and G. Wilkinson, *J. Am. Chem. Soc.*, **77**, 3689 (1955).
56. Fritz, H. P., *Ber.*, **92**, 781 (1959).
57. Fritz, H. P., and R. Schneider, *Ber.*, **93**, 1171 (1960).
58. Fritz, H. P., and H. Keller, *Ber.*, **95**, 158 (1962).
59. Goldberg, S. I., *Anal. Chem.*, **31**, 486 (1959).
60. Goldberg, S. I., D. W. Mayo, M. Vogel, H. Rosenberg, and M. Rausch, *J. Org. Chem.*, **24**, 824 (1959).
61. Goldberg, S. I., and D. W. Mayo, Abstracts of papers of the 135th meeting of the American Chemical Society, April 1959, p. 86–O.
62. Golding, R. M., and L. E. Orgel, *J. Chem. Soc.*, 363 (1962).
63. Green, M. L. H., L. Pratt, and G. Wilkinson, *J. Chem. Soc.*, 3916 (1958).
64. Green, M. L. H., L. Pratt, and G. Wilkinson, *J. Chem. Soc.*, 3753 (1959).
65. Green, M. L. H., L. Pratt, and G. Wilkinson, *J. Chem. Soc.*, 989 (1960).
66. Green, M. L. H., *Angew. Chem.*, 719 (1960).
67. Green, M. L. H., J. A. McCleverty, L. Pratt, and G. Wilkinson, *J. Chem. Soc.*, 4854 (1961).
68. Gubin, S. P., and E. G. Perevalova, *Doklady Akad. Nauk, SSSR*, **143**, 1351 (1962).
69. Hall, D. W., and J. H. Richards, *J. Org. Chem.*, **28**, 1549 (1963).
70. Hardgrove, G. L., and D. H. Templeton, UCRL, No. 8141 (1957), Radiation Laboratory, Univ. of California, Berkeley, p. 72.
71. Hardgrove, G. L., and D. H. Templeton, *Acta Cryst.*, **12**, 28 (1959).
72. Harjee, P. H., and N. C. Peterson, *North Dakota Acad. Sci.*, XI (1957).
73. Hartley, A. M., and R. E. Visco, Abstracts of papers of the 140th meeting of the American Chemical Society, Sept. 1961, p. 29–B.
74. Hartley, A. M., and R. E. Visco, *Anal. Chem.*, **35**, 1871 (1963).
75. Hawthorne, M. F., *J. Org. Chem.*, **21**, 363 (1956).
76. Hieber, W., and E. Weiss, *Z. Anorg. Allgem. Chem.*, **287**, 223 (1956).
77. Hill, E. A., and J. H. Richards, *J. Am. Chem. Soc.*, **83**, 4216 (1961).
78. Hoh, G. L. K., W. E. McEwen, and J. Kleinberg, *J. Am. Chem. Soc.*, **83**, 3949 (1961).
79. Holm, C. H., and J. A. Ibers, *J. Chem. Phys.*, **26**, 1753 (1957).
80. Holm, C. H., and J. A. Ibers, *J. Chem. Phys.*, **30**, 885 (1959).
81. Jach, J., and N. Sutin, *J. Inorg. Nucl. Chem.*, **7**, 5 (1958).
82. Jellinek, F., *Z. Naturforsch.*, **14b**, 737 (1959).
83. Jones, N. D., California Institute of Technology, unpublished work.
84. Joos, G., and K. H. Peter, *Z. Physik. Chem.*, **18**, 74 (1958).
85. Kaluskii, Z. L., R. L. Avoyan, and Yu T. Struchkov, *Zh. Strukt. Khim.*, **3**, 599 (1962).
86. Kaplan, L., W. Kester, and J. Katz, *J. Am. Chem. Soc.*, **74**, 5531 (1952).
87. Katz, S., *Dissertation Abstr.*, **19**, 2242 (1959)
88. Kauer, E., *Z. Physik. Chem. (Frankfurt)*, **6**, 105 (1956).
89. Kazitsyna, L. A., B. V. Lokshin, and A. N. Nesmeyanov, *Doklady Akad. Nauk SSSR*, **127**, 333 (1959).
90. Komenda, J., and J. Tirouflet, *Compt. Rend.*, **254**, 3093 (1962).
91. Kuwana, T., D. E. Bublitz, and G. L. K. Hoh, *J. Am. Chem. Soc.*, **82**, 5811 (1960).
92. Lauterbur, P. C., *J. Am. Chem. Soc.*, **83**, 1838 (1961).
93. Leto, J. R., F. A. Cotton, and J. S. Waugh, *Nature*, **180**, 978 (1957).

94. Levy, D. A., and L. E. Orgel, *Mol. Phys.*, **4**, 93 (1961).
95. Lippincott, E. R., and R. D. Nelson, *J. Chem. Phys.*, **21**, 1307 (1953).
96. Lippincott, E. R., and R. D. Nelson, *J. Am. Chem. Soc.*, **77**, 4990 (1955).
97. Lippincott, E. R., and R. D. Nelson, *Spectrochim. Acta*, **10**, 307 (1958).
98. Little, W. F., R. A. Berry, and P. Kannan, *J. Am. Chem. Soc.*, **84**, 2525 (1962).
99. Little, W. F., C. N. Reilley, J. D. Johnson, K. N. Lynn, and A. P. Sanders, *J. Am. Chem. Soc.*, **86**, 1376 (1964).
99a. Little, W. F., C. N. Reilley, J. D. Johnson, and A. P. Sanders, *J. Am. Chem. Soc.*, **86**, 1382 (1964).
100. Lundquist, R. T., and M. Cais, *J. Org. Chem.*, **27**, 1167 (1962).
101. Mailey, E. A., C. R. Dickey, G. M. Goodale, and V. E. Matthews, *J. Org. Chem.* **27**, 616 (1962).
102. Mason, J. G., and M. Rosenblum, *J. Am. Chem. Soc.*, **82**, 4206 (1960).
103. Mayants, L. S., B. V. Lokshin, and G. B. Shaltuper, *Opt. i Spektroskopiya*, **8**, 317 (1962).
104. McConnell, H. M., and C. H. Holm, *J. Chem. Phys.*, **27**, 314 (1957).
105. McConnell, H. M., and C. H. Holm, *J. Chem. Phys.*, **28**, 749 (1958).
106. Mulay, L. N., E. G. Rochow, and E. O. Fischer, *J. Inorg. Nucl. Chem.*, **4**, 231 (1957).
107. Mulay, L. N., E. G. Rochow, E. O. Stejkal, and N. E. Weliky, *J. Inorg. Nucl. Chem.*, **16**, 23 (1960).
108. Mulay, L. N., and A. Attalla, Abstracts of papers of the 142nd meeting of the American Chemical Society, Sept. 1962, 32–T.
109. Mulay, L. N., and A. Attalla, *Naturwiss.*, **50**, 151 (1963).
110. Mulay, L. N., and Sr. M. E. Fox, *J. Am. Chem. Soc.*, **84**, 1308 (1962).
111. Mulay, L. N., and Sr. M. E. Fox, *Naturwiss.*, **49**, 446A (1962).
112. Mulay, L. N., and Sr. M. E. Fox, *J. Chem. Phys.*, **38**, 760 (1963).
113. Mulay, L. N., and A. Attalla, *J. Am. Chem. Soc.*, **85**, 702 (1963).
114. Nöth, H., J. Voitlander, and M. Nussbaum, *Naturwiss.*, **47**, 57 (1960).
115. Nesmeyanov, A. N., and N. A. Vol'kenau, *Doklady Akad. Nauk SSSR*, **107**, 262 (1956).
116. Nesmeyanov, A. N., E. G. Perevalova, R. V. Golovnya, T. V. Nikitina, and N. A. Simoukova, *Izvest. Akad. Nauk SSSR, Otdel. Khim. Nauk*, 739 (1956).
117. Nesmeyanov, A. N., L. A. Kazitsina, B. V. Lokshin, and I. I. Kritskaya, *Doklady Akad. Nauk SSSR*, **117**, 433 (1957).
118. Nesmeyanov, A. N., and L. A. Kazitsyna et al., *Doklady Akad. Nauk SSSR*, **125**, 1037 (1959).
119. Nesmeyanov, A. N., A. M. Rubinshtein, G. L. Slonimskii, A. A. Slinkin, N. S. Kochetkova, and R. B. Materikova, *Doklady Akad. Nauk SSSR*, **138**, 125 (1961).
120. Nesmeyanov, A. N., et al., *Doklady Akad. Nauk SSSR*, **137**, 1370 (1961).
121. Nesmeyanov, A. N., and D. N. Kursanov et al., *Izvestia Akad. Nauk SSSR, Otdel., Khim. Nauk*, 1932 (1962).
122. Nesmeyanov, A. N., E. G. Perevalova, and S. P. Gubin, Abstracts of the XIX International Congress of Pure and Applied Chemistry, Paper AB4-51, p. 187.
123. Neuse, E. W., and D. S. Trifan, *J. Am. Chem. Soc.*, **84**, 1850 (1962).
124. Page, J. A., and G. Wilkinson, *J. Am. Chem. Soc.*, **74**, 6149 (1952).
125. Pauling, L., *J. Chem. Phys.*, **4**, 673 (1936).
126. Pauling, L., *The Nature of the Chemical Bond*, 3rd ed., Cornell Univ. Press, Ithaca, 1960.
127. Pauson, P. L., and G. Wilkinson, *J. Am. Chem. Soc.*, **76**, 2024 (1954).
128. Perevalova, E. G., S. P. Gubin, S. A. Smirnova, and A. N. Nesmeyanov, *Doklady Akad. Nauk SSSR*, **147**, 384 (1962).

129. Pfab, W., and E. O. Fischer, Z. Anorg. Chem., 274, 316 (1953).
130. Rausch, M. D., E. O. Fischer, and H. Grubert, Chem. & Ind. (London), 756 (1958).
131. Rausch, M. D., E. O. Fischer, and H. Grubert, J. Am. Chem. Soc., 82, 76 (1960).
132. Reed, R. I., and F. M. Tabrizi, Appl. Spectry., 17, 124 (1963).
133. Reynolds, L. T., and G. Wilkinson, J. Inorg. Nucl. Chem., 9, 86 (1959).
134. Richmond, H. H., and H. Freiser, J. Am. Chem. Soc., 77, 2022 (1954).
135. Rinehart, K. L., K. L. Motz, and S. Moon, J. Am. Chem. Soc., 79, 2749 (1957).
136. Rinehart, K. L., R. J. Curby, and P. E. Sokol, J. Am. Chem. Soc., 79, 3420 (1957).
137. Rinehart, K. L., et al., J. Am. Chem. Soc., 82, 4111 (1960).
137a. Rinehart, K. L., C. J. Michejda, and P. A. Kittle, J. Am. Chem. Soc., 81, 3162 (1959).
138. Robertson, R. E., and H. M. McConnell, J. Phys. Chem., 64, 70 (1960).
139. Rogers, M., private communication.
140. Rosenberg, H. M., and C. Riber, Microchem. J., 6, 103 (1962).
141. Rosenblum, M., Thesis, Harvard University, 1953.
142. Rosenblum, M., and R. B. Woodward, J. Am. Chem. Soc., 80, 5443 (1958).
143. Rosenblum, M., Chem. & Ind. (London), 953 (1958).
144. Rosenblum, M., J. Am. Chem. Soc., 81, 4530 (1959).
145. Rosenblum, M., and W. G. Howells, J. Am. Chem. Soc., 84, 1167 (1962).
146. Rosenblum, M., W. G. Howells, A. K. Banerjee, and C. Bennett, J. Am. Chem. Soc., 84, 2726 (1962).
147. Rosenblum, M., J. O. Santer, and W. G. Howells, J. Am. Chem. Soc., 85, 1450 (1963).
148. Rosenblum, M., and R. W. Fish, unpublished results.
149. Rosenblum, M., and G. Hoh, unpublished results.
150. Rosenblum, M., and W. G. Howells, unpublished results.
151. Savitsky, A. V., and Y. K. Syrkin, Doklady Akad. Nauk SSSR, 120, 119 (1958).
152. Savitsky, A. V., and Y. K. Syrkin, Izvest. Akad. Nauk SSSR, Otdel., Khim. Nauk, 2254 (1960).
153. Savitsky, A. V., and Y. K. Syrkin, Tr. o Khim. i Khim. Tekhnol., 1, 165 (1961).
154. Savitsky, A. V., J. Gen. Chem. SSSR, 30, 3167 (1960).
155. Schlögl, K., and H. Seiler, Monatsh., 91, 79 (1960).
156. Schlögl, K., H. Pelousek, and A. Mohar, Monatsh., 92, 533 (1961).
157. Schlögl, K., and A. Mohar, Monatsh., 93, 861 (1962).
158. Schlögl, K., and M. Fried, Monatsh., 94, 537 (1963).
159. Schwab, G. M., and J. Voitlander, Z. Physik. Chem., 3, 341 (1955).
160. Scott, D. R., and R. S. Becker, J. Chem. Phys., 35, 516 (1962).
161. Scott, D. R., and R. S. Becker, J. Chem. Phys., 35, 2246 (1962).
162. Shriver, D. H., J. Am. Chem. Soc., 85, 3509 (1963).
163. Siebold, E. A., and L. E. Sutton, J. Chem. Phys., 23, 1967 (1955).
164. Semenov, D. A., and J. D. Roberts, J. Am. Chem. Soc., 79, 2741 (1957).
165. Shustorovich, E. M., and M. E. Dyatkina, Doklady Akad. Nauk SSSR, 131, 113 (1960).
166. Smith, T. D., J. Inorg. Nucl. Chem., 14, 290 (1960).
167. Smith, T. D., J. Chem. Soc., 473 (1961).
168. Starovskii, O. V., and Y. T. Struchkov, Izvest. Akad. Nauk SSSR, Otdel. Khim. Nauk, 6, 1001 (1960).
169. Starovskii, O. V., and Y. T. Struchkov, Zh. Strukt. Khim., 2, 612 (1961).
170. Stolzle, G., Dissertation, Univ. of Munich, 1961.
171. Stranks, O. R., Discussions Faraday Soc., 29, 73 (1960).

Physical Properties 61

172. Strohmeier, W., and D. von Hobe, Z. *Elektrochem.*, **64**, 945 (1960).
173. Struchkov, Y. T., *Doklady Akad. Nauk SSSR, Otdel. Khim. Nauk*, **110**, 67 (1956).
174. Struchkov, Y. T., *Zh. Obshch. Khim.*, **27**, 2039 (1957).
175. Struchkov, Y. T., and T. L. Khotsyanova, *Kristallografiya*, **2**, 382 (1957).
176. Sutin, N., and R. W. Dodson, *J. Inorg. Nucl. Chem.*, **6**, 91 (1958).
177. Taft, R. W., in *Steric Effects in Organic Chemistry*, Wiley, New York, 1956, p. 556.
178. Taft, R. W., S. Ehrenson, I. C. Lewis, and R. E. Glick, *J. Am. Chem. Soc.*, **81**, 5353 (1959).
179. Tirouflet, J., E. Laviron, J. Metzger, and J. Boichard, *Coll. Czech. Chem. Comm.* **25**, 3277 (1960).
180. Tirouflet, J., and M. Person, *Ric. Sci.*, **30**, Suppl. No. 5, 269 (1960); *C.A.*, **55**, 20898i (1961).
181. Tirouflet, J., and J. Boichard, *Compt. Rend.*, **250**, 1861 (1960).
182. Tirouflet, J., E. Laviron, R. Dabard, and J. Komenda, *Bull. Soc. Chim. France*, 857 (1963).
183. Tirouflet, J., R. Dabard, and E. Laviron, *Bull Soc. Chim. France*, 1655 (1963).
184. Trifan, D. S., and L. Nicholas, *J. Am. Chem. Soc.*, **79**, 2746 (1957).
185. Trotter, J., *Acta Cryst.*, **11**, 355 (1958).
186. Trotter, J., *Acta Cryst.*, **16**, 571 (1963).
187. Vainshtein, E. E., U. F. Kopelev, and B. I. Kotliar, *Doklady Akad. Nauk SSSR*, **137**, 1117 (1961).
188. Vainshtein, E. E., and U. F. Kopelev, *Doklady Akad. Nauk SSSR*, **149**, 1360 (1963).
189. Vrublovsky, P., R. Kubicek, and F. Santavy, *Chem. Listy*, **52**, 974 (1958). Collection *Czechoslov. Chem. Communs.*, **24**, 645 (1959).
190. Weiss, E., *Z. Anorg. Chem.*, **287**, 236 (1956).
191. Wertheim, G. K., and R. H. Herber, *J. Chem. Phys.*, **38**, 2106 (1963).
192. Wilkinson, G., M. Rosenblum, M. C. Whiting, and R. B. Woodward, *J. Am. Chem. Soc.*, **74**, 2125 (1952).
193. Wilkinson, G., *J. Am. Chem. Soc.*, **74**, 6146 (1952).
194. Wilkinson, G., *J. Am. Chem. Soc.*, **74**, 6148 (1952).
195. Wilkinson, G., P. L. Pauson, and F. A. Cotton, *J. Am. Chem. Soc.*, **76**, 1970 (1954).
196. Wilkinson, G., F. A. Cotton, and J. M. Birmingham, *J. Inorg. Nucl. Chem.*, **2**, 95 (1956).
197. Wilkinson, G., and F. A. Cotton, "Cyclopentadienyl and Diene Metal Compounds," in *Progress in Organic Chemistry*, Vol. I, Interscience, New York, 1959.
198. Wilkinson, G., *Angew. Chem.*, 35 (1960).
199. Wolf, L., H. Franz, and H. Hennig, *Z. Chem.*, **1**, 27 (1960); *C.A.*, **55**, 7160d-e (1961).
200. Wolf, L., H. Franz, and H. Hennig, *Z. Chem.*, **1**, 220 (1960); *C.A.*, **55**, 26852g-h (1961).
201. Woodward, R. B., M. Rosenblum, and M. C. Whiting, *J. Am. Chem. Soc.*, **74**, 3458 (1952).
202. Yamada, S., A. Nakahara, and R. Tsuchida, *J. Chem. Phys.*, **22**, 1620 (1954).
203. Yamada, S., A. Nakahara, and R. Tsuchida, *Bull. Chem. Soc. Japan*, **28**, 465 (1955).
204. Zahn, U., P. Kienle, and H. Eicher, *Z. Physik.*, **166**, 220 (1962).

4 Acylmetallocenes

GENERAL ASPECTS

Both historically as well as from the point of view of its preparative value, the Friedel-Crafts acylation reaction occupies a position of central importance in the chemistry of ferrocene. The discovery that ferrocene entered into this typical aromatic substitution reaction marked the beginning of a chapter in its chemistry which, in large measure, parallels the earlier explorations of benzenoid systems. During the past decade a considerable number of other substitution reactions have been successfully applied to the parent compound, thereby providing new routes to a wide spectrum of its derivatives. Nevertheless, the acylation reaction remains among the most useful of these transformations and has been the most thoroughly examined. In general, the reaction proceeds under relatively mild conditions with both acid halides and anhydrides and affords excellent yields of mono- and diacylferrocenes. These, in turn, have served as versatile intermediates in the preparation of other, less accessible derivatives.

While oxidation of the metal atom often intervenes in reactions of metallocenes with many electrophiles, such complications are only infrequently encountered in the acylation reaction (139).*

The most commonly employed Lewis acid has been aluminum chloride, although milder reagents such as stannic chloride (69), boron trifluoride (45), phosphoric acid (42), and hydrogen fluoride (162) have also been

---

* In addition to the examples of this side reaction with such acid halides as chloroacetyl chloride, ethyl oxalyl chloride, and *p*-nitrobenzoyl chloride cited in ref. 139, the Friedel-Crafts reaction with *o*-nitrobenzoyl chloride also fails to give any detectable ketonic product (134).

used in the preparation of acetylferrocene. The reaction is generally carried out at or below room temperature in either methylene chloride, chloroform, or carbon disulfide solution, and its progress is evidenced by the formation of a dark red or purple solution characteristic of the acylferrocene-Lewis acid complex. When the reaction is carried out in carbon disulfide, this complex may separate from solution as a crystalline solid. Acylferrocenes are generally stable, highly crystalline, red or orange substances whose chemical and physical properties are not unlike those of acylbenzenes. Table 4-4 (pages 91–100), sections I to III, lists those derivatives reported in the literature.

COMPARATIVE REACTIVITIES OF FERROCENE AND BENZENOID AROMATICS

The high reactivity of ferrocene is evidenced qualitatively by the relatively mild conditions under which acylation may be effected and, more strikingly, by the observation that it is acetylated even in the presence of a tenfold excess of anisole (13). A more quantitative measure of this reactivity has been obtained through competitive acylation studies, the results of which are shown in Table 4-1 (135).

Table 4-1
Relative Rates of Friedel-Crafts Acetylation
of Aromatic Compounds[a]

COMPOUND	RELATIVE RATE
Benzene	1.0
Acetylferrocene	1.9×10^2
Mesitylene	2.9×10^3
Pentamethylbenzene	1.3×10^4
Ferrocene	3.3×10^6

[a] In methylene chloride at 0°.

Because of the great disparity in relative rates for pentamethylbenzene and ferrocene, the accuracy of the latter figure is not high. Nevertheless, its magnitude illustrates the extraordinary reactivity of ferrocene. It is of further interst to note that even the unsubstituted ring of acetylferrocene, which is strongly deactivated by the acyl substituent, retains a reactivity considerably greater than that of benzene.*

* The relative reactivity assigned in the table to acetylferrocene is more accurately attributed to the aluminum chloride complex of this substance, which is the predominant species in solution under the reaction conditions, and in which the deactivating effect of the carbonyl group is undoubtedly greatly enhanced.

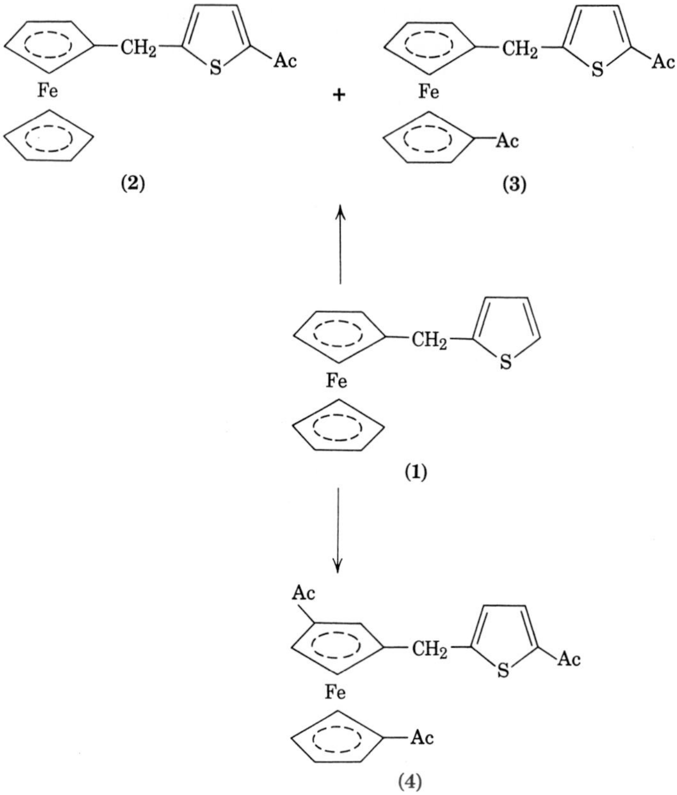

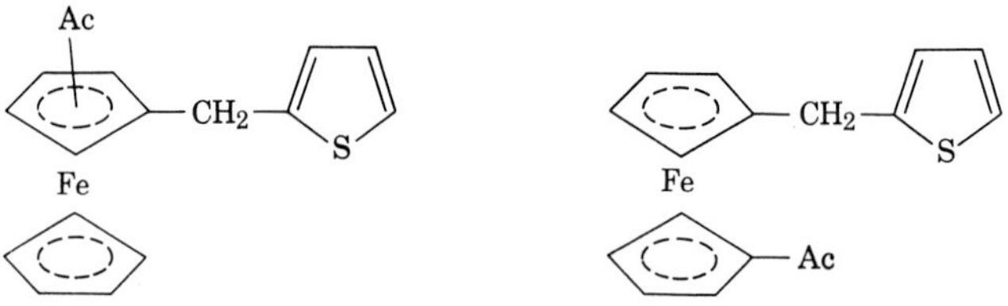

(2)   +   (3)

(1)

(4)

(2a)   (2b)

Nesmeyanov's group has recently reported specific rate constants for nuclear hydrogen exchange reactions of ferrocene, acetylferrocene, 1,1'-diacetylferrocene, and toluene in deuterotrifluoroacetic acid at 25° (85, 86). Under these conditions the relative rates of exchange were found to be 5333, 5.0, 2.6, and 1, respectively. If we adopt a value of 100 for the relative rates of hydrogen exchange for toluene and benzene,*

* The rate of deuterium exchange of toluene has been reported to be 100 times that of benzene in trifluoroacetic acid-deuterium oxide solution (57).

the differences in reactivities of ferrocene, acetylferrocene, and benzene are comparable to those observed in the Friedel-Crafts reaction. However, the relative rate of hydrogen exchange for 1,1'-diacetylferrocene is unexpectedly high, especially since this substance is quite resistant to acetylation.

A study of the comparative reactivities of thiophene and ferrocene, by internal competition, has recently been reported by Schlögl and Pelousek (148). Acetylation of 2-thienylferrocene (**1**) gave a mixture of **2** and **3** in a ratio of approximately 1:2. The absence of products such as **2a** or **2b** would imply that the thiophene ring is somewhat more reactive than is the ferrocene nucleus. However, the recovery of starting material and the yields of products ($\sim$8%) were rather poor, so that even this conclusion may not be warranted.

It is somewhat surprising that no homoannular acetylation product isomeric with **3** was isolated, since other studies indicate that alkylferrocenes are somewhat more reactive than ferrocene itself. With excess acetylating reagent, homoannular substitution does occur with the formation of **4**.

MONO- VERSUS DIACYLATION

The relative reactivities of ferrocene and monoacylferrocenes are generally so disparate that acylation of ferrocene with equimolar amounts of reagents yields preponderantly, if not exclusively, the monoacyl derivative. However, in the presence of excess aluminum chloride significant amounts of diacylferrocenes are formed even when equimolar quantities of ferrocene and acid halide are employed. The explanation for this apparent and anomalous change in the relative reactivities of ferrocene and its monoacyl derivatives lies in the fact that ferrocene is protonated by hydrogen chloride in the presence of the excess aluminum chloride (129). The resulting cation is inert toward acylation, and thus ferrocene is effectively removed from competition with the intermediate monoacylated derivative (equations 1 to 3). The complex salt has been isolated by precipitation from methylene chloride solutions (129) and shown to have the composition indicated in equation 3.

$$C_{10}H_{10}Fe + AlCl_3 \cdot AcCl \rightarrow C_{10}H_9FeAc \cdot AlCl_3 + HCl \qquad (1)$$

$$C_{10}H_9FeAc + AlCl_3 \cdot AcCl \rightarrow C_{10}H_8FeAc_2 + HCl \qquad (2)$$

$$C_{10}H_{10}Fe + AlCl_3 + HCl \rightarrow [(C_{10}H_{11}Fe)^+(AlCl_4)^-]_n \qquad (3)$$

Ferrocene is also protonated in boron trifluoride hydrate (26) and apparently in sulfuric acid solutions as well (6, 61). N.M.R. studies have shown that, in solutions of boron trifluoride hydrate, protonation is complete and occurs on the metal atom rather than on the rings (26) (see Chapter III, p. 47).

Diacylferrocenes may be prepared in high yield by treatment of ferrocene with two or more molar equivalents of acid halide or anhydride and a Lewis acid.* Acylation does not proceed beyond the stage of disubstitution† and, generally, the only product is the symmetrically substituted 1,1'-diacylferrocene, although in two reactions minor amounts of 1,2-diacylferrocenes have been isolated (96, 127). The assignment of a heteroannular structure to the principal diacetyl derivative and, by analogy, to other similarly prepared diacylferrocenes was initially based on the observation that the difference between the first and second dissociation constants of ferrocene dicarboxylic acid, derived by oxidation of this substance, was very small ($K_1/K_2 = 11.5$), indicating that the carboxyl groups interact little and were therefore far apart (166). These assignments have since been substantiated in a number of cases by degradation and synthesis. Thus, drastic hydrogenation of diacetylferrocene yields ethylcyclopentane to the exclusion of cyclopentane and diethylcyclopentane (71). Pauson (95) has also shown that the dibenzhydrylferrocene (7), prepared by reduction of dibenzoylferrocene (5), is identical with the derivative obtained directly from benzhydrylcyclopentadiene (6) (140) and ferrous chloride. There can be little doubt, then, that in general the Friedel-Crafts acylation reaction gives principally symmetrically disubstituted ferrocenes.

* The synthesis of 1,1'-diacetylferrocene directly from sodium cyclopentadienide, acetyl chloride, and ferrous chloride has been claimed in a patent (65), but the yield is apparently quite low (2%) (93).

† In the acetylation of 1,1'-dimethylferrocene the formation of a triacyl derivative is claimed (78).

As noted above, in two reactions involving the acetylation and benzoylation of ferrocene, in which the products have been carefully examined, minor amounts of derivatives isomeric with the 1,1′-diacylferrocenes have been isolated. The homoannular character of substitution in the acetylation product was deduced from the fact that its infrared spectrum possessed bands at 9 and 10 μ characteristic of an unsubstituted cyclopentadienyl ring (76, 124, 127) (see Chapter 3, page 38).

Richards and Curphey (109) subsequently established the structure of this substance as 1,2-diacetylferrocene (**8**) by oxidation with hypochlorite to the diacid (**9**) and conversion to a five-membered anhydride (**10**) with dicyclohexylcarbodiimide.

Ac ⟨Fe⟩ Ac $\xrightarrow{OCl^-}$ CO₂H ⟨Fe⟩ CO₂H $\xrightarrow{C_6H_{11}N=C=NC_6H_{11}}$ anhydride ⟨Fe⟩

(**8**)   (**9**)   (**10**)

Presumably, the minor dibenzoylferrocene isomer is likewise a 1,2-disubstituted derivative, although no evidence for this has been presented. To data, no 1,3-diacylferrocenes have been reported as products of the Friedel-Crafts reaction.*

RELATIVE REACTIVITIES OF THE IRON GROUP METALLOCENES

Comparatively little has been reported on the electrophilic substitution of ruthenocene and osmocene. The acylation studies of Rausch, Fischer, and Grubert (104, 105) indicate that the reactivity of the iron group metallocenes decreases in the order: ferrocene, ruthenocene, osmocene. Although ferrocene affords only diacetyl- and dibenzoylferrocene when treated with a three molar proportion of acid halide and aluminum chloride, ruthenocene gives mixtures containing significant amounts of the monoacyl derivative. Under these as well as more vigorous reaction conditions, osmocene yields only monoacylated compounds (111). The diacylruthenocenes are heteroannular derivatives as evidenced by absence

---

* The formation of minor amounts of such derivatives in these reactions may not be excluded, since normally 1,3-disubstituted ferrocenes are, with considerable difficulty, separated from their 1,1′-isomers. 1,3-Diacetylferrocene has been prepared by manganese dioxide oxidation of 1-acetyl-3-ethylferrocene (122b).

of absorption at 9 and 10 μ in their infrared spectra. Like ferrocene, ruthenocene is extensively protonated by strong acids and, consequently, acetylation in the presence of excess aluminum chloride similarly affords mainly the diacyl derivative (105). The lower reactivity of ruthenocene is likewise manifest in its poor conversion to the aldehyde on treatment with N-methylformanilide and phosphorus oxychloride (18, 105). By contrast ferrocene is smoothly converted to formylferrocene in high yield under these conditions.

Acyl derivatives of ruthenocene and osmocene are listed in section IV of Table 4-4, while those having two metallocene nuclei, exclusive of bimetallocenyl derivatives, are listed in section V (page 101–102).

ACYLATION OF CYCLOPENTADIENYL METAL CARBONYLS

Attempts to effect substitution of biscyclopentadienyl complexes other than the iron group metallocenes have not been successful, owing primarily to their susceptibility to oxidation. However, several cyclopentadienyl complexes having nitrosyl or carbonyl ligands have been converted to their acyl derivatives.

The acylation of cyclopentadienylmanganese tricarbonyl was first reported by Fischer and Plesske (33) and by Cotton and Leto (24) in 1958. Somewhat more vigorous conditions are required in this reaction than in those involving ferrocene. The lower reactivity of the manganese compound may also be inferred from the fact that it is not formylated with N-methylformanilide and phosphorus oxychloride.* In a series of competitive acetylation and benzoylation reactions, Kozikowski, Maginn, and Klove (56) have shown that its reactivity is somewhat greater than benzene. Methylcyclopentadienylmanganese tricarbonyl is, as expected, slightly more reactive than the parent compound, but is considerably less reactive than anisole in these reactions. Several other acyl derivatives of cyclopentadienylmanganese tricarbonyl and of its methyl and ethyl homologues have also been reported (19a, 23, 33, 84, 112, 115).

The acylation of cyclopentadienylvanadium tetracarbonyl has been reported independently by three groups (21, 34, 113) and, more recently, Fischer and Plesske have prepared acetylcyclopentadienylchromium nitrosyl carbonyl (35).

FORMYLATION

Ferrocenecarboxaldehyde constitutes one of the most useful of the acylferrocenes. It enters into a variety of condensation reactions and

* Formylation can, however, be achieved by use of dichloromethyl ethyl ether and aluminum chloride (20).

thereby serves as an important starting material for the synthesis of many ferrocene derivatives.

The aldehyde is most advantageously prepared by the reaction of ferrocene with N-methylformanilide and phosphorus oxychloride (12, 13, 42, 125, 141). The fact that ferrocene is acylated under these conditions again attests to its high reactivity since, normally, the Vilsmeier reaction is applicable to only the most reactive benzenoid compounds (32, 101, 160).

Jutz (54) has isolated the intermediate immonium cation (11) as the perchlorate. When treated with ferrocene, the immonium salt (11) is converted to diferrocenylmethyl perchlorate (12) and, by neutralization, to diferrocenylcarbinol (13). The carbonium ion (12) is also said to be formed directly from ferrocene and formic acid in the presence of a Lewis acid (54).

The deactivating effect of an acyl substituent on the reactivity of the ferrocene nucleus is particularly well illustrated in the Vilsmeier reaction, since it fails to proceed beyond the stage of monoacylation even in the presence of an excess of reagent and under more vigorous conditions of reaction.

The aldehyde has also been prepared less directly from the quaternary ammonium salt (14) through either the Sommelet reaction with hexamethylene tetramine (12, 13) or by conversion to ferrocenylmethanol followed by oxidation with manganese dioxide (46, 48, 49, 60). Treatment of ferrocenecarboxylic acid hydrazide (15) under conditions of the McFayden-Stevens reaction (93) or of cyanoferrocene by the method of Stephen (90) also yields the aldehyde, although in poor yield. Recently Pauson and Watts (98) have reported its preparation by the Friedel-Crafts reaction of ferrocene with dichloromethyl ether. The yield of aldehyde from this reaction is comparable to that obtained in the Vilsmeier reaction, although the conversion is considerably lower and some diferrocenylcarbinol (13)* is formed as well. Apparently no dialdehyde is formed in this reaction.

These various routes to the aldehyde are summarized in Fig. 4-1.

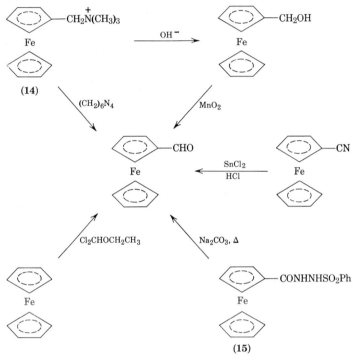

FIG. 4-1   Other routes to ferrocene aldehyde.

The aldehyde is a dark red crystalline substance which exhibits a liquid crystalline state between 45 and 124.5° (42, 43). Its exceptional basicity is evidenced by high solubility in aqueous acids and by formation of a crystalline hydrochloride (12).

ACYLFERROCENES BY OXIDATION OF ALKYLFERROCENES

Oxidation of hydroxymethylferrocene to ferrocenecarboxaldehyde with manganese dioxide was first reported by Lindsay and Hauser (60). Ferrocene-1,1'-dicarboxaldehyde (17) has recently been prepared by

* This method of preparing the aldehyde is said to be preferable to the Vilsmeier method in terms of "ease of operation and isolation of the product" (98).

Osgerby and Pauson (93) by similar oxidation of 1,1′-di(hydroxymethyl)-
ferrocene (16), obtained in turn by reduction of ferrocene-1,1′-dicarboxylic
acid with lithium aluminum hydride. The product of partial oxidation,
1′-hydroxymethylferrocenecarboxaldehyde (18), was also isolated.*

Manganese dioxide has also found application in the oxidation of
alkylferrocenes to the related carbonyl derivatives (117). Thus methyl-
and ethylferrocene are transformed to ferrocenecarboxaldehyde and
acetylferrocene, respectively. An attempt to prepare ferrocene-1,1′-
dicarboxaldehyde by oxidation of 1,1′-dimethylferrocene gave only the
product of partial oxidation, 1′-methylferrocenecarboxaldehyde. The
yields in these reactions are moderate but conversion is poor. However,
the reaction is markedly facilitated by additional activation of the methylene group, and good over-all yields of diferrocenyl ketone and ferrocil are
reported from the oxidation of diferrocenylmethane (98, 117) and
desoxyferrocoin (117). Rinehart and co-workers have also reported
isolation of the interesting quinone (20) by oxidation of α-keto-1,2-
tetramethyleneferrocene (19) with manganese dioxide (117).

The rather exceptional activation of saturated carbon centers bonded
to the ferrocene nucleus, which is suggested by these reactions, manifests
itself as well in the facile air oxidation of ferrocenylethynylmethanes to the
corresponding ketones (147).

* Goldberg had earlier attempted to prepare the dialdehyde by reduction of ferrocene-
dicarboxylic acid chloride with lithium tri-t-butoxyaluminum hydride, but the properties
of the product obtained suggest it to be a polymer (41).

ACYLATION OF SUBSTITUTED FERROCENES

The Friedel-Crafts ketone synthesis has been applied to a number of substituted ferrocenes. Aside from their synthetic interest, these studies provide useful information regarding the steric, inductive, and resonance effects of the substituent on the reaction.

Alkylferrocenes

The apparent steric requirements of alkyl substituents on a ferrocene ring are considerably smaller than in benzenoid systems, and may in part be accounted for by the larger projected angle of meeting of adjacent substituents in a five-, compared with a six-membered aromatic ring (121). This point is well illustrated by the relative amounts of isomeric ketones formed in the acetylation of 1,1'-dimethyl- and 1,1'-diisopropyl-ferrocene (121), shown in Fig. 4-2. By contrast, the ratio of $o:p$ isomers formed in the acetylation of toluene is 1:167 (15), and acetylation of cumene is reported to yield no detectable amount of *ortho* product by vapor phase chromatographic analysis (16).

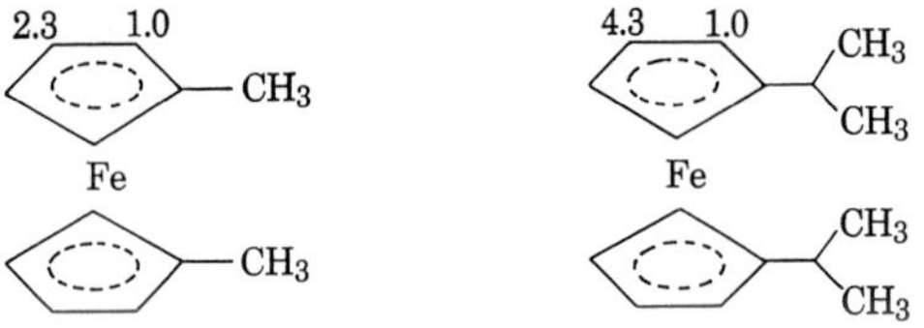

FIG. 4-2   Relative site reactivities in dialkylferrocenes (acetylation).

The relatively low order of steric effects exerted by alkyl groups in these reactions is also evidenced by the comparatively small difference in the ratio of isomers formed in the acetylation and *i*-butrylation of 1,1'-dimethylferrocene (133). The data shown in Fig. 4-3 were obtained by vapor-phase chromatographic analysis of products, and differences between

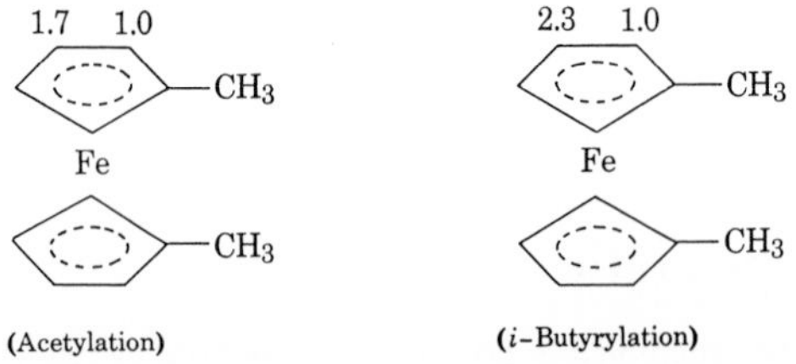

FIG. 4-3   Isomer distribution in the acylation of 1,1'-dimethylferrocene as a function of the electrophile.

these figures and those given in Fig. 4-2 for acetylation may in part be due to differences in the reaction conditions employed in each of these studies.

While no measure of the relative reactivities of ferrocene and simple alkylferrocenes is available, the activating effect of alkyl substituents would not be expected to be pronounced, in view of the intrinsically high reactivity of the parent substance and of the relatively weak activating effect of these substituents (16).

The results of competitive acetylation experiments between ferrocene and 1,1'-trimethyleneferrocene (134), summarized in Fig. 4-4, support such a conclusion, although some caution must be exercised in extrapolating these results to open chain derivatives. The data given in this and all succeeding figures are corrected for statistical factors.

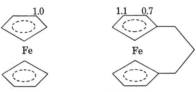

FIG. 4-4   Reactivities of ferrocene and 1,1'-trimethyleneferrocene (acetylation).

Not only is the over-all activity of ferrocene little enhanced by alkyl substitution but, as expected, there is comparatively little difference in the reactivity of the two rings in monoalkylferrocenes. This point is illustrated by the relative site reactivities in ethylferrocene, determined from the proportion of isomers formed on Friedel-Crafts acetylation (124, 127). These are shown in Fig. 4-5.

FIG. 4-5   Relative site reactivities in ethylferrocene (acetylation).

The effects of structural variations in bridged ferrocenes on both isomer ratios and relative reactivities of these substances, determined by competitive *i*-butyrylation reactions, are illustrated by the data in Fig. 4-6 (133). In comparing the relative site reactivities in these substances, the 2 position in 1,1'-trimethyleneferrocene has been assigned unit activity.

  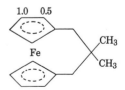

FIG. 4-6   Effect of structural variations on relative reactivity and isomer distribution in the isobutyrylation of bridged ferrocenes.

It is of interest to note that the isomer ratios for these substances show a much smaller variation with structural change than do the site reactivities themselves. The origin of these small but significant differences in site reactivities, especially between the closely related 1,1'-trimethylene- and β,β-dimethyl-1,1'-trimethyleneferrocenes is not clear, but may derive from a preferred endocyclic mode of electrophilic substitution (page 77.)

Arylferrocenes

Arylferrocenes and, in particular, the p-substituted phenylferrocenes are more suited to the purpose of examining substituent resonance interactions than are the alkylferrocenes. While alkyl groups tend to enhance the reactivity of the ferrocene nucleus, aryl substituents exert a deactivating effect due to a combination of inductive and ground state resonance interactions. The greater electronegativity of the benzenoid ring compared with the ferrocene nucleus is well supported by a variety of physical evidence. This includes the relative carbonyl absorption frequencies of phenyl and ferrocenyl ketones (page 85), the dissociation constants of structurally related acids (4, 62, 166) and bases (70), and the dipole moments of p-chlorobiphenyl and p-chlorophenylferrocene.* The data summarized in Fig. 4-7, derived from a series of competitive acetylation reactions, illustrate the deactivating effect of aryl groups of differing electronegativity (130).

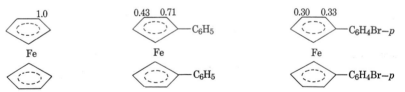

FIG. 4-7   Relative reactivities of ferrocene and diarylferrocenes (acetylation).

Nesmeyanov and co-workers have recently reported (83) that competitive acetylation of equimolar quantities of ferrocene and phenylferrocene gave acetylferrocene and a mixture of acetylphenylferrocenes in a ratio of 5:1. However, the material balance in these experiments was poor and apparently no attempt was made to separate isomeric products.

As might be anticipated, the deactivating effect of the substituent in monoarylferrocenes is more pronounced in the arylated ring. This point is illustrated by the proportion of isomers formed in the acetylation of two such compounds (130). Relative site reactivities, for these substances,

* Determined by Prof. M. T. Rogers, Michigan State University, and reported in ref. 128.

with that for the 1′ position of each taken as an internal standard, are shown in Fig. 4-8. The small activation of the 2 position in *p*-anisylferrocene compared with the deactivation of the corresponding position in phenylferrocene must be attributed to a decreased electronegativity and, possibly, to enhanced transition state resonance interactions of the *p*-anisyl substituent.

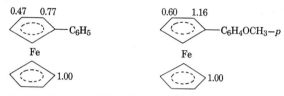

FIG. 4-8 Site reactivities of monoarylferrocenes (acetylation).

A comparison of relative site reactivities for the three diarylferrocenes, shown in Fig. 4-9, demonstrates the unequal deactivating effects of these substituents on positions in the ferrocene ring. In each of these derivatives the 3 position has been assigned unit reactivity (130).

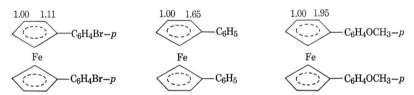

FIG. 4-9 Site reactivities in diarylferrocenes (acetylation).

The inequivalence of resonance interactions must be somewhat greater than is suggested simply by the ratio of isomers, since both inductive as well as steric factors are undoubtedly more effective in retarding substitution at the 2 position than at the more remote 3 position.

A simple molecular orbital treatment of transition-state localization energies for electrophilic substitution predicts a higher reactivity for the 2 position in ferrocenes bearing either electron donating or withdrawing groups. In the latter derivatives, the difference in localization energies between the two positions is rather small, and the predicted relative reactivities might well be reversed on inclusion of electronegativity parameters (109, 130).*

It is of interest to note that similar theoretical treatments of benzenoid systems likewise ascribe a higher reactivity to the *ortho* compared with the

---

* A reasonably good model for ferrocene derivatives substituted by electron withdrawing groups is diazocyclopentadiene, which has recently been shown by Cram and Partos (25) to undergo electrophilic substitution preferentially at the 2 position.

para position in derivatives bearing either electron withdrawing or donating groups. These relative reactivities are experimentally demonstrable for the latter such derivatives (28, 123). Thus a close analogy exists between the 2 and 3 positions in ferrocenes and the *ortho* and *para* positions in benzene derivatives.

Other derivatives

Friedel-Crafts acetylation of chloro- , bromo- , cyano- , and carbomethoxyferrocene, not unexpectedly, has been found to give the 1′-acetyl derivatives (44, 75, 80). Hall and Richards (44) have also examined the Friedel-Crafts acetylation of acetamido- , carbomethoxyamino- , and carbethoxyaminoferrocene under a variety of reaction conditions. Each of these compounds afforded the 1′-acetyl derivative, but small amounts of isomeric ketones, shown to be the 1,2 derivatives, were also isolated. In view of the accepted activating effect of these substituents in benzenoid aromatics, their directive effects in the above reactions would appear somewhat anomalous. Hill and Richards further observed that acetamidoferrocene was about one half as reactive as ferrocene and, in order to account for these observations, have suggested that the acylamino derivatives exist largely in their Lewis-acid complexed form in these reactions.

Since similar effects in Friedel-Crafts acylations of acylaminobenzenes are not generally observed, such an explanation does not appear particularly convincing. Moreover, the implicit assumption that the gross electronic effects of all substituents will be the same for both benzene and ferrocene derivatives is questionable especially since the electronegativities of the two parent systems differ so markedly. Thus, the methylthio group, which activates benzenoid aromatics toward electrophilic substitution (14), deactivates ferrocene in the aminomethylation reaction in which complexation of the substituent is not likely to be an important process (see below).

Morrison and Pauson (68) have reported that attempts to carry out the Friedel-Crafts acetylation of methoxy- and methylthioferrocene in the presence of aluminum chloride led instead to the formation of ferrocene and acetylferrocene, and Hall and Richards (44) have encountered similar difficulties in attempting to acetylate iodoferrocene.* These reactions probably proceed, like their analogs in benzenoid systems, through electrophilic displacement of the substituent by protons generated in this

---

* Morrison and Pauson were also unable to effect acetylation of chloroferrocene, although Hall and Richards, under presumably the same conditions, reported the formation of 1-acetyl-1′-chloroferrocene.

instance by partial and inadvertent hydrolysis of the Lewis acid catalyst. Substituent transfer, as in the Jacobsen rearrangement (150) and in deacylations of hindered aromatic ketones (40), was also observed to occur when methoxy- or methylthioferrocene was treated with aluminum chloride. Under these conditions, ferrocene and mixtures of isomeric dimethoxy- and dimethylthioferrocenes were formed.

Although Friedel-Crafts acylation of methylthio- and 1,1'-dimethyl-thioferrocene have been unsuccessful, Knox, Pauson, and Tiers have carried out the aminomethylation of these compounds (55) with formalde-hyde and dimethylamine. The latter compound gave the 2-alkyl and 3-alkyl derivatives (**21** and **22**) in a ratio of 2:1. The methylthio group is apparently mildly deactivating in these reactions as judged by the relative extent of reaction of ferrocene and methylthioferrocene under comparable conditions of reaction.

(21)   (22)

MECHANISM OF ELECTROPHILIC SUBSTITUTION

Although considerable use has been made of the acylation reaction and of other electrophilic substitution processes for the preparation of metallo-cene derivatives, comparatively little has been said about the mechanism of these reactions. Richards (108) was the first to suggest that the mechanism of electrophilic substitution of benzenoid aromatics and metallocenes might differ significantly, and that the metal atom might play a critical role in reactions of the metallocenes. A more detailed exposition of this view has recently been given (135).

This mechanism, summarized in Fig. 4-10, pictures the initial step in ring substitution as the formation of a charge-transfer type of complex (**23**) involving the electrophile and the e_{2g} orbital electrons of the metal. These electrons, which lie in the equatorial plane between the rings, are energetically the most accessible, since they occupy the highest filled molecular orbital of the metallocenes and are essentially nonbonding within the molecular framework.

The fact that protonation of ferrocene and ruthenocene has been shown to take place on the metal atom (Chapter 3, page 47) lends some support for the view that similar complexes may be formed with other

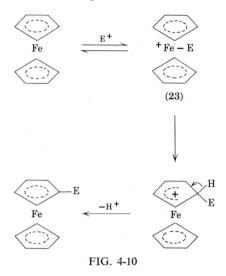

FIG. 4-10

electrophiles, although it does not follow that ring substitution need take place through such intermediates. Nevertheless, the effect of ring-metal bonding in the metallocenes may be to concentrate the electronic charge of the rings largely on their *endo* faces and thus render this side of each ring more susceptible to electrophilic attack than the *exo* side.

The cyclization of β-ferrocenylpropionic acid **(24)** to α-keto-1,1'-trimethyleneferrocene **(25)** provides compelling evidence that endocyclic substitution is at the very least allowed, since the bridging reaction must be constrained by the length of the chain to proceed in this sense.

Since the ionization potential of the nonbonding metal electrons is known to differ for each of the metallocenes and to be sensitive to the nature and degree of ring substitution, a parallel effect on the stability of the charge-transfer complex and hence on the rate of electrophilic substitution is to be expected. The mechanism thus provides a reasonable accounting for the relative reactivities of the metallocenes and for apparent interannular substituent effects in monoacylferrocenes, which appear to operate in the absence of any appreciable conjugation between the rings.

GENERAL TRANSFORMATIONS OF ACYLFERROCENES

In general, acylferrocenes undergo many of the reactions typical of carbonyl compounds. In their physical properties and reactivities these substances bear a closer relation to aromatic than to aliphatic ketones and aldehydes. However, in some circumstances, participation of the metal atom may give rise to reactions not encountered with either of these substances.

Side chain oxidation

Acylferrocenes are much less susceptible to oxidation than the parent substance. Thus, while ferrocene itself is rapidly oxidized to the cation by ferric chloride, diacetylferrocene is unattacked by this reagent. This circumstance makes it possible to carry out side chain oxidations with mild oxidants which would otherwise lead exclusively to nuclear oxidation. For example, diacetylferrocene is oxidized with hypoiodite in aqueous methanol to the dicarboxylic acid (124, 166). With hypochlorite the product of partial oxidation, 1'-acetylferrocenecarboxylic acid, may also be isolated (124). Acetylferrocene is similarly converted to ferrocenecarboxylic acid (124, 162), and Rinehart, Motz, and Moon have applied the reaction in the preparation of isomeric dialkylferrocenecarboxylic acids (121).

While the synthesis of carboxylic acids from acetylferrocenes finds special applications, as in the proof of structure of 1,2-diacetylferrocene (109), it has been largely supplanted in recent years by more general synthetic methods.

The Willgerodt reaction has been employed for the conversion of acetyl-, propionyl-, and diacetylferrocene to the corresponding ferrocenylalkanecarboxylic acids (42, 120). The reaction has not found wide use for the synthesis of these acids, since yields are generally poor.

Ferrocenecarboxaldehyde is reported to resist oxidation by permanganate under conditions which effect the conversion of benzaldehyde to benzoic acid (42, 48). More vigorous treatment with this oxidant or with ceric sulfate leads through the unstable ferricenium salts to products of nuclear decomposition (42, 48).

Side chain reduction

These reactions have proved to be of much greater synthetic value than the oxidative transformations of acylferrocenes. Since the primary reduction products are either alkyl and α-hydroxyalkylferrocenes, these transformations are treated in detail in Chapter 5.

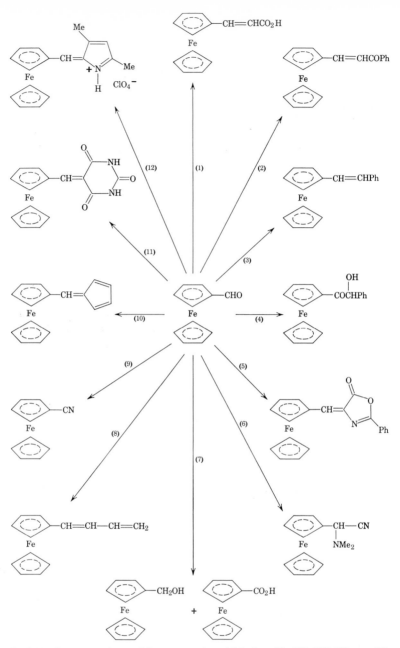

FIG. 4-11 Some reactions of ferrocenecarboxaldehyde. (1) $CH_2(CO_2H)_2$, pyridine, piperidine. (2) $PhCOCH_3$, OH^- or BF_3. (3) $PhCH=PPh_3$. (4) PhCHO, KCN. (5) $PhCONHCH_2CO_2H$, Ac_2O. (6) NaCN, $HNMe_2$ (on bisulfite addition product). (7) Fifty per cent alcoholic KOH. (8) $CH_2=CH-CH=PPh_3$. (9) Ac_2O or PCl_5 or $(C_6H_{11}N)_2C$ on oxime. (10) C_5H_6, NaOEt. (11) Barbituric acid. (12) 2,4-Dimethyl-pyrrole, $HClO_4$ (on bisulfite addition product).

80

Condensation reactions

Acylferrocenes and, in particular, ferrocenecarboxaldehyde serve as valuable intermediates for the preparation of a wide variety of derivatives. Selected examples of these transformations are illustrated in Figs. 4-11 and 4-12. Primary, base-catalyzed condensation products of acylferrocenes are listed in Table 4-4, section VI (pages 102–114).

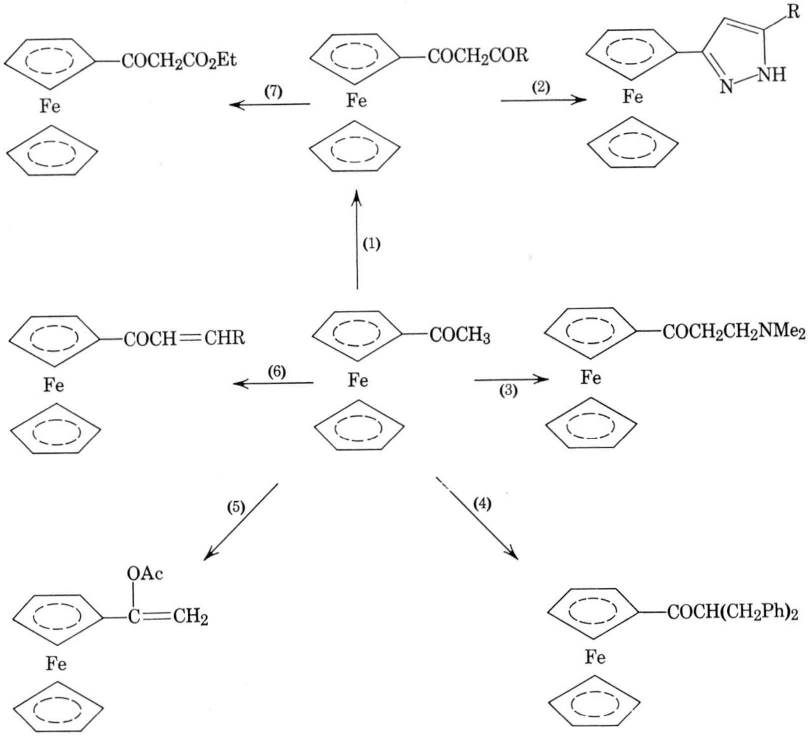

FIG. 4-12 Some reactions of acetylferrocene. (1) RCO_2Et, KNH_2. (2) NH_2NH_2. (3) CH_2O, $HNMe_2 \cdot HCl$. (4) $PhCH_2Cl$, KNH_2. (5) $CH_2=C(OAc)CH_3$, H_2SO_4. (6) $RCHO$, $NaOH$. (7) $(EtO)_2CO$, NaH.

The exceptional electron releasing capacity of the ferrocene nucleus manifests itself in a pronounced stabilization of adjacent electron deficient centers and, as a consequence, the electrophilic character of the carbonyl group in acylferrocenes is greatly diminished. Thus Broadhead, Osgerby, and Pauson (13) have noted that the aldehyde is not extracted into saturated bisulfite from an ethereal solution, and that its ethylene glycol acetal undergoes acid hydrolysis with extreme ease. The fact that the cyanohydrin as well as the derived hydantoin can be prepared only from the bisulfite addition product of the aldehyde may also be a consequence of the diminished reactivity of the carbonyl function (42). The rather severe conditions required to effect the Cannizzaro reaction and the failure of the aldehyde to undergo self-condensation under conditions of the benzoin reaction are also noteworthy (13). In the latter respect the compound resembles such typically unreactive aldehydes as *p*-dimethylaminobenzaldehyde and the methoxybenzaldehydes which likewise fail to yield symmetrical acyloins (53). However, like these latter aldehydes, ferrocenecarboxaldehyde enters into a mixed benzoin condensation with benzaldehyde (13). The position of the carbonyl group in the product, adjacent to the ferrocene nucleus (Fig. 4-11), reflects the greater resonance stabilization associated with this isomer, rather than the roles played by the separate carbonyl components in the reaction.

Unfortunately the azlactone prepared by condensation of the aldehyde with hippuric acid has not proved to be useful in the synthesis of β-ferrocenylalanine since the final step, involving hydrolysis of the benzoyl derivative of the amino acid proceeds in very poor yield (94, 141). This amino acid has, however, been made by two alternate routes (94, 141).

The Knoevenagel condensation of the aldehyde with malonic acid serves as a useful starting point for the synthesis of ferrocenes bridged by a three carbon chain (119, 132, 142, 143).

Hauser and co-workers have reported that the potassium amide catalyzed condensation of diacetylferrocene with esters (19, 47) or with benzyl chloride (50) yields only the diacyl and tetrabenzyl derivatives of the diketone respectively, even when equimolar amounts of combining components are used. No alkylation or acylation was observed in the presence of only one molar equivalent of base.

A possible explanation for these observations may lie in the existence of the monoanion (26), preponderantly in its internally condensed form (27). The products of C-alkylation or acylation can then arise only through the dianion (28), formed in the presence of excess base. The explanation advanced by Hauser (19, 50), that condensation proceeds through the cyclic dianion (29), does not appear plausible since the bridged compound α-keto-1,1'-trimethyleneferrocene (25) has been shown to resist alkylation (132).

Rearrangements

Attempts to carry out reactions such as the Schmidt and Beckmann rearrangements with acylferrocenes have been without success. Although nitrogen is rapidly evolved when diacetylferrocene is treated with hydrazoic acid under conditions of the Schmidt reaction, extensive decomposition of the ferrocene nucelus occurs (124). A similar experience has attended various attempts to carry out a Beckman rearrangement on the oximes of either acetylferrocene (42) or diacetylferrocene (124). It seems likely that the cause of these misfortunes lies in the intervention of electron transfer processes involving the metal atom and the proximate cationic nitrogen center in the intermediate common to these arrangements.* Weliky and Gould (164) have successfully rearranged the oxime of benzoylferrocene, but the product, ferrocenecarboxanilide, indicates that the stereochemistry of the oxime was such as to preclude migration of the ferrocene nucleus. Even then the yield in the reaction (25%) is not particularly good.

Two forms of the oxime of ferrocenecarboxaldehyde have been isolated and assigned structures on the basis of their comparative melting points, acidities, and modes of preparation (13). Like the isomeric oximes of benzaldehyde, each of these oximes is converted by a variety of dehydrating reagents to cyanoferrocene (13).

Attempts to effect a Hofmann rearrangement of ferrocenecarboxamide have likewise proved fruitless, although these results may be as much due to destruction of the product by the oxidizing medium as to complications arising from participation by the metal atom.

* Such a reaction has also been proposed by Nesmeyanov, Perevalova, and Nikitina to account for the failure of azoferrocene to undergo a benzidine rearrangement. Aminoferrocene was the only product isolated from these reactions (82).

BASICITY

The pronounced basicity of ferrocenecarboxaldehyde has already been noted (page 70). A more quantitative estimation of the electron releasing effect of the ferrocene nucleus upon the basicities of the carbonyl groups in acetylferrocene and in diferrocenyl ketone has been provided by Arnett and Bushick (2). The pK_a's of the conjugate acids of acetylferrocene and diferrocenyl ketone, determined in aqueous sulfuric acid, were found to be -2.80 and -2.55, respectively. These values may be compared with those of -6.15 for acetophenone and -6.16 for benzophenone. The ferrocenyl ketones are therefore 2000 to 4000 times more basic than their benzenoid analogs. From these data and those of Stewart and Yates (152), an average σ^+ substituent constant (14) of -1.31 was calculated for the ferrocenyl group. This value places the ferrocenyl group between the p-hydroxyphenyl ($\sigma^+ = -0.92$) and p-dimethylaminophenyl ($\sigma^+ = -1.7$) groups in its electron-releasing capacity. Similar conclusions were reached by these authors from an estimation of the Hammett σ substituent constant for the ferrocenyl group (see Chapter 6, page 211).

Some qualitative observations by Arnett and Bushick (2) suggest that ferrocenyl ruthenocenyl ketone is less basic than diferrocenyl ketone.

Rubalcava and Thompson (136, 137) have recently reported the solid-state infrared spectra of several acylferrocenes taken in the presence of gaseous hydrogen chloride and deuterium chloride. Extensive protonation on oxygen was evidenced by a rather large decrease in the frequency of carbonyl absorption and the appearance of a hydroxyl band.

PHYSICAL PROPERTIES

Infrared spectra

The very great electron releasing capacity of the ferrocene nucleus is likewise reflected in the comparative positions of infrared carbonyl absorption in acylferrocenes and acylbenzenes.* These data are summarized in Table 4-2.

This table also summarizes the spectral data of Rausch, Fischer, and Grubert (105) for various metallocenyl ketones. A comparison of these data suggests very little difference in the electron-releasing capacity of the various metallocene nuclei.

---

* Dvoryantseva and Sheinker have recently compared the relative carbonyl absorption frequencies and band intensities of a number of acylferrocenes with their benzenoid and aliphatic analogs (31).

The infrared spectra of a number of homoannularly substituted acetyl-alkylferrocenes and acetyl-arylferrocenes provide valuable data with which structures may be assigned to these substances. These generalizations are based in part on some early observations of Rinehart, Motz, and Moon (121). For the acetyl-alkylferrrocenes, the peak at 11.20 μ, characteristic

Table 4-2
Carbonyl Absorption Peak Positions in Metallocenes

	COMPARISON OF FERROCENE AND BENZENE DERIVATIVES[a]		
COMPOUND	R = ferrocenyl	R = phenyl	REFERENCE
$\begin{matrix} O \\ \| \\ HCR \end{matrix}$	5.97, 6.01	5.87	13
$\begin{matrix} O \\ \| \\ CH_3CR \end{matrix}$	5.98	5.94	13, 124
$\begin{matrix} O \\ \| \\ PhCR \end{matrix}$	6.09	6.03	124
$\begin{matrix} O \\ \| \\ RCR \end{matrix}$	6.20	6.03	124

	COMPARISON OF METALLOCENE DERIVATIVES[b]			
	R = ferrocenyl	R = ruthenocenyl	R = osmocenyl	
$\begin{matrix} O \\ \| \\ CH_3-C-R \end{matrix}$	6.03	6.00	5.99	105
$\begin{matrix} O \\ \| \\ Ph-C-R \end{matrix}$	6.15	6.13	6.15	105
$\begin{matrix} O \\ \| \\ C_{10}H_9FeC-R \end{matrix}$	6.20	6.16		105

[a] Determined in chloroform solution.
[b] Determined in KBr.

of a ferrocene ring substituted by an acetyl group alone, is shifted to a position near 10.90 μ in the 1,2 isomers. The corresponding 1,3 isomers are identified by a characteristic doublet absorption near 10.85 and 11.05 μ. These generalizations appear to apply to acetylated mono- and dimethyl- (5, 121), ethyl- (127), i-propyl- (5, 121), and t-butylferrocenes (5), as well as to the bridged compounds 2-acetyl- and 3-acetyl-1,1′-trimethylene-ferrocene (134), and to α-keto-1,1′,3,3′-bis(trimethylene)ferrocene (134, 143).

Similar observations apply to the spectra of various acetyl-arylferro-cenes (126, 128, 130). In these, the absorption peak at 11.27 μ, indicative

Table 4-3
Ultraviolet Absorption Maxima of Acetylferrocenes[a]

DERIVATIVE	λ_{max}	ε_{max}	λ_{max}	ε_{max}	REFERENCE
Acetyl-	225	14,600[b]	335	1120[c]	127
	268	5400[b]	455	420[c]	
1,1'-Diacetyl-	220[d]	—	334	1410	124
	263	10,500	470	440	
1,2-Diacetyl-	220[d]	—	330	1450	124
	260	11,200	370	1550	
			450	630	
2-Acetyl-1,1'-dimethyl-	227	18,600	e		121
	271	6800	e		
3-Acetyl-1,1'-dimethyl-	232	15,800	e		121
	271	6600	e		
2-Acetyl-1,1'-diisopropyl-	226	18,200	e		121
	271	6700	e		
3-Acetyl-1,1'-diisopropyl-	231	15,600	e		121
	273	6700	e		
1-Acetyl-1'-ethyl-	228	15,100	340	1290	124, 127
	270	5800	460	540	
1-Acetyl-2-ethyl-	225	18,600	335	1120	124, 127
	268	7100	460	430	
1-Acetyl-2-phenyl-	227	17,400	346	1540	128
	265	11,500	457	610	
1-Acetyl-3-phenyl-	245	23,600	340	2100	128
	270	11,300	465	560	
1-Acetyl-1'-phenyl	236	16,500	e		128
	267	10,500	e		
1,1'-Diphenyl-2-acetyl-	235	26,200	350[d]	2200	128
	265	19,200	465	960	
1,1'-Diphenyl-3-acetyl-	237	24,900	370[d]	2000	128
	270[d]	19,400	465	720	
1-Acetyl-1'-acetamido-	222[f]	18,300	e		44
	262[f]	8000	e		44
1-Acetyl-2-acetamido-	233	21,250	338[f]	3750	44
	265–70[f]	10,700			
2-Acetyl-1,1'-dicarbethoxyamino-	230[f]	22,500	e		44
	280[d,f]	7550	e		44
3-Acetyl-1,1'-dicarbethoxyamino-	226[f]	22,150	e		44
	290[d,f]	6100	e		44
1-Acetyl-1'-bromo-	223[f]	e	e		44
	250–60[d,f]	—	e		44
1-Acetyl-1'-chloro-	224[f]	e	e		44
	270[f]	e	e		44
1-Acetyl-1'-cyano-	221[f]	19,900	325[d,f]	950	44
	253[f]	10,600	e		

[a] Determined in 95% ethanol unless otherwise noted.
[b] Ref. 121 gives λ_{max} 226; ε, 16,500; λ_{max} 269; ε, 6500.
[c] Ref. 64 gives λ_{max} 337; ε, 1713; λ_{max} 456; ε, 544.
[d] Shoulder.
[e] Not given.
[f] Determined in methanol.

of an aryl-substituted ferrocene ring, is replaced in the 1,2-isomers by absorption near 10.95 μ, and in the 1,3-isomers by two peaks at 11.05 and 11.15 μ.

These generalizations have recently been extended to the isomeric diarylferrocenes (131) and apply as well to 1,2-diacetylferrocene (127). It seems likely that these characteristic absorption peaks are associated with C—H out-of-plane bending modes on the ferrocene ring similar to those which are responsible for diagnostically useful absorption patterns in benzenoid derivatives (67).

Rinehart and co-workers (121, 122) have noted that 2-acetyl-alkyl-ferrocenes exhibit a band near 7.9 μ (1270 cm.$^{-1}$) while the 1,3 isomers show absorption near 7.8 μ (1290 cm.$^{-1}$). Unfortunately these correlations are not applicable to isomeric acetyl-arylferrocenes or diarylferrocenes.

Ultraviolet spectra

The ultraviolet absorption spectra of acylferrocenes preserve many of the features of the spectrum of the parent substance. In general the two weak absorption bands in ferrocene at 325 and 440 mμ are not greatly shifted in position in the simple acyl derivatives. However, the intensity of these bands is significantly increased. This effect is generally confined to derivatives bearing electron-withdrawing substituents and is therefore manifest in the spectra of arylferrocenes as well. By contrast, the spectra of alkylferrocenes are practically identical with that of ferrocene itself.

Below 300 mμ, the relatively intense, broad end absorption in the spectrum of ferrocene is replaced by two well-defined, intense peaks near 230 and 270 mμ in the spectra of most acyl derivatives. These may be associated in part with electronic interactions of the substituent with the ring, superimposed upon metal to ring charge-transfer bands.

The spectra of acylferrocenes have been recorded and discussed by a number of authors (64, 121, 127, 128). A compilation of spectral data for a number of acetylated ferrocene derivatives is presented in Table 4-3.

Nuclear magnetic resonance spectra

In general, acyl substituents lead to pronounced deshielding of protons in the substituted cyclopentadienyl ring. In mono- or 1,1'-diacylmetallo-cenes these protons appear as a pair of closely spaced unsymmetrical

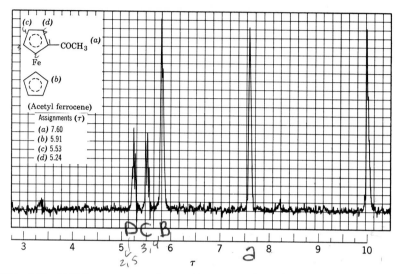

FIG. 4-13   N.M.R. spectrum of acetylferrocene (determined at 60 Mc. in 5% deuterochloroform solution).

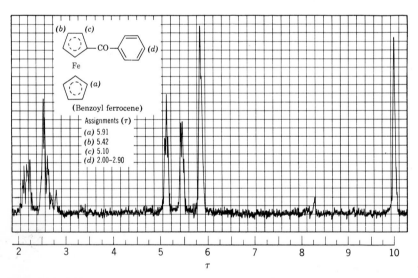

FIG. 4-14   N.M.R. spectrum of benzoylferrocene (determined at 60 Mc. in 5% deuterochloroform solution).

triplets corresponding to the spectrum of an A_2B_2 system in which J_{AB} and $J_{A'B}$ (or $J_{AB'}$) are equal and considerably smaller than the chemical shifts between A and B.* The low field triplet in these derivatives is assigned to $H_{2,5}$ and the higher field triplet to $H_{3,4}$. The spectra of acetyl- and benzoylferrocene are reproduced in Fig. 4-13 and 4-14 as typical examples.

Rausch and Mark (106) have recently published n.m.r. data for a series of acylmetallocenes. In general it appears that the average down-field shift of $H_{2,5}$ and of $H_{3,4}$ in these substances is somewhat greater in ferrocene derivatives (0.6 and 0.3 p.p.m. respectively) than in either the corresponding ruthenocene or osmocene derivatives (0.5 and 0.2 p.p.m. respectively for each of these metallocenes). As noted by these authors, the magnitude of the deshielding of $H_{2,5}$ and $H_{3,4}$ as well as the chemical shift difference between these pairs of protons in the acylmetallocenes very closely parallels the deshielding effects of acyl substituents on the *ortho* and *meta* protons in benzene derivatives.

N.M.R. spectral data, like infrared spectral data, have been particularly valuable in assigning structures to isomeric homoannularly substituted ferrocenes, and have the significant advantage of being analytic rather than correlative in nature.

This point is well illustrated by the n.m.r. spectra of a series of isomeric acetyl-alkylferrocenes recently reported by Nagai, Hooz, and Benkeser (5). The spectra of 1-acetyl-1'-alkylferrocenes are readily identified by the characteristic pair of low field triplets near 5.4 and 5.6 τ, which are assigned to $H_{2,5}$ and $H_{3,4}$ respectively of the acetylated ring. Protons in the alkylated ring give rise to singlet absorption which is generally shifted by about 0.1 p.p.m. to higher field compared with the proton resonance of ferrocene. The spectra of the 1-acetyl-2-alkylferrocenes exhibit a singlet peak near 5.9 τ, corresponding to the five protons of the un-substituted ring, and three complex lower field peaks, near 5.5, 5.7, and 5.8 τ, assigned in order of increasing shielding to H_5, H_4, and H_3 of the disubstituted ring. By contrast, the spectra of 1-acetyl-3-alkylferrocenes exhibit, in addition to the five proton singlet peak near 5.9 τ, two low field absorptions near 5.4 and 5.7 τ, in the intensity ratio of 2:1, which are assigned to $H_{2,5}$ and H_4 respectively of the disubstituted ring.

---

* These coupling constants, corresponding to $J_{2,3}$ or $J_{4,5}$ and $J_{2,4}$ or $J_{3,5}$ in mono-acylmetallocenes are not exactly equal, but are very nearly so. The values of these coupling constants in bridged acetylferrocenes has recently been determined by Rinehart, Bublitz, and Gustafson (122a) and are probably not significantly different in the simple acyl derivatives. These are: $J_{2,3} = J_{4,5} \sim 2.5$ c.p.s., $J_{2,4} = J_{3,5} \sim 1.5$ c.p.s., $J_{3,4} \sim 2.5$ c.p.s., $J_{2,5} \sim 1.5$ c.p.s. The spectrum of furan, discussed recently by Reddy and Goldstein (107), has many features paralleling those of the acylmetallocenes.

PREFACE TO TABLE 4-4

Organization

The table is divided into six sections.

Melting points

In general the highest melting point reported in the literature is given, except where there appears to be agreement from several independent sources on a lower value. In cases where substantial differences occur in the literature, both values are recorded.

Refractive indices

Where two or more values of the index of refraction at the same temperature are reported, the upper and lower values are given. The temperature at which the refractive index was determined is given in parentheses.

Footnotes

[a] The highest melting point reported is given.
[b] By Friedel-Crafts type reaction.
[c] Structural assignment given in the literature is incorrect.
[d] Bracketed numbers refer to the orientation of groups within the aromatic ring.
[e] By indirect synthesis.
[f] From the ester by saponification.
[g] Not isolated.
[h] From the acid by esterification.
[k] By side chain oxidation.
[l] Directly from the substituted cyclopentadiene.
[m] Not well characterized, probably a mixture.
[n] Structural assignment not certain.
[p] No structure given.

Table 4-4

I. Monoacylferrocenes

ACYL GROUP	M.P.–B.P.^{a}	METHOD OF SYNTHESIS	LITERATURE REFERENCE
—CHO	124.5	b	12, 13, 42, 125, 141, 145,
—COCH$_3$	85–86	b	13, 42, 45, 69, 127, 162, 166
		e	89
		b	103
—COCH$_2$CH$_3$	38.0–38.2	e	89
—CO(CH$_2$)$_2$CH$_3$	b.p. 144–6/1.5	b	29
—CO(CH$_2$)$_4$CH$_3$	b.p. 161–3/1.5	b	29
—CO(CH$_2$)$_6$CH$_3$	26–27	b	29
—CO(CH$_2$)$_8$CH$_3$	b.p. 203–4/1.6	b	29
—CO(CH$_2$)$_{10}$CH$_3$	36–37	b	29
—CO(CH$_2$)$_{14}$CH$_3$	59–59.8	b	29
—COC(CH$_3$)$_3$	92	b	161
—COCH$_2$C$_6$H$_{11}$	84	b	27a, 59, 151, 151a
—COCH$_2$Cl	92–93	b	58
—COCH$_2$Cl$_2$	93–94	b, e	141
—COCH=CH$_2$	73.5–74	b	141
		b	124
		k	147
		e	51
—COC≡CH	78–80	c	166
		k	147

Table 4-4 Continued
I. Monoacylferrocenes

ACYL GROUP	M.P.–B.P.[a]	METHOD OF SYNTHESIS	LITERATURE REFERENCE
—COCO$_2$CH$_3$	71.5–72.5	b	124
—COCH$_2$CH$_2$CO$_2$H	166.5–167.5	b	77, 120, 269
		f	142
—COCH$_2$CH$_2$CO$_2$CH$_3$	60	b	77, 142
—COCH$_2$CH(CH$_3$)CO$_2$H	—	b	153
—CO(CH$_2$)$_3$CO$_2$H	136–137	b	120
—CO(CH$_2$)$_3$CO$_2$CH$_3$	b.p. 150–200/0.2	b	142
—CO(CH$_2$)$_4$CO$_2$H	83.5–84.5	f	120
—CO(CH$_2$)$_4$CO$_2$C$_2$H$_5$	—[g]	b	120
—CO–(cyclohexyl, CO$_2$H)	176	b	27
—CO–(pyridyl, N–H)	163	b	27
—CO–(furyl, O)	80	b	27
—CO–(thienyl, S)	125	b	27

Substituent	m.p. (°C)		Refs.
—COC$_6$H$_5$	111.5–112	b	102, 124, 164, 167
—COC$_6$H$_4$OH-o	87.5–88.5	e	81, 138
—COC$_6$H$_3$(OH)$_2$-(2,4)^d	175–176	e	138
—COC$_6$H$_4$OCH$_3$-o	136–137	b	88, 138
—COC$_6$H$_4$OCOCH$_3$-o	111–113	b	88
—COC$_6$H$_4$OCH$_3$-p	82–83	b	164
—CO— (2-OCH$_3$, 4-OH–C$_6$H$_3$)	123.5–125.5	e	138
—COC$_6$H$_3$(OCH$_3$)$_2$-(2,4)^d	133.5–133.8	b	138
—COC$_6$H$_4$CH$_3$-o	b.p. 135/1.5	b	27
—COC$_6$H$_4$CH$_3$-m	b.p. 220/1.5	b	27
—COC$_6$H$_4$CH$_3$-p	132	b	27
—COC$_6$H$_4$CO$_2$CH$_3$-o	134–135	b	74
—COC$_6$H$_4$CO$_2$H-o	171–172	b	8, 9
—COCH$_2$C$_6$H$_5$	130	b	27, 154
—COCH$_2$C$_6$H$_4$CO$_2$H-o	174–176	b	8, 9
—COCH$_2$C$_6$H$_4$C$_6$H$_5$	85.5–86	b	66
—COCH=CHC$_6$H$_5$ (cis)	130–131	e	66, 147
—COCH=CHC$_6$H$_5$ (trans)	139–140	k	147
—CO—CH=CH—C$_6$H$_4$NO$_2$-o	168–172	k	147
—CO—CH=CH—C$_6$H$_4$NO$_2$-m	172–173	b	36
—CO—CH=CH—C$_6$H$_4$NO$_2$-p	198	b	36
—CO—CH=CH—C$_6$H$_4$Cl-o	116–118	b	36
—COC≡CC$_6$H$_5$	103–106	k	147

Table 4-4 Continued
II. Diacylferrocenes

ACYL GROUP	M.P.–B.P.[a]	METHOD OF SYNTHESIS	LITERATURE REFERENCE
1,1'—CHO	183–184	e	93
1,1'—COCH$_3$	130–131	b	13, 72, 105, 110, 127, 161, 166
		l	65
1,2—COCH$_3$	105–106	b	109, 124, 127, 202
1,1'—COCH$_2$CH$_3$	53–54	b	73
1,1'—COCH$_2$CH$_2$Cl	117–121	b	124, 166,
1,1'—COCH$_2$CH$_2$CN	133–134	e	42
1,1'—COCH$_2$CO$_2$C$_2$H$_5$	Oil	e	142
1,1'—CO(CH$_2$)$_2$CO$_2$H	167–169	b	42, 74
		f	142
1,1'—CO(CH$_2$)$_2$CO$_2$CH$_3$	102–105	b	74, 142
1,1'—CO(CH$_2$)$_2$CO$_2$C$_2$H$_5$	134–136	h	42
1,1'—CO(CH$_2$)$_3$CO$_2$H	190–191 (dec.)	b	144
		f	142
1,1'—CO(CH$_2$)$_2$CO$_2$CH$_3$, —CO(CH$_2$)$_3$CO$_2$CH$_3$	Oil	b	142, 144
1,1'—CO(CH$_2$)$_2$CO$_2$H, —CO(CH$_2$)$_3$CO$_2$H	Oil	b	142, 144
	142–149 (dec.)	b	144
		f	142
1,1'—CO(CH$_2$)$_2$CH$_3$	74–75	b	73, 139
1,1'—CO(CH$_2$)$_4$CH$_3$	38–39	b	29

1,1'—CO(CH₂)₆CH₃	54.8–56.0	b	161
1,1'—CO(CH₂)₈CH₃	68.6–69.0	b	161
1,1'—CO(CH₂)₁₀CH₃	76.7–77.1	b	161
1,1'—CO(CH₂)₁₁CH₃	80.0–80.4	b	161
1,1'—CO(CH₂)₁₄CH₃	82.4–83.4	b	161
1,1'—COC(CH₃)₃	126	b	59, 151
1,1'—COCH₂C(CH₃)₃	94	b	58
1,1'—COCH₂CH(CH₃)₂	61	b	58
1,1'—COCH₃, —COC₆H₅	71–72	b	161
1,1'—COC₆H₅	106.5–106.7	b	73, 102, 110, 114
1,2—COC₆H₅	124	b	96, 124
1,1'—COC₆H₄Cl-*p*	186	b	114
1,1'—COC₆H₄F-*p*	129–130.5	b	139
1,1'—COC₆H₄CO₂CH₃-*o*	144–144.5	h	166
1,1'—COCH₂C₆H₅	202–204	b	27

1,1'—COCHC₆H₃(CH₃)₂-(3, 4)ᵈ
      |
    CH₃
	77	b	58

Table 4-4 Continued

III. Acyl Derivatives of Substituted Ferrocenes

FERROCENE SUBSTITUENT	ACYL GROUP	M.P.–B.P.[a]	METHOD OF SYNTHESIS	LITERATURE REFERENCE
1—CH$_3$	1'—CHO	79.5–80.5	k	117
1,1'—CH$_3$	2—COCH$_3$	15–16	b	78[m], 121
	3—COCH$_3$	48.4–48.6	b	78[m], 121
	2,2'—COCH$_3$ (*meso*)[n]	87.5–88.5	b	78, 122
	2,2'—COCH$_3$ (*d, l*)[n]	130–131	b	122
	3,3'—COCH$_3$ (*meso*)[n]	73–73.5	b	122
	3,3'—COCH$_3$ (*d, l*)[n]	130–131	b	122
	Triacetyl	—	b	78[g]
1—C$_2$H$_5$	1'—COCH$_3$	12.5–13.2	b	72, 127
	2—COCH$_3$	42.5–44.5	b	127
	3—COCH$_3$	11.6–12.6	b	72[m], 127
	1'—COCH$_2$CH$_2$CO$_2$CH$_3$	94–96	b	157
	2—COCH$_2$CH$_2$CO$_2$CH$_3$	120	b	157
	3—COCH$_2$CH$_2$CO$_2$CH$_3$	106–108	b	157
	1',X—COCH$_3$	Oil	b	72[m,p] 124[p]
	1',Y—COCH$_3$	34–37	b	124[p]
1,1'—C$_2$H$_5$	2—COCH$_2$CH$_2$CO$_2$H	54	b	157
	3—COCH$_2$CH$_2$CO$_2$H	52	b	157
1—CH$_2$CH$_2$CH$_3$	1'—COC(CH$_3$)$_3$	b.p. 166/2	b	27a, 151a
	3—COC(CH$_3$)$_3$[n]	b.p. 158–160/2	b	27a, 151a

1—CH$_2$CH(CH$_3$)$_2$	1'—COC(CH$_3$)$_3$	b.p. 150/1	b	27a, 151a
1,1'—CH(CH$_3$)$_2$	2—COCH$_3$	b.p. 120–125/0.4	b	121
	3—COCH$_3$	b.p. 150–155/1.3	b	121
1—CH$_2$C(CH$_3$)$_3$	1'—COCH$_3$	73–74	b	7
	3—COCH$_3$^{n}	76–78	b	7
	1'—COC$_6$H$_{11}$	37–38	b	27a
	3—COC$_6$H$_{11}$^{n}	64–66	b	27a
	1'—COC$_6$H$_4$Cl-p	118–120	b	7
	1'—COC$_6$H$_4$Cl-o	113–114	b	7
	1'—COCH=CHC$_6$H$_5$ (*trans*)	125–126	b	7
	1'—COCH$_2$C$_6$H$_5$	100–101	b	7
		54–54.5	b	27a
	3—COCH$_2$C$_6$H$_5$^{n}	111–112	b	7
	1'—COCH$_2$CH$_3$	125–130	b	27a
	3—COCH$_2$CH$_3$^{n}	40–42	b	7
	1'—COCH(CH$_3$)$_2$	b.p. 150/2	b	7
	3—COCH(CH$_3$)$_2$^{n}	118–122/0.5	b	27a
	1'—COC(CH$_3$)$_3$	56–57	b	7, 27a
	3—COC(CH$_3$)$_3$^{n}	56–57	b	151a
	1'—COC$_6$H$_5$	110	b	151a
		85–86	b	7
1—CH$_2$C(CH$_3$)$_3$	3—COC$_6$H$_{11}$^{n}	100–105	b	7
	1'—COCH$_2$CHCH$_2$C(CH$_3$)$_3$ CH$_3$	b.p. 154/2	b	7, 27a

Table 4-4 Continued

FERROCENE SUBSTITUENT	ACYL GROUP	M.P.–B.P.[a]	METHOD OF SYNTHESIS	LITERATURE REFERENCE
1—$CH_2CH_2C_6H_5$	1'—$COC(CH_3)_3$	93–94	b	151a
	3—$COC(CH_3)_3$[n]	81–82	b	151a
1—CH_2OH	1'—CHO	39–40	k	93
1,1'—$CH_2CH_2CH_2$—	2—$COCH_3$	77.5–78.5	b	52, 132
	3—$COCH_3$	103–104	b	52, 132
1—$CH_2CH_2CH_2CO_2H$	1'—$COCH_2CH_2CO_2H$	120–123	f	142
	1'—$COCH_2CH_2CO_2CH_3$	40–65	b	142
1—$CH_2C_6H_5$	1'—$COCH_3$	78–81	b	148
1—$CH_2C_6H_4COCH_3$-p	1,3—$COCH_3$	132–134	b	148[n]
1—$CH_2C_6H_4COCH_3$-p	1',X,Y—$COCH_3$	114–117	b	148[p]

1—C$_6$H$_5$	1'—COCH$_3$	92.5–93.5	b	83, 128
	2—COCH$_3$	72.5–74.0	b	128
	3—COCH$_3$	113–114	b	128
1,1'—C$_6$H$_5$	2—COCH$_3$	Oil	b	128
	3—COCH$_3$	113–114	b	128
1—C$_6$H$_4$OCH$_3$-p	1'—COCH$_3$	97–98	b	130
	2—COCH$_3$	137–139	b	130
1,1'—C$_6$H$_4$OCH$_3$-p	2—COCH$_3$	Oil	b	130
	3—COCH$_3$	147–148	b	130
1,1'—C$_6$H$_4$Br-p	2—COCH$_3$	126.4–127.5	b	130
	3—COCH$_3$	145–147	b	130
1—C$_6$H$_4$NO$_2$-p	1'—COCH$_3$	122–123 (dec.)	e	99
	2 or 3—COCH$_3$	158–160 (dec.)	e	99
1—CH$_2$ [thiophene]—COCH$_3$	1'—COCH$_3$	110–116	b	148
	1',X—COCH$_3$	123–125	b	148[D]
1—OH	1—COCH$_3$	115.5–118.5	e	80
1—OCOC$_6$H$_5$	1'—COCH$_3$	84–85	e	80

Table 4-4 Continued

FERROCENE SUBSTITUENT	ACYL GROUP	M.P.–B.P.[a]	METHOD OF SYNTHESIS	LITERATURE REFERENCE
1—Br	1'—COCH$_3$	61.5–63	b	44, 80
1—Cl	1'—COCH$_3$	53–55	b	44
1—CO$_2$CH$_3$	1'—COCH$_3$	101.5–103.5	k	75, 124
	1'—COCH$_2$CH$_2$CH$_3$	54.5–55.5	b	75
1—CO$_2$H	1'—COCH$_3$	153–155	f	75
	1'—COCH$_2$CH$_2$CH$_3$	114–115	b	75
1—CN	1'—COCH$_3$	99.8–101	b	44, 87
1—NHCOCH$_3$	1'—COCH$_3$	115.5–116	b	44
	2—COCH$_3$	109–109.5	b	44
1—NHCO$_2$C$_2$H$_5$	1'—COCH$_3$	149.5–150	b	44
	2—COCH$_3$	Oil	b	44
1,1'—NHCO$_2$C$_2$H$_5$	2—COCH	109.5–110	b	44
	3—COCH$_3$	140.8–142	b	44
1—NHCO$_2$CH$_3$	1'—COCH$_3$	135–136	b	44
	2—COCH$_3$	Oil	b	44

IV. Acyl Derivatives of Ruthenocene and Osmocene

METALLOCENE	ACYL GROUP	M.P.–B.P.[a]	METHOD OF SYNTHESIS	LITERATURE REFERENCE
Ruthenocene				
	—CHO	100.2–100.8	b	18
	—COCH$_3$	111–112	b	104, 105
	1,1'—COCH$_3$	149–150	b	104, 105
	—COC$_6$H$_5$	124.5–125	b	104, 105
	1,1'—COC$_6$H$_5$	125–126	b	104, 105
	1,X—COC$_6$H$_5$	141.8–142.4	b	17, 18
Osmocene				
	—COCH$_3$	127	b	104, 105, 111
	—COC$_6$H$_5$	131–132	b	18, 105, 111

V. Acyl Derivatives with Two Metallocene Nuclei

—C$_{10}$H$_9$Fe, —C$_{10}$H$_9$Fe

ACYL GROUP	M.P.–B.P.[a]	METHOD OF SYNTHESIS	LITERATURE REFERENCE
—CO—	204[d]	b	41, 105, 145,
		k	98, 117
		e	89
—COCO—	193–195	k	117
—COCH$_2$CH$_2$CO—	185–186	b	153, 154
—COCH$_2$CH(CH$_3$)CO—	—	b	153
—CH$_2$CO—	159–161	b	97, 118
—CH$_2$CH$_2$CO—	127–130	e	149
—CHCH$_2$CO—	147–149	e	98
CH$_3$ —CH=CHCO—	207–210	b	149

Table 4-4 Continued

METALLOCENE	ACYL GROUP	M.P.–B.P.[a]	METHOD OF SYNTHESIS	LITERATURE REFERENCE
—C₁₀H₉Fe, —C₁₀H₉Fe				
	—C=CHCO— (CH₃)	118–120	e	98, 116
	—COC≡CCO—	158–161	k	147
	—COC≡C—C≡CCO—	161–164	k	147
—C₁₀H₉Fe, C₁₀H₉Ru				
	—CO—	216	b	105
"Pentaethanodiferrocene"[c]				
	—COCH₃	105–110	b	79ᴅ
	X,Y—COCH₃	80 (dec.)	b	79ᴅ

VI. Primary Condensation Products of Acylferrocenes

ACYL SUBSTITUENT	DERIVED SUBSTITUENT	M.P.–B.P.	LITERATURE REFERENCE
—CHO			
	—CH=CHCO₂H	186–187 (dec.)	13, 46, 141
	—CH=C(CN)CO₂H	158–160	42
	—CH=C(CN)CO₂C₂H₅	88–90	3
	—CH=CHCOC₆H₅	126–128	46
		138–140	141
		α 136–137	11
		β 140	11

Structure	M.p.	Refs.
—CH=CHCOC$_6$H$_4$OH-o	157–158	11, 141, 156
—CH=CHCOC$_6$H$_4$NO$_2$-m	149	10, 11
—CH=CHCH=CH$_2$	80°	93
—CH= (cyclopentadienylidene)	59–60	39, 93
—CH= (oxazolone, C$_6$H$_5$)	188	12, 94, 141
—CH=CH— (N-methylpyridinium I$^-$)	—	13
—COCHOHC$_6$H$_5$	148–149	13
(hydantoin)	192–197	42
	250–252	63
	217–219	141

Table 4-4 Continued

ACYL SUBSTITUENT	DERIVED SUBSTITUENT	M.P.–B.P.	LITERATURE REFERENCE
—CHO		>360	42
		245 (dec.)	42
		α 128 β 140	11 11, 156
		191–192	10
		α 188–189 β 158	11, 156 11

Structure	mp (°C)	References
—CH=CHCO (2-pyridyl)	157–158	10
—CH=CHCOC$_{10}$H$_9$Fe "α"	198	10, 11
"β"	210	10, 11
—CH= (isocoumarin)	189	10, 11
—CH= (indandione)	167–168	10, 11
—CH= (isoquinolinedione, N—R) R = H	240	10, 11
R = CH$_3$	182	10, 11
R = C$_2$H$_5$	223	10
R = C$_6$H$_5$	234	10, 11
—CH=NC$_6$H$_5$	77	10, 11
—CH=NC$_{10}$H$_7$—(1)[a]	128	10, 11

Table 4-4 Continued

ACYL SUBSTITUENT	DERIVED SUBSTITUENT	M.P.–B.P.	LITERATURE REFERENCE
—CHO	—CH=NC$_{10}$H$_7$–(2)[d]	106	10, 11
	—CH=N– (thiazol-2-yl)	128	10, 11
	—CH=N$^+$C$_6$H$_5$ · CH$_3$ ClO$_4$$^-$	—	54
	—CH= (2,4-dimethyl-5-ethylpyrrolium) C$_2$H$_5$, CH$_3$, N$^+$H ClO$_4$$^-$	167 (dec.)	158
	—CH= (pyrrolium, C$_2$H$_5$, CH$_3$, N$^+$H) CH$_3$ ClO$_4$$^-$	173 (dec.)	158
	—CH= (pyrrolium, CO$_2$CH$_3$, CH$_3$, N$^+$H) CH$_3$ ClO$_4$$^-$	178 (dec.)	158

Structure / Substituent		
Ferrocene —CH—OH	176–177	54, 98
—CH—CN	104	42
OH / —CH—CN		
—N(CH₃)₂ → $-N(CH_3)_2$	86	46
—CH=CHNO₂ → $-CH=CHNO_2$	Oil	63
—CH=CHC₆H₅ → $-CH=CHC_6H_5$	118	30
—CH=CHC₆H₄CH₃-p → $-CH=CHC_6H_4CH_3\text{-}p$	131	30
—CH=CH (anthracene)	168	30
—CH=CHCH=CHC₆H₅ → $-CH=CHCH=CHC_6H_5$	192	30
—CH=CH—C₆H₄—CH=CHC₆H₅ → $-CH=CH-C_6H_4-CH=CHC_6H_5$	220	30

Table 4-4 Continued

ACYL SUBSTITUENT	DERIVED SUBSTITUENT	M.P.–B.P.	LITERATURE REFERENCE
—CHO	—CH=CH—⬡—CH=CHC$_{10}$H$_9$Fe	141–142	30
	Oxime		
	α	96–99	13, 42, 60, 125
	β	155–157	13
	Oxime acetate	80–81	42, 60
	Semicarbazone	217–219	42, 49, 120
		240–242	11
	2,4-Dinitrophenylhydrazone	248 (dec.)	125
	Azine	245	42
	Isonicotinylcarbonylhydrazone	212–213	42
	Thiosemicarbazone	190–191 (dec.)	11
1,1'—CHO	1—CH=CHCOCH$_3$, 1'—CHO	300	93[n]
	1,1'—CH=N—⬡—CH=N—	210	93[n]
	Dioxime	135	93
—COCH$_3$	—COCH$_2$COCH$_3$	97–97.5	19, 163, 165
	—COCH$_2$CO$_2$C$_2$H$_5$	57–58	45, 116, 120

Substituent	mp (°C)	References
$-COCH_2COC_6H_5$	106–107	45
$-C(CH_3)=$ (cyclopentadienylidene)	88–89	38
$-COCH=CHC_6H_5$ (*trans*)	139–140	11, 45, 103, 141, 156
Oxime	116–118	11
$-COCH=CH-CH=CHC_6H_5$	142	11
$-COCH=CHC_6H_4CN\text{-}p$	225	11, 156
$-COCH=CHC_6H_4Cl\text{-}p$	119	11, 156
α	160	11, 156
β	150	11, 156
$-COCH=CHC_6H_4OCH_3\text{-}p$	169–170°	36
$-COCH=CH$ (2,3-dihydrobenzofuranyl)	190	11, 156
$-COCH=CHC_6H_4NO_2\text{-}p$	204	11, 156
$-COCH=CHC_{10}H_7\text{-}(2)^{[d]}$	147	11, 156
$-COCH=CH$ (2-thienyl, S)	158	11, 36, 156
$-COCH=CH$ (2-furyl, O)		

Table 4-4 Continued

ACYL SUBSTITUENT	DERIVED SUBSTITUENT	M.P.–B.P.	LITERATURE REFERENCE
—$COCH_3$	—$COCH=CH$- (pyrrole)	208	11, 156
	—$COCH=CH$- (5-NO_2 pyrrole)	241 (dec.)	11, 156
	—$COCH=CH$- (NO_2 pyrrole)	275 (dec.)	11, 156
	—$COCH=CHC_5H_4N$-(2)[d]	153	11, 156
	-(3)[d]	172	11, 156
	-(4)[d]	196	11, 156
	—$COCH=CH$- (quinoline)	202	11
	—$COCH(CH_2C_6H_5)_2$	154–155	50
	—$COCH_2CH_2N(CH_3)_2 \cdot HCl$	159–160	51

—$COCH_2CH_2N(CH_3)_2$	72–73	51
—$COCH_2CH_2N(C_2H_5)_2$	Oil	51
—$C(CH_3)=CHCO$—	118–120	98, 116
(pyrazole ring: $N\!-\!N$ with C_6H_5 substituent)	142, 144	51
—$CH(NH_2)CH_3 \cdot HCl$	163–165 (dec.)	42
Oxime	169–170	1, 69
Semicarbazone	184–185	11
	198–201	69
	226–227	11
Thiosemicarbazone	195–196	11
1,1'—$COCH_2COCH_3$	142.5–144	9, 19
1,1'—$COCH_2COCH_3$	142.5–144	9, 19
1,1'—$COCH_2COC_2H_5$	114–115.5	19
1,1'—$COCH_2CO_2C_2H_5$	Oil	142
1,1'—$COCH_2COC_6H_5$	213–215	19, 47
1,1'—$C(CH_3)=$ (cyclopentadiene)	134	38
1,1'—$COCH=CHC_6H_5$	208–210	66

1,1'—$COCH_3$

Table 4-4 Continued

ACYL SUBSTITUENT	DERIVED SUBSTITUENT	M.P.–B.P.	LITERATURE REFERENCE
1,1'—COCH₃	1—COCH₃, 1'—COCH=CHC₆H₄NO₂		
	$-o$	Oil	37
	$-m$	200–202	37
	$-p$	265	37
	1,1'—COCH(CH₂C₆H₅)₂	185–186	50
	Dioxime	200 (dec.)	166
	Bis-hydantoin	192–196 (dec.)	42
	$\overset{\text{OCOCH}_3}{\underset{}{1,1'—\text{C}=\text{CH}_2}}$		
—COCH₂CH₃	—COCH(CH₃)CH₂N(CH₃)₂·HCl	b.p. 100°/1 mm.	100
—COC≡CH	isoxazole ring (O—N)		103
		93–95	147
	pyrazole ring (NH—N)	148–152	147

—COCH$_2$CO$_2$C$_2$H$_5$		186–188	45
—COCH$_2$COC$_6$H$_5$		267–269	45, 47
1,1'—COCH$_2$COCH$_3$		300 (dec.)	19
1,1'—COCH$_2$COC$_2$H$_5$		300 (dec.)	19

Table 4-4 Continued

ACYL SUBSTITUENT	DERIVED SUBSTITUENT	M.P.–B.P.	LITERATURE REFERENCE
1,1'—$COCH_2COC_6H_5$	1,1' (C₆H₅, NH, N pyrazole structure)	300° (dec.)	47
—$COCH_2CH_2CO$—	(bicyclic N–N ring structure)	266	153

[a] The highest melting point reported is given.
[b] By Friedel-Crafts type reaction.
[c] Structural assignment given in the literature is incorrect.
[d] Bracketed numbers refer to the orientation of groups within the aromatic ring.
[e] By indirect synthesis.
[f] From the ester by saponification.
[g] Not isolated.
[h] From the acid by esterification.
[k] By side chain oxidation.
[l] Directly from the substituted cyclopentadiene.
[m] Not well characterized, probably a mixture.
[n] Structural assignment not certain.
[p] No structure given.

REFERENCES

1. Arimoto, F. S., and A. C. Haven, *J. Am. Chem. Soc.*, **77**, 6295 (1955).
2. Arnett, E. M., and R. D. Bushick, *J. Org. Chem.*, **27**, 111 (1962).
3. Barben, I. K., *J. Chem. Soc.*, 1827 (1961).
4. Benkeser, R. A., D. Goggin, and G. Schroll, *J. Am. Chem. Soc.*, **76**, 4025 (1954).
5. Benkeser, R. A., J. Hooz, and Y. Nagai, *Bull. Chem. Soc., Japan*, **37**, 53 (1964).
6. Berger, A., W. E. McEwen, and J. Kleinberg, *J. Am. Chem. Soc.*, **83**, 2274 (1961).
7. Birtwell, S., Brit. Pat. 861, 832 (March 1, 1961).
8. Boichard, J., and J. Tirouflet, *Compt. Rend.*, **253**, 1337 (1961).
9. Boichard, J., and M. Delepine, *Compt. Rend.*, **253**, 2702 (1961).
10. Boichard, J., and J. Tirouflet, *Compt. Rend.*, **251**, 1394 (1960).
11. Boichard, J., J. P. Monin, and J. Tirouflet, *Bull. Soc. Chim. France*, 851 (1963).
12. Broadhead, G. D., J. M. Osgerby, and P. L. Pauson, *Chem. & Ind. (London)*, 209 (1957).
13. Broadhead, G. D., J. M. Osgerby, and P. L. Pauson, *J. Chem. Soc.*, 650 (1958).
14. Brown, H. C., and Y. Okamoto, *J. Am. Chem. Soc.*, **80**, 4979 (1958).
15. Brown, H. C., G. Marino, and L. M. Stock, *J. Am. Chem. Soc.*, **81**, 3310 (1959).
16. Brown, H. C., and G. Marino, *J. Am. Chem. Soc.*, **81**, 5611 (1959).
17. Bublitz, D. E., J. Kleinberg, and W. E. McEwen, *Chem. & Ind. (London)*, 936 (1960).
18. Bublitz, D. E., W. E. MeEwen, and J. Kleinberg, *J. Am. Chem. Soc.*, **84**, 1845 (1962).
19. Cain, E. C., T. A. Mashburn, and C. R. Hauser, *J. Org. Chem.*, **26**, 1030 (1961).
19a Cais, M., and A. Modiano, *Chem. & Ind. (London)*, 202 (1960).
20. Cais, M. et al., Abstracts of the 19th International Congress of Pure and Applied Chemistry, July 1963, Paper AB4-12, p. 166.
21. Calderazzo, F., and R. Ercoli et al., *Chimica Ind. (Milan)*, **42**, 52 (1960).
22. Cannon, C. G., and G. B. B. M. Sutherland, *Spectrochim. Acta*, **4**, 373 (1951).
23. Coffield, T. H., K. G. Ihrman, and W. Burns, *J. Am. Chem. Soc.*, **82**, 4209 (1960).
24. Cotton, F. A., and R. Leto, *Chem. & Ind. (London)*, 1368 (1958).
25. Cram, D. J., and R. D. Partos, *J. Am. Chem. Soc.*, **85**, 1273 (1963).
26. Curphey, T. J., J. O. Santer, M. Rosenblum, and J. H. Richards, *J. Am. Chem. Soc.*, **82**, 5249 (1960).
27. Dabard, R., and B. Gatheron, *Compt. Rend.*, **254**, 2014 (1962).
27a Day, L. A., Brit. Pat. 864, 198 (March 29, 1961) *C. A.*, **55**, 17647 (1961).
28. Dewar, M. J. S., *J. Chem. Soc.*, 463 (1949); *J. Am. Chem. Soc.*, **74**, 3357 (1952).
29. DeYoung, E. L., *J. Org. Chem.*, **26**, 1312 (1961).
30. Drefahl, G., G. Plötner, and I. Winnefeld, *Ber.*, **94**, 2788 (1962).
31. Dvoryantseva, G. G., and Yu. N. Sheinker, *Izvestia Akad. Nauk SSSR, Otdel. Khim. Nauk*, 924 (1963).
32. Ferguson, L. N., *Chem. Rev.*, **38**, 227 (1946).
33. Fischer, E. O., and K. Plesske, *Ber.*, **91**, 2719 (1958).
34. Fischer, E. O., and K. Plesske, *Ber.*, **93**, 1006 (1960).
35. Fischer, E. O., and K. Plesske, *Ber.*, **94**, 93 (1961).
36. Furdik, M., P. Elecko, S. Toma, and J. Suchy, *Chem. Zvesti*, **15**, 501 (1960).
37. Furdik, M., S. Toma, J. Suchy, and D. Elecko, *Chem. Zvesti*, **15**, 45 (1961).
38. Furdik, M., S. Toma, and J. Suchy, *Chem. Zvesti*, **15**, 547 (1961).
39. Furdik, M., S. Toma, and J. Suchy, *Chem. Zvesti*, **16**, 719 (1962).

40. Fuson, R. C., G. R. Bakker, and B. Vittimberga, *J. Am. Chem. Soc.*, **81,** 4858 (1959).
41. Goldberg, S. I., *J. Org. Chem.*, **25,** 482 (1960).
42. Graham, P. J., R. V. Lindsey, G. W. Parshall, M. L. Peterson, and G. M. Whitman, *J. Am. Chem. Soc.*, **79,** 3416 (1957).
43. Gray, G., *Molecular Structure and the Properties of Liquid Crystals*, Academic Press, New York, 1962.
44. Hall, D. W., and J. H. Richards, *J. Org. Chem.*, **28,** 1549 (1963).
45. Hauser, C. R., and J. K. Lindsay, *J. Org. Chem.*, **22,** 428 (1957).
46. Hauser, C. R., and J. K. Lindsay, *J. Org. Chem.*, **22,** 906 (1957).
47. Hauser, C. R., and C. E. Cain, *J. Org. Chem.*, **23,** 1142 (1958).
48. Hauser, C. R., and C. E. Cain, *J. Org. Chem.*, **23,** 2007 (1958).
49. Hauser, C. R., J. K. Lindsay, D. Lednicer, and C. E. Cain, *J. Org. Chem.*, **22,** 717 (1959).
50. Hauser, C. R., and T. A. Mashburn, Jr., *J. Org. Chem.*, **26,** 1795 (1961).
51. Hauser, C. R., R. L. Pruett, and T. A. Mashburn, *J. Org. Chem.*, **26,** 1800 (1961).
52. Hill, E. A., and J. H. Richards, *J. Am. Chem. Soc.*, **83,** 4216 (1961).
53. Ide, W. S., and J. S. Buck, in *Organic Reactions*, Vol. IV, Wiley, New York, 1958, p. 269.
54. Jutz, C., *Tetrahedron Letters*, No. 21, 1 (1959).
55. Knox, G. R., P. L. Pauson, and G. V. D. Tiers, *Chem. & Ind.* (*London*), 1046 (1959).
56. Kozikowski, J., R. E. Maginn, and M. S. Klove, *J. Am. Chem. Soc.*, **81,** 2995 (1959).
57. Lauer, W. M., W. G. Matson, and G. Stedman, *J. Am. Chem. Soc.*, **80,** 6433 (1958).
58. Leigh, T., Brit. Pat. 869,504 (May 31, 1961). *C. A.*, **55,** 24790 (1961).
59. Leigh, T., Brit. Pat. 819,108 (August 26, 1959). *C. A.*, **54,** 7732 (1960).
60. Lindsay, J. K., and C. R. Hauser, *J. Org. Chem.*, **22,** 355 (1957).
61. Little, W. F., R. A. Berry, and P. Kannan, *J. Am. Chem. Soc.*, **84,** 2525 (1962).
62. Little, W. F., and R. Eisenthal, *J. Org. Chem.*, **26,** 3609 (1961).
63. Loev, B., and M. Flores, *J. Org. Chem.*, **26,** 3595 (1961).
64. Lundquist, R. T., and M. Cais, *J. Org. Chem.*, **27,** 1167 (1962).
65. Lynch, M. A., and J. C. Brantley, Brit. Pat. 785,760 (November 6, 1957); *C. A.*, 11126 (1958).
66. Mashburn, T. A., C. E. Cain, and C. R. Hauser, *J. Org. Chem.*, **25,** 1982 (1960).
67. McMurray, H. L., and V. Thornton, *Anal. Chem.*, **24,** 318 (1952).
68. Morrison, I. G., and P. L. Pauson, *Proc. Chem. Soc.*, 177 (1962).
69. Nesmeyanov, A. N., E. G. Perevalova, R. V. Golovnya, and O. A. Nesmeyanova, *Doklady Akad. Nauk SSSR*, **97,** 459 (1954).
70. Nesmeyanov, A. N., E. G. Perevalova, and R. V. Golovnya, *Doklady Akad. Nauk SSSR*, **103,** 81 (1955).
71. Nesmeyanov, A. N., E. G. Perevalova, R. V. Golovnya, T. V. Nikitina, and N. A. Simukova, *Izvestia Akad. Nauk SSSR, Otdel. Khim. Nauk*, 739 (1956).
72. Nesmeyanov, A. N., and N. A. Vol'kenau, *Doklady Akad. Nauk SSSR*, **111,** 605 (1956).
73. Nesmeyanov, A. N., and N. A. Vol'kenau, *Doklady Akad. Nauk SSSR*, **107,** 262 (1956).
74. Nesmeyanov, A. N., N. A. Vol'kenau, and V. D. Vil'chevskaya, *Doklady Akad. Nauk SSSR*, **111,** 362 (1956).

75. Nesmeyanov, A. N., and O. A. Reutov, *Doklady Akad. Nauk SSSR*, **115**, 518 (1957).
76. Nesmeyanov, A. N., L. A. Kazitsina, V. Lokshin, and I. I. Kritskaya, *Doklady Akad. Nauk SSSR*, **117**, 433 (1957).
77. Nesmeyanov, A. N., N. A. Vol'kenau, and V. D. Vil'chevskaya, *Doklady Akad. Nauk SSSR*, **118**, 512 (1958).
78. Nesmeyanov, A. N., E. G. Perevalova et al., *Doklady Akad. Nauk SSSR*, **120**, 1263 (1958).
79. Nesmeyanov, A. N., N. S. Kochetkova, and R. B. Materikova, *Doklady Akad. Nauk SSSR*, **136**, 1096 (1961).
80. Nesmeyanov, A. N., V. A. Sazonova, and V. N. Drozd, *Doklady Akad. Nauk SSSR*, **137**, 102 (1961).
81. Nesmeyanov, A. N., V. D. Vil'chevskaya, and N. S. Kochetkova, *Doklady Akad. Nauk SSSR*, **138**, 390 (1961).
82. Nesmeyanov, A. N., E. G. Perevalova, and T. N. Nikitina, *Doklady Akad. Nauk SSSR*, **138**, 1118 (1961).
83. Nesmeyanov, A. N., et al., *Doklady Akad. Nauk SSSR*, **139**, 888 (1961).
84. Nesmeyanov, A. N., K. N. Anisimov, and Z. P. Valeuva, *Izvestia Akad. Nauk SSSR Otdel. Khim. Nauk*, 1780 (1961).
85. Nesmeyanov, A. N., D. N. Kursanov, and V. N. Setkina, *Tetrahedron Letters*, No. 21, 41 (1961).
86. Nesmeyanov, A. N., D. N. Kursanov, V. N. Setkina, N. V. Kislyakova, and N. S. Kochetkova, *Izvestia Akad. Nauk SSSR Otdel. Khim. Nauk*, 1932 (1962).
87. Nesmeyanov, A. N., E. G. Perevalova, L. P. Yur'eva, and K. I. Grandberg, *Izvestia Akad. Nauk SSSR Otdel. Khim. Nauk*, 1772 (1962).
88. Nesmeyanov, A. N. et al., *Izvestia Akad. Nauk SSSR Otdel. Khim. Nauk*, 1990 (1962).
89. Nesmeyanov, A. N., E. G. Perevalova, L. P. Yur'eva, and L. I. Denisovich, *Izvestia Akad. Nauk SSSR Otdel. Khim. Nauk*, 2241 (1962).
90. Nesmeyanov, A. N., et al., *Izvestia Akad. Nauk SSSR Otdel. Khim. Nauk*, 1377 (1963).
91. Nesmeyanov, A. N., E. G. Perevalova, and S. P. Gubin, Abstracts of the 19th International Congress of Pure and Applied Chemistry, July 1963, Paper AB4-51, p. 187.
92. Nystrom, R. F., and C. R. A. Berger, *J. Am. Chem. Soc.*, **80**, 2896 (1958).
93. Osgerby, J. M., and P. L. Pauson, *J. Chem. Soc.*, 4604 (1961).
94. Osgerby, J. M., and P. L. Pauson, *J. Chem. Soc.*, 656 (1958).
95. Pauson, P. L., *J. Am. Chem. Soc.*, **76**, 2187 (1954).
96. Pauson, P. L., *Quart. Rev. (London)*, **9**, 391 (1955).
97. Pauson, P. L., and W. E. Watts, *J. Chem. Soc.*, 2990 (1963).
98. Pauson, P. L., and W. E. Watts, *J. Chem. Soc.*, 3880 (1962).
99. Perevalova, E. G. et al., *Izvestia Akad. Nauk SSSR Otdel. Khim. Nauk*, 77 (1961).
100. Pruett, R. L., U.S. Pat. 2,947,769 (August 2, 1960). *C. A.*, **55**, 565 (1961).
101. Raisen, C. G., *J. Chem. Soc.*, 3319 (1949).
102. Rausch, M., M. Vogel, and H. Rosenberg, *J. Org. Chem.*, **22**, 903 (1957).
103. Rausch, M. D., and L. E. Coleman, *J. Org. Chem.*, **23**, 107 (1958).
104. Rausch, M. D., E. O. Fischer, and H. Grubert, *Chem. & Ind. (London)*, 756 (1958).
105. Rausch, M. D., E. O. Fischer, and H. Grubert, *J. Am. Chem. Soc.*, **82**, 76 (1960).
106. Rausch, M. D., and V. Mark, *J. Org. Chem.*, **28**, 3225 (1963).
107. Reddy, G. S., and J. H. Goldstein, *J. Am. Chem. Soc.*, **84**, 583 (1962).

108. Richards, J. H., Abstracts of the 135th Meeting of the American Chemical Society, April, 1959, p. 86–0.
109. Richards, J. H., and T. J. Curphey, *Chem. & Ind.* (*London*), 1456 (1956).
110. Riemschneider, R., and D. Helm, *Ber.*, **89**, 155 (1956).
111. Riemschneider, R., *Monatsch. Chem.*, **90**, 658 (1959).
112. Riemschneider, R., and H. G. Kassahn, *Z. Naturforsch.*, **14b**, 348 (1959).
113. Riemschneider, R., O. Goehring, and M. Krüger, *Monatsch. Chem.*, **91**, 305 (1960).
114. Riemschneider, R., and D. Helm, *Ann.*, **646**, 10 (1961).
115. Riemschneider, R., and H. Kassahn, *Ber.*, **92**, 3208 (1962).
116. Rinehart, K. L., R. J. Curby, D. H. Gustafson, K. G. Harrison, R. E. Bozak, and D. E. Bublitz, *J. Am. Chem. Soc.*, **84**, 3263 (1962).
117. Rinehart, K. L., A. F. Ellis, C. J. Michejda, and P. A. Kittle, *J. Am. Chem. Soc.*, **82**, 4112 (1962).
118. Rinehart, K. L., C. J. Michejda, and P. A. Kittle, *J. Am. Chem. Soc.*, **81**, 3162 (1959).
119. Rinehart, K. L., and R. J. Curby, *J. Am. Chem. Soc.*, **79**, 3290 (1957).
120. Rinehart, K. L., R. J. Curby, and P. E. Sokol, *J. Am. Chem. Soc.*, **79**, 3420 (1957).
121. Rinehart, K. L., K. L. Motz, and S. Moon, *J. Am. Chem. Soc.*, **79**, 2749 (1957).
122. Rinehart, K. L., and K. L. Motz, *Chem. & Ind.* (*London*), 1150 (1957).
122a Rinehart, K. L., D. E. Bublitz, and D. H. Gustafson, *J. Am. Chem. Soc.*, **85**, 970 (1963).
122b Rinehart, K. L., unpublished results.
123. Roberts, J. D., and A. Streitweiser, *J. Am. Chem. Soc.*, **74**, 4723 (1952).
124. Rosenblum, M., Thesis, Harvard University, 1953.
125. Rosenblum, M. *Chem. & Ind.* (*London*), 72 (1957).
126. Rosenblum, M. *Chem. & Ind.* (*London*), 953 (1958).
127. Rosenblum, M., and R. B. Woodward, *J. Am. Chem. Soc.*, **80**, 5443 (1958).
128. Rosenblum, M., *J. Am. Chem. Soc.*, **81**, 4530 (1959).
129. Rosenblum, M., and J. O. Santer, *J. Am. Chem. Soc.*, **81**, 5517 (1959).
130. Rosenblum, M., and W. G. Howells, *J. Am. Chem. Soc.*, **84**, 1167 (1962).
131. Rosenblum, M., W. G. Howells, A. K. Banerjee, and C. Bennett, *J. Am. Chem. Soc.*, **84**, 2726 (1962).
132. Rosenblum, M., A. K. Banerjee, N. Danieli, R. W. Fish, and V. Schlatter, *J. Am. Chem. Soc.*, **85**, 316 (1963).
133. Rosenblum, M., and G. Hoh, unpublished work.
134. Rosenblum, M., unpublished results.
135. Rosenblum, M., J. O. Santer, and W. G. Howells, *J. Am. Chem. Soc.*, **85**, 1450 (1963).
136. Rubalcava, H. E., and J. B. Thompson, *Spectrochim. Acta*, **18**, 449 (1962).
137. Rubalcava, H. E., and J. B. Thompson, *J. Phys. Chem.*, **67**, 310 (1963).
138. Schaaf, R. L., *J. Org. Chem.*, **27**, 107 (1962).
139. Schaaf, R. L., and C. T. Lenk, *J. Org. Chem.*, **28**, 3238 (1963).
140. Schlenk, W., and E. Bergman, *Ann.*, **463**, 1 (1928).
141. Schlögl, K., *Monatsch. Chem.*, **88**, 601 (1957).
142. Schlögl, K., and H. Seiler, *Monatsch. Chem.*, **91**, 79 (1960).
143. Schlögl, K., and H. Seiler, *Tetrahedron Letters*, No. 7, p. 4 (1960).
144. Schlögl, K., and H. Seiler, *Angew. Chem.*, **72**, 38 (1960).
145. Schlögl, K., and A. Mohar, *Monatsch. Chem.*, **92**, 219 (1961).
146. Schlögl, K., A. Mohar, and M. Peterlik, *Monatsch. Chem.*, **92**, 921 (1961).

147. Schlögl, K., and A. Mohar, *Monatsch. Chem.*, **93**, 861 (1962).
148. Schlögl, K., and H. Pelousek, *Ann.*, **651**, 1 (1962).
149. Schlögl, K., and H. Egger, *Monatsch. Chem.*, **94**, 376 (1963).
150. Smith, L. I., in *Organic Reactions*, Vol. I, Wiley, New York, 1942, p. 370.
151. Stephenson, R. J., Brit. Pat. 861,833 (March 1, 1961); *C. A.*, **55**, 25981 (1961).
151a Stephenson, R. J., Brit. Pat. 864,197 (March 29, 1961); *C. A.*, **55**, 17647 (1961).
152. Stewart, R., and K. Yates, *J. Am. Chem. Soc.*, **80**, 6355 (1958).
153. Sugiyama, N., and T. Teitei, *Bull. Chem. Soc., Japan*, **35**, 1423 (1962).
154. Sugiyama, N., H. Suzuki, Y. Shioura, and T. Teitei, *Bull. Chem. Soc., Japan*, **35**, 767 (1962).
155. Thompson, J. B., *Chem. & Ind.* (*London*), 1122 (1959).
156. Tirouflet, J., and J. Boichard, *Compt. Rend.*, **250**, 1861 (1960).
157. Tirouflet, J., J. P. Monin, G. Tainturier, and R. Dabard, *Compt. Rend.*, **256**, 433 (1963).
158. Treibs, A., and R. Zimmer-Galler, *Ber.*, **93**, 2539 (1960).
159. Trifan, D. A., and L. Nicholas, *J. Am. Chem. Soc.*, **79**, 2746 (1957).
160. Vilsmeier, A. V., and A. Haack, *Ber.*, **60b**, 119 (1927).
161. Vogel, M., M. Rausch, and H. Rosenberg, *J. Org. Chem.*, **22**, 1016 (1957).
162. Weinmayr, V., *J. Am. Chem. Soc.*, **77**, 3009 (1955).
163. Weinmayr, V., *Naturwiss.*, **45**, 311 (1958).
164. Weliky, N., and E. S. Gould, *J. Am. Chem. Soc.*, **79**, 2742 (1957).
165. Wolf, L., and M. Beer, *Naturwiss.*, **44**, 442 (1957).
166. Woodward, R. B., M. Rosenblum, and M. C. Whiting, *J. Am. Chem. Soc.*, **74**, 3458 (1952).
167. Woodward, R. B., and E. Csendes, unpublished results, quoted by P. L. Pauson, *J. Am. Chem. Soc.*, **76**, 2187 (1954).

5 Alkylmetallocenes

A very considerable number of alkylmetallocenes have been prepared either by electrophilic substitution reactions, indirectly from the acyl-metallocenes, or from substituted cyclopentadienides. Of these synthetic routes, those involving the transformation of acylmetallocenes are the most generally applicable for the preparation of both simple alkylmetallocenes as well as those possessing functional groups on the side chain. However, the Mannich-type aminoalkylation reaction also provides a uniquely important origin for the synthesis of a variety of derivatives which are not otherwise readily accessible.

Metallocenes derivatives whose synthesis and chemistry are treated in this chapter include those with aliphatic saturated and unsaturated substituents which may also possess oxygen, nitrogen, and other hetero-atomic functional groups bonded to the side chain. These are listed in Table 5-3 (pages 153–192).

FRIEDEL-CRAFTS ALKYLATION

Use of alkyl halides and olefins

The alkylation of ferrocene with alkyl halides (79, 84, 85, 174) or olefins (85, 90, 107, 116) under Friedel-Crafts conditions has been explored largely by the Russian school. Although the method is, in principle, the most direct for the preparation of alkylmetallocenes, its synthetic value is severely proscribed since conversions are for the most part poor and the products are generally intractable mixtures of mono- and polyalkyl derivatives.*

* Reasonable yields of polyalkylated ferrocenes are claimed in a recent patent when alkylation is carried out with *t*-butyl and *t*-amyl chlorides (68).

Alkylation of ruthenocene or osmocene by these procedures has not been reported, although the alkylation of cyclopentadienylmanganese tricarbonyl with isobutylene and with cyclohexyl chloride has been described by Kozikowski, Maginn, and Klove (62).

Ferrocene does not exhibit as high a reactivity in alkylation reactions as in Friedel-Crafts acylation. Indeed, the earliest attempts at alkylation were reported to have failed (118, 132), and even under forcing conditions the yields of ethyl- , i-propyl and t-butylferrocenes from the olefins are not especially good (90). This apparent decrease in reactivity may in large measure be due to extensive oxidation and protonation of the metallocene and its alkylation products (equations 2 and 3) which must compete with the alkylation reaction.

$$C_{10}H_{10}Fe + RX + AlCl_3 \rightarrow C_{10}H_9RFe + HX{\cdot}AlCl_3 \qquad (1)$$
$$C_{10}H_{10}Fe + RX + AlCl_3 \rightarrow C_{10}H_{10}Fe^+ + R{\cdot} + AlCl_4^- \qquad (2)$$
$$C_{10}H_{10}Fe + HX{\cdot}AlCl_3 \rightarrow C_{10}H_{11}Fe^+ + AlXCl_3^- \qquad (3)$$

Alkylation of ferrocene with n-butyl chloride and aluminum chloride gives a mixture of akyl derivatives (79)* which may contain products derived from rearrangement of the alkyl halide (2). An example of such a rearrangement is provided by the alkylation of ferrocene with 1,2-dichloroethane, which gives largely 1,1-diferrocenylethane (2) and some 1,2-diferrocenylethane (3) (96, 138).† The result illustrates the high order of stability associated with the cation (1) since under similar reaction conditions benzene is reported to give only bibenzyl (61, 165).

Nesmeyanov and Kotchetkova (92) reported that prolonged treatment of ferrocene with 1,2-dichloroethane and aluminum chloride gave a product to which they assigned the rather unusual structure 4a. The NMR spectrum of the substance was said to confirm the presence of only one type of methylene proton (173)‡ and on Friedel-Crafts acetylation the compound afforded a mono- and diacetyl derivative (96). § Definitive

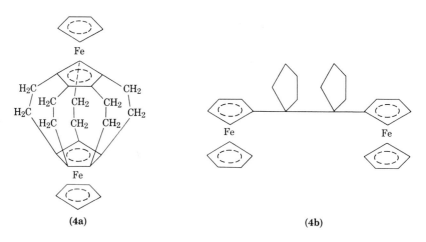

(4a)   (4b)

evidence excluding structure 4a has been provided by Goldberg (33), who observed the formation of an identical substance when ferrocene was heated with aluminum chloride in the absence of ethylene chloride. It seems most likely that the substance in question has the structure 4b, and is formed through dimerization of cyclopentenylferrocene (5) by the general mechanism outlined on page 127. This suggestion has recently

* Judging from the analytical data given for some of these products as well as those from other alkylations (79), even the gross homogeneity of some of the liquid fractions reported in this paper must be doubted.
† The product was first described simply as diferrocenylethane (79) but was later found to be a mixture of 2 and 3 (96).
‡ The resonance peak is quite broad.
§ Neither the parent substance nor its acetyl derivative exhibit well-defined melting points raising some doubts as to the homogeneity of these substances.

been made by Nesmeyanov (105), who found that a substance identical with "pentaethanodiferrocene" was formed when cyclopentenylferrocene was heated in heptane solution in the presence of aluminum chloride.

(5)   (6)

The formation of cyclopentenylferrocene in these reactions, probably through alkylation of ferrocene by products derived from decomposition of the ferricenium ion, is not without precedent. Prolonged treatment of ferrocene with hydrogen fluoride or phosphoric acid has been shown to give this substance (139, 176) in addition to the bridged compound (6) (25). Both these compounds probably derive from a common unconjugated cyclopentenylferrocene.

Use of alcohols

Alcohols have been employed in the alkylation of ferrocene with only limited success. Neuse and Trifan (107) have reported that good yields of mono- and 1,1'-dialkylferrocenes can be obtained from *sec*- and *tert*-arylcarbinols and arylalkylcarbinols by carrying out the reaction in the melt phase at 100 to 140°.* However, the procedure appears to be confined to this class of alcohol since *t*-butanol gave little product. It is of interest to note that the disubstituted products obtained by Neuse and Trifan are almost exclusively the 1,1'-dialkylferrocenes, while those derived from alkylation with alkyl halides and olefins under normal Friedel-Crafts conditions are said to be of homoannular constitution (84, 85).†

Reactions of alkylmetallocenes

Side Chain Oxidation. Several reports of the autoxidation of alkyl-ferrocenes have appeared in the literature. Nesmeyanov, Kritskaya, and

* Pauson and Watts (121) have prepared tritylferrocene and 1,1'-ditritylferrocene by treatment of ferrocene with trityl fluoroborate at reflux temperatures in methylene chloride solution.
† It is not unlikely that these latter substances, which were reported to be liquids, were actually mixtures of heteroannular and homoannular derivatives.

Antipina (99, 101) have noted the oxidation of derivatives such as benzyl-ferrocene (7) and 1,2-diferrocenylbibenzyl (8) to benzoylferrocene (9) when these substances are chromatographed on alumina, and Schlögl and Mohar (157) have reported that propargylferrocene (10) is readily oxidized by air to ferrocenyl ethynyl ketone (11). Simple alkylferrocenes are apparently considerably more resistant to autoxidation. These reactions bear a close resemblance to the familiar autoxidations of hydrocarbons possessing benyl or allyl C—H bonds (175), and it seems most probable that they also proceed by a radical chain mechanism involving the formation and subsequent decomposition of α-ferrocenylalkyl hydro-peroxides (12).

The oxidation of alkylferrocenes to acylferrocenes by the use of activated manganese dioxide has been described in Chapter 4 (page 70).

Metalation. Unlike benzyl carbanions, little stabilization of charge appears to accrue to α-ferrocenyl carbanions by virtue of conjugation with the aromatic ring. Westman and Rinehart (180) have carried out the metalation of 1,1'-dimethylferrocene with *n*-butyllithium and, on carboxy-lation, obtained only the 2- and 3-carboxylic acids (13 and 14). The latter acid was resolved through its cinconidine and quinidine salts to the optically active acids.

Furthermore, Nesmeyanov and Perevalova (88) have reported that treatment of dimethylferrocene with n-amylsodium and subsequent carboxylation gave a dicarboxylic acid in 52% yield which was not identical with the known (136) ferrocene-1,1'diacetic acid. It seems likely that both of the carboxyl groups in this compound are on the rings, although their disposition relative to the methyl groups is not known. In addition to this substance, two minor products were isolated, neither of which appear to be ferrocene-1,1'-diacetic acid.

A considerably more definitive study of the metalation of alkyl-substituted ferrocenes has recently been provided by Benkeser and Bach (8a). The monometalation of methyl-, ethyl-, i-propyl-, and t-butyl-ferrocene with n-amylsodium or n-amylpotassium, followed by carboxylation, gave 1'-alkyl- and 3-alkylferrocenoic acids as the major products in the approximately statistical ratio of 2.6:1. Dimetalation, which is a side reaction of some importance even when equimolar quantities of reagents are used, led to the formation of mixtures of 2-alkyl- and 3-alkylferrocene-1,1'-dicarboxylic acids in which the predominance of the latter isomer increases significantly as the size of the alkyl group is increased. In none of these reactions were any products of side chain metalation observed.

Ferrocenylmethyllithium (16) has been prepared indirectly by Nes-meyanov, Perevalova, and Ustynyuk (94) by cleavage of methoxymethyl-ferrocene (15) with lithium in tetrahydrofuran.

ALKYLATION WITH ALDEHYDES—α-HYDROXYALKYLMETALLOCENES

Ferrocene reacts with formaldehyde in the presence of hydrogen fluoride or concentrated sulfuric acid to give a dinuclear product incor-porating two methylene units (82, 176). The substance was initially assigned the structure 17 by Nesmeyanov (86), but was later shown by Rinehart, Michejda, and Kittle (137) to be 1,2-diferrocenylethane (3). With benzaldehyde, the two diasteriomeric 1,2-diphenyl-1,2-diferrocenyl-ethanes (8) are obtained (82, 99, 137a).

Although the mechanism of these reactions has not been examined, it seems probable that the products arise through coupling of the diradical

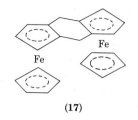

(17)

(8)   (3)

cation (20) generated from the ion (19) by internal electron transfer (137).* The observation that both hydroxymethylferrocene (18a) (137) and phenylferrocenylcarbinol (18b) (82) are converted to the dimeric products (3 and 8) on treatment with sulfuric acid is in accord with this suggestion. Furthermore, the dimeric products do appear to be present at the conclusion of the reaction largely if not exclusively as the diferricenium salts (137), which also accounts for the absence of higher condensation products.

Pauson and Watts (119) have recently reported that the reaction of ferrocene with formaldehyde in concentrated sulfuric acid takes quite a different course when paraformaldehyde rather than an aqueous 40% solution of the aldehyde is used. Under these conditions the only product formed is diferrocenylmethane (21). The alcohol (18a) is also a likely intermediate in this reaction as in the formation of 3, since it is converted to 21 by treatment with ferrocene in the presence of sulfuric acid (119). It is not unlikely that the observed change in the course of the reaction

* Rinehart, Michejda and Kittle (137) have also suggested the possibility of an intermolecular oxidation-reduction chain reaction involving the cation (19).

when paraformaldehyde is employed is due to a lower effective concentration of the monomeric aldehyde. This suggests that the internal oxidation-reduction step (**19** → **20**) is either reversible or relatively slow compared to the rate at which ferrocene is alkylated by the cation (**19**).

(**18**)

(**a**, R = H)
(**b**, R = Ph)

(**19**)

(**20**)

(**21**)

(**3**, R = H)
(**8**, R = Ph)

Diferrocenylcarbinol, triferrocenylcarbinol, and triferrocenylmethane

Diferrocenylcarbinol (**22**) may be obtained by reduction of diferrocenyl ketone (**23**) with lithium aluminum hydride (119), or more directly by the reaction of ferrocene with ferrocenecarboxaldehyde under conditions of the Vilsmeier reaction, or with formic acid (53) or ethyl orthoformate (146) in the presence of a Lewis acid.* The corresponding *tert*-alcohol, triferrocenylcarbinol (**24**), is obtained by treatment of the ketone (**23**) with ferrocenyllithium, and is converted to triferrocenylmethane (**25**) on reduction with zinc and hydrochloric acid (104, 119)† Triferrocenylmethane undergoes hydride abstraction by triphenylmethyl perchlorate to give the blue cation (**26**) which, on hydrolysis, affords the alcohol (**24**).

It is unfortunate that no detailed study of the stabilities of the triferrocenylmethyl anion, radical and cation has as yet been reported, since a

---

* Evidently, the diradical state corresponding to **20** is not readily accessible at room temperature to the 2° cation derived from diferrocenylcarbinol, since the perchlorate salt is reported to be diamagnetic ($X_M^{295.5} - 79.1 \pm 1.09 \times 10^{-6}$) (53).

† Triferrocenylcarbinol is also formed in the reaction of ferrocenecarboxylic acid and phosphorus oxychloride with ferrocene (54).

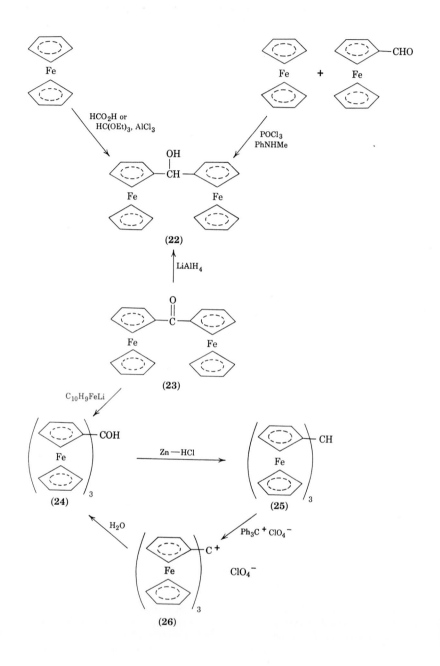

comparison of the properties of these species with their triphenylmethyl analogs would be of some interest.

Reactions of *a*-Hydroxyalkylmetallocenes

Solvolysis Reactions—The α-Metallocenyl Carbonium Ion. Richards and Hill (48, 131) have provided some very convincing evidence for the exceptional stability of the α-metallocenyl carbonium ion through a study of the kinetics of the solvolysis of α-metallocenylethyl acetates (**27**, M = Fe, Ru, Os). In 80% acetone-water, these esters solvolyze exclusively by uncatalyzed ionization to give the carbinols (**28**) and acetic acid. The conclusion that these reactions proceed by alkyl-oxygen fission is supported by the correspondence of activation parameters for these solvolyses with those for trityl acetate, for which an S_N1 mechanism is well established (23), from the observation than ethanolysis of **27** (M = Fe) gives exclusively the ethyl ether and acetic acid, and from the very pronounced dependence of its solvolysis rate on the ionizing power of the solvent and the concentration of added acetate ions.* The data obtained by Richards and Hill from these studies are summarized in Table 5-1. The very high

Table 5-1
Solvolysis Rates of α-Metallocenylethyl Acetates in 80%
Acetone-Water at 30°[a]

M	$k \times 10^5$ sec.$^{-1}$	ΔH^* (kcal./mole)	ΔS^* (e.u.)	RELATIVE RATE
Fe	17.02 ± 0.15 (18.4)[b]	19.0 ± 0.6	−13.2	1.00
Ru	23.22 ± 1.10	19.34	−11.4	1.36
Os	91.5 ± 1.6	18.54	−11.2	5.37
Ph_3COAc	2.58 ± 0.033	21.1	−6.7	0.152

[a] Refs. 48, 49, 131,
[b] Ref. 170.

* Neither the olefin nor the products of radical coupling similar to those encountered in the hydroxyalkylation reactions are observed in these solvolyses.

order of stability associated with the α-metallocenyl carbonium ion is apparent from a comparison of the rates of solvolyses of the metallocene esters with that of trityl acetate. It is of interest to note that the reactivity sequence observed for these derivatives is the reverse of that found for Friedel-Crafts acylation of the parent metallocenes. However, the differences in rates of solvolyses are rather small and appear to arise as much from differences in entropies of activation as from the enthalpy term.

A further striking aspect of these reactions is their stereospecificity, which is best illustrated by the solvolysis reactions of the *exo* and *endo* acetates (**29** and **30**). Both of these esters give exlusively the *exo* alcohol (**31**), but the rate of solvolysis of the *exo* isomer differs from that of the *endo* isomer by a factor of 2500 (49, 170) at 30°. The difference in rates, which is due entirely to a lower enthalpy of activation for the *exo* isomer, cannot be ascribed to differences in ground state energies of the two isomers, since the *exo* isomer is manifestly the more stable (49).*

Both Trifan and Bacskai (170), as well as Richards and Hill (48, 49, 131), have suggestedt ha tthese results are best accommodated in terms of neighboring group participation by the metal atom in these reactions. Without defining for the moment the precise mode of such an interaction, it is nevertheless clear that it would be expected to promote ionization of the *exo* acetate as well as *exo* attack of a nucleophile on the resulting cationic center.

A similar stereochemical discrimination is observed in the solvolysis reactions of the esters (**32, 33,** and **34**), which exist in two diastereomeric forms owing to the presence of the asymmetric methinyl group in an otherwise asymmetric molecule. The two diastereomeric forms of the acetate (**32**) are depicted by structures **32a** and **32b**. These are distinguished as ψ-*exo* and ψ-*endo* respectively, since each would be expected to

* The ruthenocene derivatives corresponding to **29** and **30** do not exhibit as pronounced a stereospecificity; the *exo* acetate gives 100% of the *exo* alcohol (**31**, Ru instead of Fe), but the *endo* acetate affords 80% of this alcohol and 20% of its *endo* isomer (123); suggesting that the transition states for the solvolyses of these esters are not identical.

preferentially adopt the conformation shown, in which steric interactions between the adjacent ring substituents are minimized.*

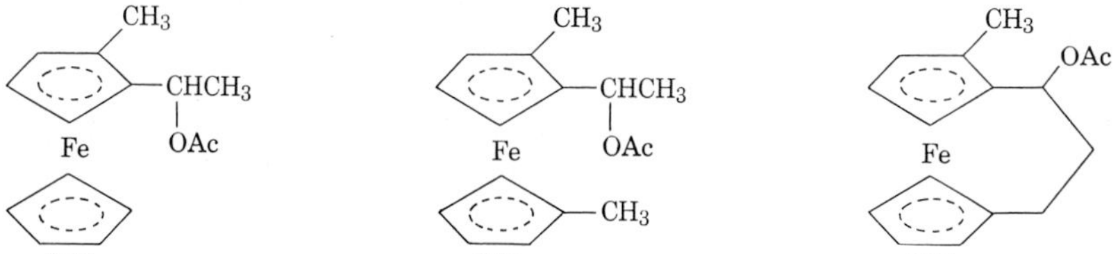

CH₃ —CHCH₃ OAc Fe (32)   CH₃ —CHCH₃ OAc Fe —CH₃ (33)   CH₃ OAc Fe (34)

Each of these esters apparently solvolyze with metal participation so that no interconversion of diastereomeric pairs is observed (Fig. 5-1). Furthermore, the ψ-*exo* isomer of each pair solvolyzes faster than its ψ-*endo* diastereomer since metal participation in the solvolyses of the latter compounds involves an energetically less favorable reaction path.

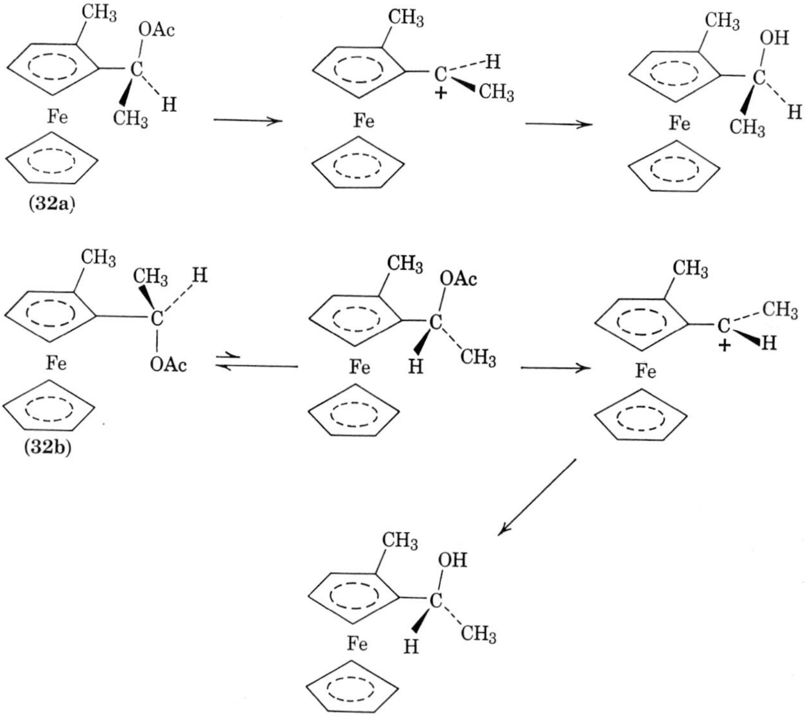

(32a)   (32b)

FIG. 5-1

---

* Assignments were made on the basis of the relative intensities of bonded and non-bonded hydroxyl absorptions in the infrared spectra of each pair of alcohols (see page 135).

As might be expected, the difference in solvolysis rates for the conformationally rigid diastereomeric esters (29 and 30) arises principally from a disparity in their enthalpies of activation, whereas the difference in rates of solvolysis of the diastereomers of 32 and 33 is derived entirely from the lower entropy of activation of each of the ψ-exo isomers. The diastereomeric esters of 34 are somewhat anomalous in this respect, but the added structural feature of a chain bridging the rings in these compounds might be expected to set them apart. An apparent consequence of the

Table 5-2

Solvolysis Rates of Diastereomeric α-Ferrocenylalkyl
Acetates in 80% Acetone-Water at 30°[a]

ACETATE		$k \times 10^5$ sec.$^{-1}$	ΔH^* (kcal./mole)	ΔS^* (e.u.)
29	exo	72.1 (74.3)[b]	18.5 ± 0.4	−12.0
30	endo	0.028 (0.0331)[b]	23.5 ± 1.3	−11.0
32	ψ-exo	72.8	19.4 ± 0.3	−8.9
	ψ-endo	5.73	19.2 ± 0.5	−14.9
33	ψ-exo	128.8	18.5 ± 0.6	−10.8
	ψ-endo	10.85	18.5 ± 0.4	−15.7
34	ψ-exo	46.7	18.2 ± 0.4	−13.8
	ψ-endo	0.297	22.2 ± 0.8	−10.6

[a] Ref. 49.
[b] Ref. 170.

relative conformational rigidity imposed by the bridge is a decrease in solvolysis rates for each of the diastereomers. The rate data and activation parameters for these diastereomeric esters are summarized in Table 5-2.*

At this point it is necessary to consider the mechanisms available for stabilization of the carbonium ion center in α-metallocenyl cations. Two such modes may be distinguished and have been discussed in some detail by Hill and Richards (48). In the first of these the vacant p-orbital of the cationic center is viewed as interacting with the localized molecular orbital

* The ruthenocene analog of 29 solvolyzes more rapidly than 29, due principally to a more favorable enthalpy of activation ($k_{30°} = 150 \times 10^{-5}$ sec.$^{-1}$, $\Delta H^* = 15.81$ kcal./mole, $\Delta S^* = -19.5$ e.u.), suggesting more effective participation of the metal in this compound. However, the rate of solvolysis of the ruthenocene endo isomer is slower than that of 30 ($k_{30°} = 0.0081 \times 10^{-5}$ sec.$^{-1}$, $\Delta H^* = 21.95$ kcal./mole, $\Delta S^* = -18.7$ e.u.). It seems unlikely that this is due entirely to increased steric resistance to departure of the acetate ion by the larger metal atom, since the ratio of solvolysis rates for the epimeric ferrocene pivalate esters corresponding to 29 and 30 (k_{exo}/k_{endo}) is only about 35% larger than this ratio for the acetates (123).

associated with the ring to which it is bonded. While, in essence, this is the classical form of π-orbital conjugation, an important distinction must be noted. Since the ring orbitals are also involved in bonding with the metal atom, the effect of such delocalization on ring-metal binding energy must be considered. Hill and Richards (48) have argued that the symmetry properties of the extended ring orbital resulting from charge delocalization are not incompatible with those of the metal,* and have also suggested that some increase in the total overlap integral may be achieved by a shift of one of the rings as shown in **35**. However, there is some question whether such a molecular distortion would inevitably lead to increased stabilization.

Supplementing this mode of stabilization, and quite independent of it, is one involving the direct interaction of nonbonding E_{2g} metal orbital electrons with the cationic center, or more properly with the localized ring orbital associated with it. Although the symmetry properties of the orbitals are not identical, appreciable overlap might nevertheless occur and would clearly provide a mechanism which accounts for the stereo-specificity of the solvolysis reactions.

The relative importance of each of these distinct interactions in stabilizing α-metallocenyl carbonium ions is difficult to assess. Both Richards and Hill, as well as Trifan and Bacskai, appear to favor the latter mechanism. However, it is of interest to note that the former mode of carbonium ion stabilization would, by itself, be capable of accounting for the stereospecificity of the solvolysis reactions, since the localized ring molecular orbital which interacts with the carbonium ion center must be unsymmetrical with respect to the ring plane, the greater electronic charge concentration lying on the endo face of each ring as indicated diagram-matically in **36**. Moreover, the obvious difference in steric environment above and below the rings cannot be neglected in a consideration of the stereochemistry of these reactions.

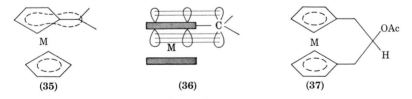

| (35) | (36) | (37) |

* Hill and Richards discussed these interactions in terms of the MO analysis of Moffitt in which the primary source of ring-metal bonding is derived from E_{1g} type inter-actions only. The arguments are somewhat strengthened by inclusion of the more extensive metal-ring orbital interactions invoked in the more recent theoretical analyses (Chapter 2).

An experimental distinction between the two possible modes of electronic interaction is not easily made, but it may be significant that the enthalpy of activation for the solvolysis of β-ferrocenylethyl p-toluenesulfonate is about 3 kcal./mole more favorable than that for the reaction of β-phenylethyl p-toluenesulfonate (170). A study of the solvolysis of the bridged ester (37) might likewise prove instructive.

Dehydration, Etherification and Disproportionation of α-*Hydroxyalkylmetallocenes.* The exceptional stability of α-metallocenyl carbonium ions is also indicated by the ease with which the α-hydroxyalkyl derivatives undergo acid-catalyzed dehydration and etherification, and by the very high reactivity of alkenylmetallocenes toward addition of acids.

Dehydration of α-hydroxyalkylferrocenes occurs with such facility that it may be effected in good yield by simply shaking a benzene solution of the alcohol in the presence of a 5 to 10 fold excess of acidic alumina (152, 154). Thus, methylferrocenylcarbinol affords vinylferrocene in 50% yield by this method, whereas methylphenylcarbinol is inert (152). The conversion of α-ferrocenylethyl acetate to vinylferrocene under similar reaction conditions has also been described (164).

Etherification of α-hydroxyalkylferrocenes by alcohols also proceeds under exceptionally mild acidic conditions and undoubtedly involves generation of the α-ferrocenyl carbonium ion (94, 101, 144, 152).

Nesmeyanov, Kritskaya, and Antipina (101) have reported that α-hydroxyalkylferrocenes such as ferrocenylphenylcarbinol (18b) partially disproportionate to benzoylferrocene (9) and benzylferrocene (7) when chromatographed on silica columns. On alumina columns these alcohols are oxidized to the corresponding ketones, especially on prolonged contact.

Both hydrazoic acid and acetic acid add to vinylferrocene with extraordinary facility affording α-ferrocenylethyl azide and acetate (21, 22). The relative reactivities of vinylferrocene, vinylruthenocene, and vinylosmocene toward addition of acetic acid have recently been reported (22). Not unexpectedly, a progressive increase in rate is exhibited by these

(31)

$(\nu_{OH}\ 3610\ cm.^{-1})$

(38)

$(\nu_{OH}\ 3561\ cm.^{-1})$

derivatives (1.00, 1.19, 4.62, respectively) which closely parallels the relative rates of solvolysis of the α-metallocenylethyl acetates (Table 5-1).

Hydrogen Bonding in Hydroxyalkylmetallocenes.   In view of the Lewis-base properties of the metal atom (Chapter 3, page 47), it is not surprising that intramolecular hydrogen bonding of this center with the alcohol group in hydroxyalkylmetallocenes is observed.   This interaction is most clearly evident from a comparison of the infrared spectra of the isomeric alcohols (**31** and **38**) which exhibit absorption at 3610 cm.$^{-1}$ (2.77 μ) and 3561 cm.$^{-1}$ (2.81 μ) respectively (49, 171) in carbon disulfide solution.*   The less rigid open chain α- and β-hydroxyalkylferrocenes exhibit both absorptions very near these frequencies (49, 169, 171).†   Hill and Richards (48) have examined the spectra of the three α-metallocenylethanols and report a progressive decrease in frequency of the metal-bonded hydroxyl absorption and a corresponding increase in the relative intensity of this band as the metal is changed from iron to osmium.‡   They have inferred from the data that the order of increasing metal-hydrogen bond strength is Os > Ru > Fe, which is opposite to that which might be expected from the relative basicities of the parent metallocenes.   However, there is evidence that the absorption shifts, of even closely related hydrogen bonded species, need not necessarily correspond directly with the enthalpies of the hydrogen bonds.   A very excellent demonstration of this fact has recently been provided by West et al. (179) in a study of hydrogen bonding between phenols and cyclohexyl halides.   While the frequency shifts observed for the hydrogen bonded hydroxyl group suggested that the proton acceptor power of the halides increased in the order F, Cl, Br, I, the measured enthalpies and free energies of the hydrogen bond were in the reverse order.

Yet another and perhaps more dramatic expression of intramolecular hydrogen bonding in these compounds is provided by a comparison of the proton magnetic resonance spectra of the *exo* and *endo* alcohols (**39** and

---

* The higher frequency absorption, exhibited by the *exo* alcohol (**31**) has been assigned by Trifan and Bacskai to an intramolecular π-bonded hydroxyl absorption (171), but there would appear to be some doubt as to the certainty of this and similar assignments.
† Three peaks at 3632, 3605, and 3533 cm.$^{-1}$ are reported to be present in the spectrum of 2-ferrocenylethanol which have been assigned by Trifan and Bacskai (171) to free, π-bonded and metal-bonded hydroxyl absorptions respectively.
‡ A similar decline in O—H stretching frequency is observed in the ruthenocene analog of **38** (ν, 3510 cm.$^{-1}$).   Moreover, the difference between the O—H frequencies in the epimers (**31** and **38**), which may be a measure of the strength of the metal-hydrogen bond in the *endo* isomer, is greater for the ruthenocene derivatives ($\Delta = 138$ cm.$^{-1}$) than for the ferrocene derivatives ($\Delta = 49$ cm.$^{-1}$) (124).   Metal-hydrogen bonding is apparently absent or very weak in the related cyclopentadienylmanganese tricarbonyl derivatives (124).

40). The *exo* alcohol (39) exhibits hydroxyl proton absorption at 5.97 τ while the resonance peak for this proton in the *endo* isomer lies more than 2 p.p.m. to higher field at 8.02 τ (145).

(39)   (40)

Preparation and Reactions of Haloalkylmetallocenes. The only simple haloalkyl derivatives thus far reported are those of ferrocene. As might be expected, the α-haloalkyl derivatives are exceedingly reactive substances.

Benkeser and Fitzgerald (8) have prepared both α-chloro- and α-bromoethylferrocene (42a and 42b) by the addition of gaseous hydrogen halide to vinylferrocene (41) at −78°. The chloride reacts at −78° with sodium azide to give α-azidoethylferrocene, while the bromide reacts almost instantaneously with aqueous sodium carbonate, affording the alcohol. Bromine adds readily to vinylferrocene, and the product, α,β-dibromoethylferrocene (43), is transformed to ferrocenylacetylene (44) by treatment with potassium amide in liquid ammonia.

The simplest chloroalkyl derivative, chloromethylferrocene (**45**), has not been isolated, but Schlögl (148) has reported the synthesis of the formamidomalonate (**46**) from hydroxymethylferrocene (**18a**) by the reaction sequence shown below, which probably involves this substance.

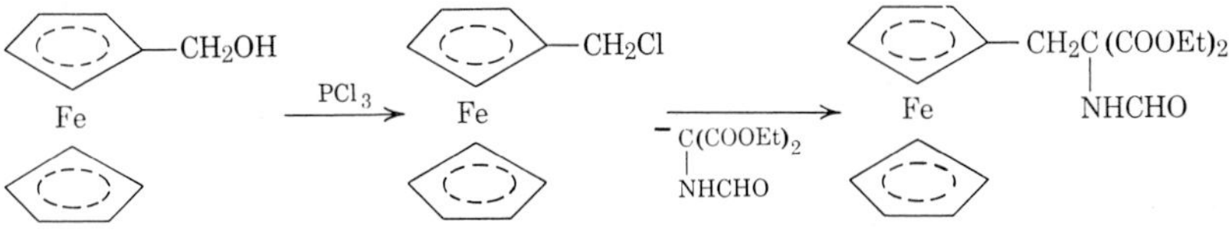

| (18a) | (45) | (46) |

A quantitative measure of the solvolytic reactivity of the α-halo-alkylferrocenes has recently been provided by Hill (50) in a study of the ethanolysis of α-chloroethylferrocene (**42a**) in ether-ethanol solutions at −42 to −82°.

$$C_{10}H_9FeCHCH_3 \underset{k_2}{\overset{k_1}{\rightleftharpoons}} C_{10}H_9Fe\overset{+}{C}HCH_3 + Cl^-$$
$$\underset{Cl}{|}$$

$$C_{10}H_9Fe\overset{+}{C}HCH_3 + C_2H_5OH \overset{k_3}{\longrightarrow} C_{10}H_9FeCHCH_3 + H^+$$
$$\underset{OC_2H_5}{|}$$

This reaction, like those of the related acetates, is characterized by its extreme rapidity and by the high selectivity of the intermediate carbonium ion, manifest in the high value of k_2/k_3 (8000 at −45°, 48,000 at −82°) and in a strong common ion effect, all of which are typical of reactions involving carbonium ions of high stability. At −45° the rate constant for solvolysis of the chloride (**42a**) is estimated to be more than 500 times larger than that for trityl chloride.

AMINOALKYLATION REACTIONS

Ferrocene

The successful aminoalkylation of ferrocene under conditions of the Mannich reaction provides yet another illustration of its exceptional reactivity, since these reactions are generally confined to only the most reactive aromatic compounds.

The first such reaction, employing formaldehyde and dimethylamine in acetic acid, was reported in 1956 by Hauser and Lindsay (40), and has since been improved somewhat by Osgerby and Pauson (112) by the addition of phosphoric acid to the reaction mixture. Owing to the relatively low electrophilic reactivity of the anhydro salt $[CH_2 = \overset{+}{N}[CH_3]_2]$ which is the alkylating species, the reaction does not proceed with the ease which characterizes other substitutions such as acylation, sulfonation, and mercuration. Moreover, it is generally interrupted at the stage of monosubstitution, probably as a consequence of the deactivating effect of the aminomethyl group which must exist under the reaction conditions largely in its protonated form. The aminoalkylation of ruthenocene or osmocene has not been reported, but these substances would be expected to be somewhat more resistant to such substitution than ferrocene.

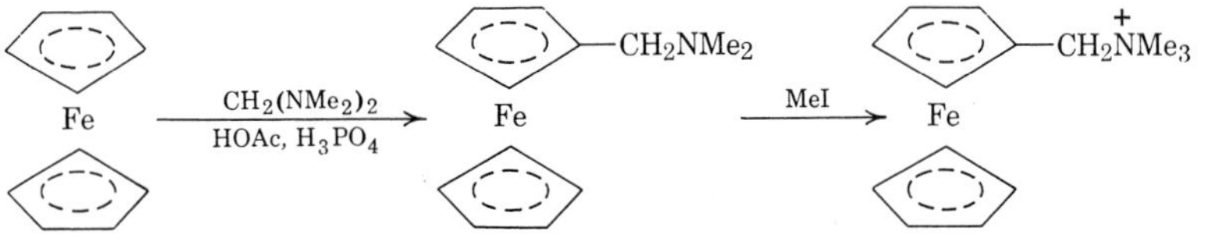

Fe $\xrightarrow[\text{HOAc, H}_3\text{PO}_4]{\text{CH}_2(\text{NMe}_2)_2}$ Fe —CH$_2$NMe$_2$ $\xrightarrow{\text{MeI}}$ Fe —CH$_2\overset{+}{\text{N}}$Me$_3$

(47)

The synthetic importance of the aminomethylation reaction lies principally in the multitude of transformation products which may be obtained from the readily available quaternary ammonium salt (47). Some of these are indicated in Fig. 5-2.

The quaternary ammonium salt (47) has also served as a useful inter-mediate in the synthesis of β-ferrocenylalanine (48) through alkylation with either sodio ethyl formamidomalonate (112) or sodio ethyl acetamido-cyanoacetate (43). The synthesis of this interesting analog of phenyl-alanine by alkylation of chloromethylferrocene (45) with sodio ethyl formamidomalonate has also been reported by Schlögl (148).

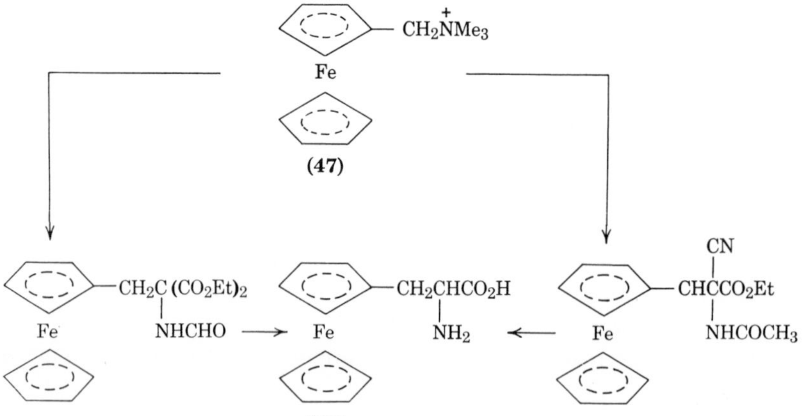

Fe — CH$_2\overset{+}{\text{N}}$Me$_3$

(47)

Fe —CH$_2$C (CO$_2$Et)$_2$ NHCHO ⟶ Fe —CH$_2$CHCO$_2$H NH$_2$ ← Fe —CHCCO$_2$Et NHCOCH$_3$ CN

(48)

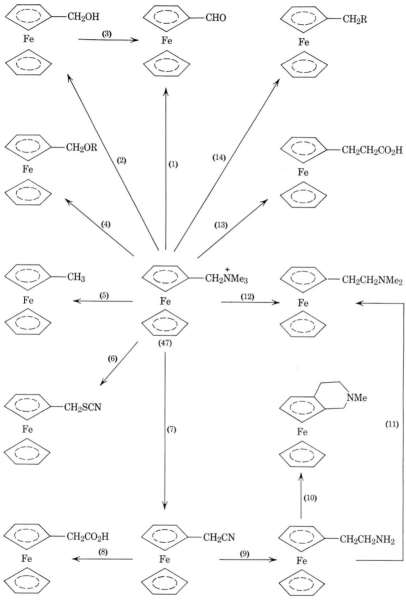

FIG. 5-2 (*1*) (CH$_2$)$_6$N$_4$, HOAc. (*2*) NaOH. (*3*) MnO$_2$, CHCl$_3$. (*4*) ROH, NaOH. (*5*) Na(Hg), H$_2$O. (*6*) KSCN, H$_2$O. (*7*) KCN, H$_2$O. (*8*) NaOH, H$_2$O. (*9*) LiAlH$_4$. (*10*) CH$_2$O, HCO$_2$H. (*11*) CH$_3$I, NaHCO$_3$. (*12*) KNH$_2$. (*13*) NaCH(CO$_2$C$_2$H$_5$)$_2$; NaOH, H$_2$O. (*14*) RMgX.

Pauson and Watts (120) have recently described the transformation of the quaternary ammonium salt (47) to the phosphorane (49) which entered normally into Wittig condensations affording a variety of unsaturated derivatives. Alternatively, treatment of the phosphorane with ferrocenoyl or benzoyl chlorides provides a route through the pyrolytic decomposition of the acylphosphoranes (34) to diferrocenylacetylene and phenylferrocenylacetylene. These transformations are summarized in Fig. 5-3.

It is of interest to note that the Stevens rearrangement of the quaternary salt (47) with potassium amide in liquid ammonia (reaction 12, Fig. 5-2) does not follow the *ortho* rearrangement path, observed with benzyltrimethylammonium salts (55), as was originally formulated by Hauser and Lindsay (40). The ylid (50), which is a probable intermediate in these reactions, rearranges instead to give only β-dimethylaminoethylferrocene (51) (41, 77, 114).

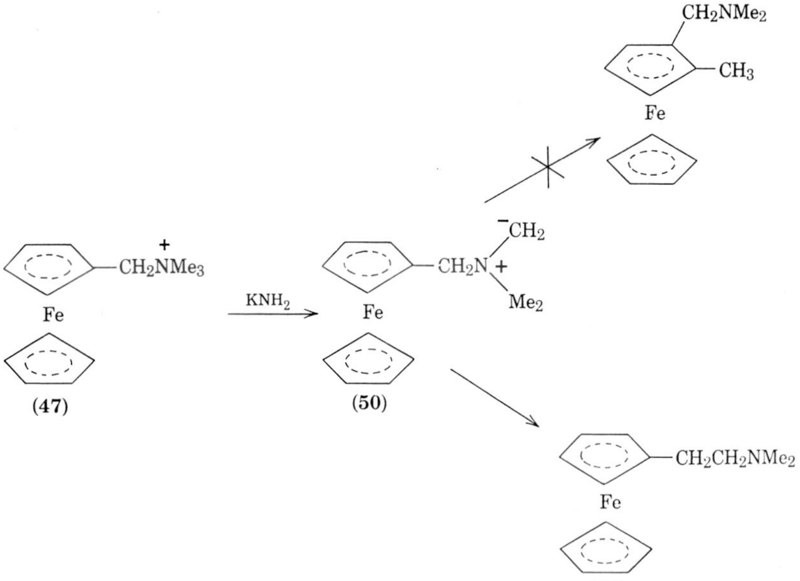

The fact that the reaction fails to take the anticipated *ortho* rearrangement path has been ascribed to steric factors (113, 114), but it is possible that more subtle electronic factors are responsible. It is perhaps significant that attempted Claisen rearrangement of allyl ferrocenyl ether gives instead only hydroxyferrocene (93). This course of reaction is identical

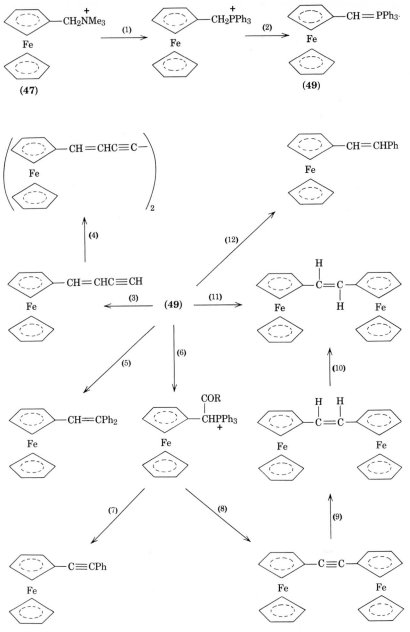

FIG. 5-3 (1) P(C₆H₅)₃. (2) C₆H₅Li. (3) CH≡CCHO. (4) Cu(OAc)₂, pyridine.
(5) (C₆H₅)₂CO. (6) RCOCl. (7) R = C₆H₅; OH⁻, Δ. (8) R = C₁₀H₉Fe; OH⁻, Δ.
(9) Pd/CaCO₃—Pb(OAc)₂, H₂. (10) H⁺. (11) C₁₀H₉FeCHO. (12) C₆H₅CHO.

with that observed for allyl phenyl ethers in which the formation of stable aromatic rearrangement products is precluded by substitution at the 2, 4, and 6 positions of the benzene ring.

Substituted ferrocenes

Aminomethylation of methylferrocene with bis(N,N,-dimethylamino)-methane has been reported by Nesmeyanov et al. (91) to give a homo-annularly substituted (N,N,-dimethylaminomethyl)methylferrocene (**52**), which was assigned a 1,3 structure. However, no extensive purification of the liquid product was carried out and consequently considerable doubt must remain as to its homogeneity and the conclusions drawn. In addition to this product, a lesser amount of a bis(N,N,-dimethylaminomethyl)-methylferrocene (**53**) was isolated. Its formation, which contrasts with the resistance of ferrocene itself to bisaminoalkylation, may be the result of the moderate activating effect of the methyl substituent. By contrast, amino-methylation of phenylferrocene (97, 100), p-tolyferrocene (100), or chloroferrocene (100) leads to the introduction of only one dimethyl-aminomethyl group at the 1′ position (**54**) in keeping with the expected deactivating effect of these substituents (Chapter 4).

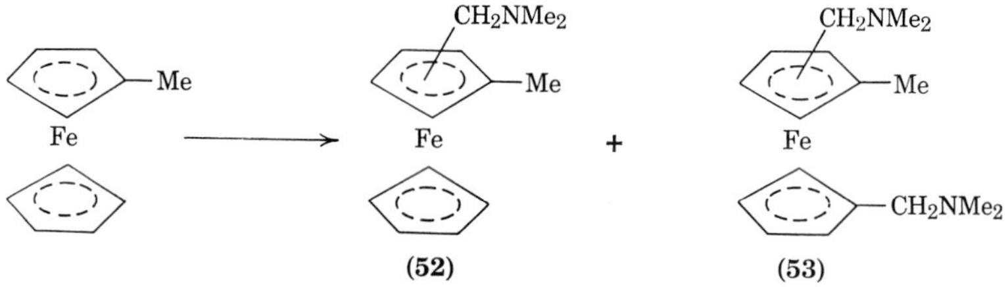

(52)   (53)

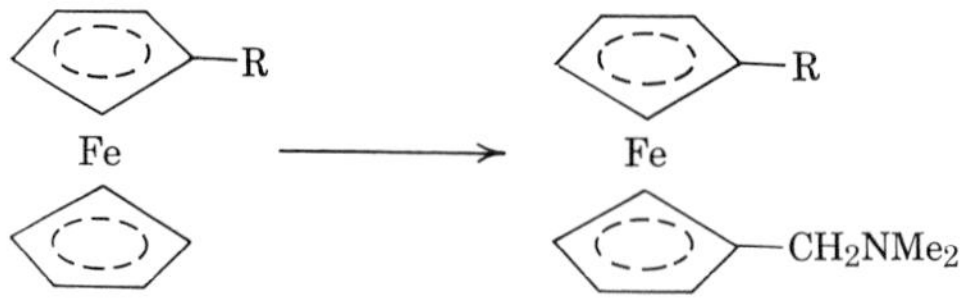

(54)

(R = C₆H₅, p−C₆H₄Me, Cl)

Knox, Pauson, and Tiers (57) have carried out the aminomethylation of methylthio- and 1,1′-dimethylthioferrocene. The methylthio sub-stituent is apparently weakly deactivating as judged by the extent of reaction of these derivatives compared with ferrocene. No details of the products obtained from methylthioferrocene are given, but the amino-methylation of 1,1'-dimethylthioferrocene is reported to give both the 1,1',2 and the 1,1',3 isomers (**55** and **56**, respectively) in a ratio of 1.9:1. Structures for these derivatives were assigned on the basis of their NMR spectra. While **56** exhibits only singlet methylene absorption at 6.84 τ, the isomer (**55**) gives rise to an AB type quarter signal ($J = 12.5$ cps) due to the inequivalence of these protons resulting from either restricted rotation of the methylene group or a greater disparity in the populations of the various side chain conformers in this compound than in **56**.

(55)   (56)

With the exception of one report, in which piperidine was employed as the amine component (112), the use of other amine and carbonyl reagents in aminoalkylation reactions has not been explored.

Rearrangements of metallocenylphenylcarbinyl azides

The acid-catalyzed decomposition of metallocenylphenylcarbinyl azides in sulfuric acid-chloroform and in sulfuric acid-acetic acid media has been studied extensively by McEwen and co-workers (10–12, 19, 20). These reactions afford a complex mixture of products whose composition is dependent to some extent on the reaction conditions but more significantly on the identity of the metallocene.

Both the ferrocene and ruthenocene derivatives give the metallo-cenecarboxaldehyde (**59**) and aniline as well as the phenylmetallocenyl ketone (**60**), evidently formed via the protonated azide (**57**) through phenyl migration or loss of a proton from the methinyl carbon atom in the inter-mediate (**58**) (Fig. 5-4). In addition, both afford the hydrolysis product metallocenylphenylcarbinol (**61**), but the yield of this product is signifi-cantly greater in the case of the ruthenocenyl azide. Moreover, the sym-metric ether (**62**) derived from this carbinol and constituting a principal product of the reaction of the ruthenocene azide in acetic acid solution is not formed from the ferrocene derivative. A further significant difference between the reaction of these two azides lies in the formation of consider-able amounts of the reduction product benzylferrocene (**63**) and its related dimer (64) from the reaction of the ferrocenyl azide, but the absence of such products from decomposition of the ruthenocenylazide. Both of these latter products are most likely formed by internal electron transfer in the carbonium ion (65), generated by loss of hydrazoic acid from the protonated azide, as indicated in Fig. 5-4. By contrast, the corresponding ruthenocenyl cation is apparently incapable of undergoing similar electron transfer, owing to the higher oxidation potential of the metal atom, with the consequence that its solvolysis products (61 and 62) are formed instead* (20).

In all of these reactions, the absence of products derived from migration of the metallocene nucleus is notable. Berger, Kleinberg, and McEwen (10, 12) have suggested that the dication (66) which is present to an appreciable extent in the acid solutions, and in which migration of the metallocene nucleus is precluded, gives rise to the observed rearrangement products. The monocation (57) leads instead through anchimerically assisted loss of hydrazoic acid to products such as 61 to 64. It may also be that migration of the metallocenyl nucleus does occur through this latter ion but that either the intermediates or products formed are irreversibly decomposed under the experimental conditions. Certainly, the relatively low yield in all of these reactions suggests that such decomposition may be an important side reaction.

The osmocene azide behaves quite differently from the other two metallocene derivatives, affording only benzoyl osmocene in relatively good yield in acetic acid solutions. Bublitz, McEwen, and Kleinberg (20) have suggested that this is due to the lower basicity of the metal atom, and to its greater ability to participate in displacement reactions which leads instead to the formation of the critical intermediate ion (67) and thence to the observed product. However, these assumptions provide no explanation for the absence of phenyl migration in the proposed cationic intermediate, since neither structural nor electronic factors implicit in the formulation of this intermediate would appear to preclude such a process.

(67)

---

* The acid-catalyzed decomposition of alkyl azides to alcohols is generally not observed except for those azides, such as triphenylmethyl azide, in which the carbonium ion formed by loss of hydrazoic acid is relatively stable (15).

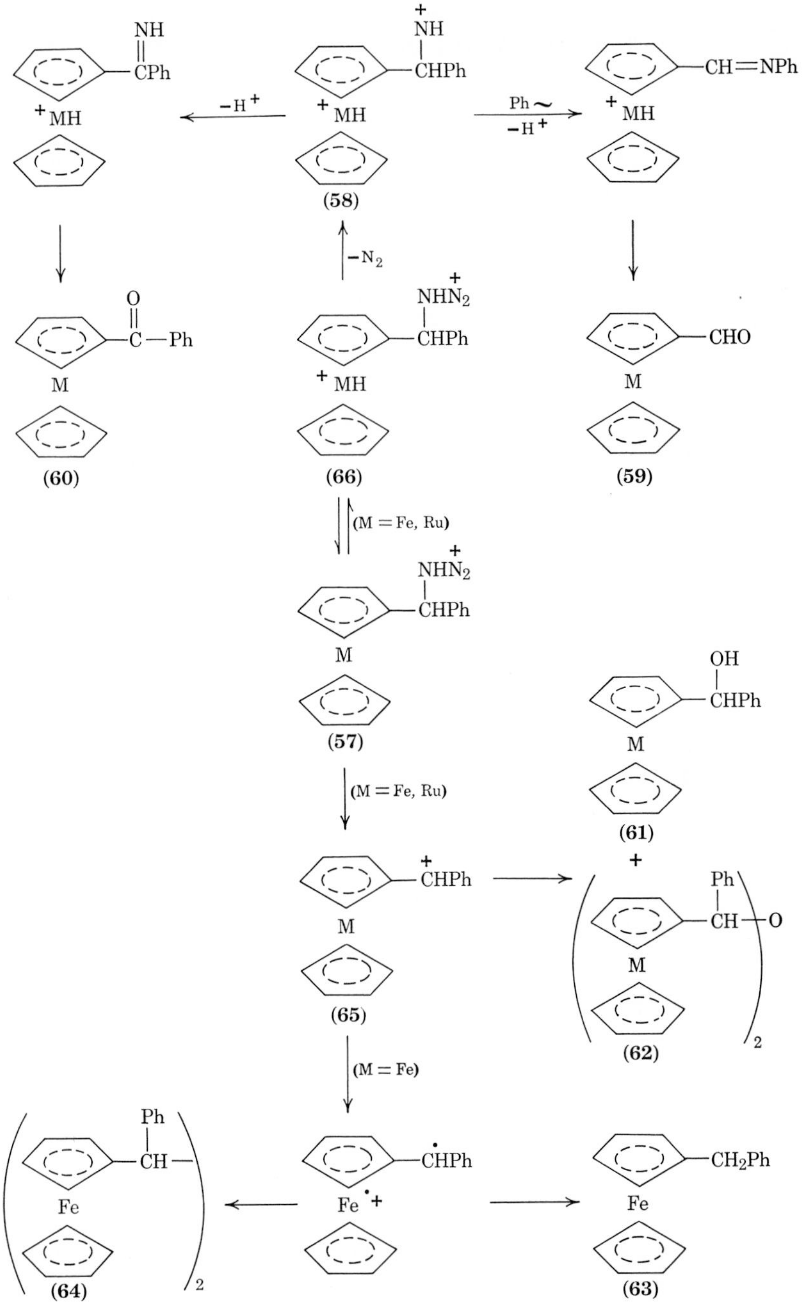

FIG. 5-4

TRANSFORMATION OF ACYLMETALLOCENES

Reduction

The reduction of acylmetallocenes constitutes the most useful and generally applicable method for the synthesis of alkylmetallocenes and α-hydroxyalkylmetallocenes.

Catalytic Reduction. Low pressure hydrogenation of acylferrocenes over platinum or palladium catalysts at room temperature has been widely employed to effect the conversion of these substances to alkyl-ferrocenes (128, 136, 142, 143, 151, 152). In general the yields are excellent, and only in a few instances is the reaction interrupted at the alcohol stage of reduction (144, 152).* Thus, in their ease of hydrogenolysis, the acylferrocenes closely resemble the aryl ketones and aldehydes (38, 39). The conversion of α-azidoalkylferrocenes (22) and α-oximinoalkyl-ferrocenes (22, 125, 127) to α-aminoalkylferrocenes by catalytic hydro-genation has also been carried out.

Chemical Reduction. Clemmensen reduction of a variety of acyl-ferrocenes has been reported (1, 29, 78, 80, 81, 87, 115, 141, 144, 166, 174, 178). In two cases, products derived from pinacol reduction and rearrange-ment have been observed.† Thus, acetylferrocene gave 3,3-diferrocenyl-2-butanone (**68**) in addition to ethylferrocene (119), and benzoylferrocene gave benzylferrocene as well as diferrocenylphenylacetophenone (**69**) and its reduction product 1,1-diferrocenyl-1,2-diphenylethane (**70**) (99, 128, 178). The latter ketone was also reported to be obtained by brief acid treatment of 1,2-diferrocenyl-1,2-diphenylethanediol (**71**). These reactions represent the only instances in which migration of a metallocenyl group to a cationic center has been observed.

Perhaps the simplest and most convenient method for the conversion of acylferrocenes to alkylferrocenes is by reduction with lithium aluminum hydride in the presence of aluminum chloride (18, 108). Excellent yields of a variety of alkylferrocenes have been obtained under mild reaction conditions with this reagent (83, 119, 137, 140, 153, 157). Nesmeyanov, Perevalova, and Beinoravichute (83), as well as Hill and Richards (49),

---

* Graham et al. (35) have also reported the use of Raney nickel and Ruthenium catalysts at higher pressures and temperatures, in the reduction of formylferrocene and 1,1'-bis-β-carboxypropionylferrocene, respectively, in which alcohol derivatives were obtained.

† Pinacol reduction of acetylcyclopentadienylmanganese tricarbonyl has also been reported by Cais and Feldkimel (24).

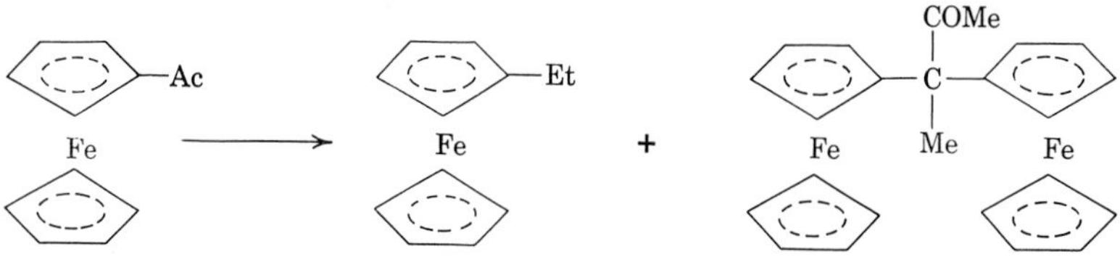

Ferrocene—Ac ⟶ Ferrocene—Et + Ferrocene—C(COMe)(Me)—Ferrocene

(68)

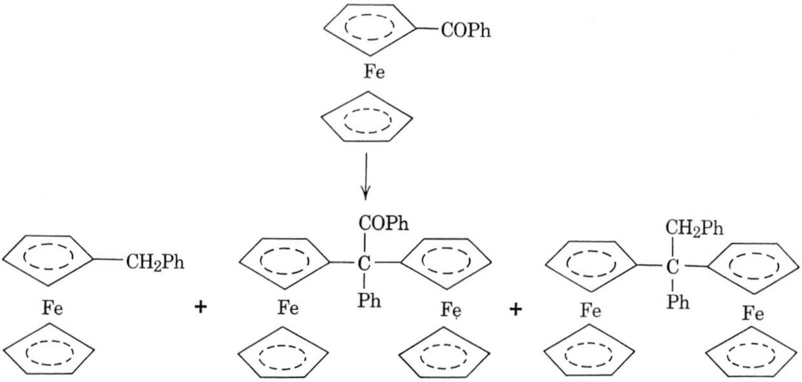

Ferrocene—COPh

↓

Ferrocene—CH₂Ph + Ferrocene—C(COPh)(Ph)—Ferrocene + Ferrocene—C(CH₂Ph)(Ph)—Ferrocene

(7)   **(69)**   **(70)**

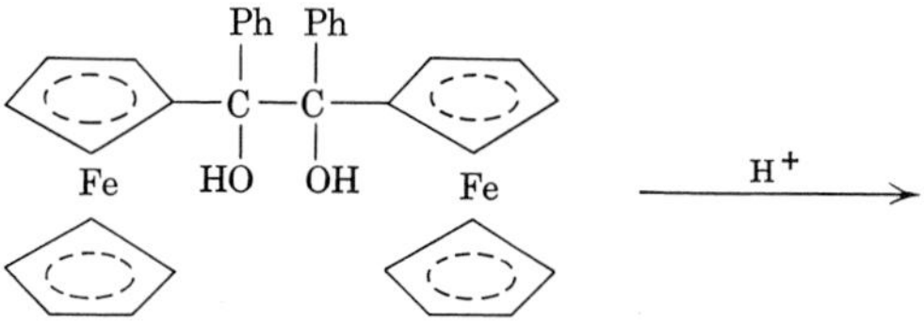

Ferrocene—C(Ph)(OH)—C(Ph)(OH)—Ferrocene $\xrightarrow{\text{H}^+}$ **(69)**

(71)

have also described the reduction of 1,1′-dicarbomethoxyferrocene to 1,1′-dimethylferrocene under these conditions.*

In the absence of aluminum chloride, reduction with either lithium aluminum hydride or sodium borohydride proceeds in the conventional manner to give α-hydroxyalkylmetallocenes in excellent yields. Representative examples of these reactions are to be found in the reduction of formylferrocene (1, 17, 35), acetylferrocene and 1,1′-diacetylferrocene (1, 35), acetylruthenocene and acetylosmocene (48), benzoylferrocene (178) and the bridged ketone α-keto-1,1′-trimethyleneferrocene (141).

* The Russian authors have stated that lithium aluminum hydride alone achieved this reduction, but their reagent was prepared from lithium hydride and aluminum chloride and was very probably contaminated with aluminum chloride.

Meerwein-Ponndorf reduction of benzoylferrocene (178) and 1,1'-dibenzoylferrocene (132) with aluminum *i*-propoxide in *i*-propanol has been reported to give the *i*-propyl ethers of the hydroxybenzylferrocenes. These products, as well as the fully reduced benzylferrocene, obtained at higher reaction temperatures in xylene solution (128), are quite typical of those ketones in which the intermediate aluminum alkoxide possesses a readily ionizable C—O bond (181).

Reduction of benzoyl- and 1,1'-dibenzoylferrocene with sodium in ethanol is reported to give the corresponding benzylferrocene in good yields (128). Weliky and Gould (178) have reported the formation of α,α-diferrocenylbenzyl alcohol in low yield when benzoylferrocene was reduced with sodium amalgam. Pauson and Watts (119) have more recently confirmed these observations and found that the best yield of this product is obtained in the presence of an equimolar quantity of ferrocene, and that water is a necessary component. The mechanism of this reaction is unknown.

Attempts to effect pinacol reduction of benzoylferrocene with Mg-MgI$_2$ or by irradiation in the presence of *i*-propanol are reported to have failed (128, 178).*

Carbanion addition

Aside from the base-catalyzed condensation reactions described in Chapter 4, the acylferrocenes react normally with Grignard reagents (63, 132) and acetylides to give α-hydroxyalkyl derivatives. Schlögl and Mohar (152, 157) have used these latter reagents to prepare a variety of acetylenic carbinols and glycols, and have converted these by oxidative and reductive procedures to acetylenic ketones, olefinic carbinols, and polyenes. The use of Wittig reagents with acylferrocenes has also been reported (30, 115).

SYNTHESIS FROM SUBSTITUTED CYCLOPENTADIENES

The use of substituted cyclopentadienes constitutes a fairly direct and useful procedure for the synthesis of substituted alkylmetallocenes. The alkylcyclopentadienes have been prepared in some cases by alkylation of cyclopentadienyl Grignard reagents (69, 133), but a more general method consists in the preparation of fulvenes and their transformation to cyclopentadienides by either reduction, proton abstraction, or addition of carbanions (56, 58, 60, 73).

* In this context it is of interest to note that the photochemical reduction of benzo-phenone to benzpinacol may be effected in the presence of ferrocene (128).

These latter three general transformations are illustrated by the conversion of dimethylfulvene to 1,1'-di-*t*-butylferrocene (**72**), 1,1'-di-*i*-propylferrocene (**73**), and 1,1'-di-*i*-propenylferrocene (**74**). In all of these reactions, the intermediate cyclopentadienide need not be isolated.

(**72**) (**73**) (**74**)

Knox and Pauson (56, 58) have also reported the use of azulene in these reactions. By treatment of the hydrocarbon with phenyllithium or lithium aluminum hydride and then with ferrous chloride, a mixture of stereo-isomeric bis-dihydroazulenyliron compounds (**75a** or **75b**) was obtained.

(**75a**, R = C_6H_5)
(**75b**, R = H)

The fulvene procedure has also been employed by Pauson and co-workers (59) in the synthesis of the nickelocene and cobalticenium compounds (76 to 78) and of the polynuclear ferrocene and cobalticenium derivatives (79 and 80). The synthesis of several bridged ferrocenes from polymethylene cyclopentadienes (76) and by treatment of fulvenes with sodium metal followed by ferrous chloride (111, 139, 163) has also been reported.

1,1′-(N,N-Dimethylaminomethyl)ferrocene (84) and cobalticenium salts (85) have also been prepared from (N,N-dimethylaminomethyl)cyclopentadienide (81), obtained by lithium aluminum hydride reduction of (N,N-dimethylaminomethyl)fulvene (82) or by reductive decomposition of (N,N-dimethylaminomethyl)ferrocene (83) with lithium (59, 115), following the method of Trifan and Nicholas (168).

RADICAL SUBSTITUTION OF FERRICENIUM SALTS

Beckwith and Leydon (6) have recently reported the preparation of 2-cyano-2-ferrocenylpropane by treatment of ferricenium salts with azobisisobutyronitrile, and of benzylferrocene from the reaction of ferrocene in toluene solution with t-butyl perbenzoate. These reactions, which probably involve radical substitution of the ferricenium ion, are discussed more fully in Chapter 6, pages 204–207. Their synthetic importance remains to be demonstrated.

PREFACE TO TABLE 5-3

Organization

The table is divided into four main sections.

Section I, containing by far the preponderant number of derivatives, is subdivided in turn according to the character of the substituent. Within each of these divisions, mono-, di-, and more highly substituted derivatives are grouped together and listed in order of increasing number of carbon atoms and of constitutional and functional group complexity.

Melting points

In general the highest melting point reported in the literature is given, except where there appears to be agreement from several independent sources on a lower value. In cases where substantial differences occur in the literature, both values are recorded.

Refractive indices

Where two or more values of the index of refraction at the same temperature are reported, the upper and lower values are given. The temperature at which the refractive index was determined is given in parentheses.

Footnotes

[a] Structure uncertain.
[b] Structure given is incorrect.
[c] No data given.
[d] Not isolated.
[e] Probably a mixture of isomers.

Table 5-3

I. Ferrocene Derivatives

A. Alkyl

SUBSTITUENT	M.P.	B.P.	REFRACTIVE INDEX	LITERATURE REFERENCE
—CH_3	35.5–36.5	86/0.4	—	89, 115, 153 84[b], 110
—CH_2CH_3	—	121–123/10 107–108/5 93–94/1 74–76/0.2	1.6002–1.6015 (20)	1, 29, 78 79, 81, 84 90, 98, 142 153
—$(CH_2)_2CH_3$	—	106–108/3	1.5880 (20) 1.5846 (25)	51, 98, 152 153, 154
—$CH(CH_3)_2$	—	106–107/3	1.5897 (20)	60, 84, 90
—$(CH_2)_3CH_3$	—	180–183/5	1.5701–1.5795 (20)	29, 79[e], 153
—$CHCH_2CH_3$ | —CH_3	—	50–70/0.2	1.5825 (20) 1.5951 (25)	51, 152, 154
—$C(CH_3)_3$	—	103–105/4	1.5790 (20)	85, 107
—$(CH_2)_4CH_3$	—	80–90/0.5	1.5711 (20)	153, 155
—$CH_2C(CH_3)_3$	62	—	—	67
—$C(CH_3)_2$ | —CH_2CH_3	—	135–136/4	1.5760 (20)	85
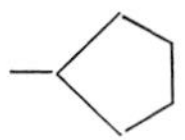 (cyclopentyl)	16.3	—	—	176
—$(CH_2)_5CH_3$	—	139–140/1.5	1.5602 (20)	29

153

Table 5-3 (Contd.)
I. Ferrocene Derivatives

SUBSTITUENT	M.P.	B.P.	REFRACTIVE INDEX	LITERATURE REFERENCE
			A. Alkyl (Contd.)	

—CHC(CH₃)₃
    |
   CH₃
	—	—	1.5687 (25)	51

—CH₂C₆H₁₁	52	—	—	67
—CH₂C₆H₅	74.5–75.5	—	—	6, 36, 79, 98, 99, 128, 153, 178
—CH₂C₆H₄OH-o	82.5–83.5	—	—	102
—CH₂C₆H₄OCH₃-o	50–52	—	—	102
—(CH₂)₇CH₃	—	154–155/1.0	1.5490 (20)	29
—CH₂CH₂C₆H₁₁	30	—	—	70
—CH₂CH₂C₆H₅	59–61	—	—	26, 51, 70, 98, 120

—CHC₆H₅
    |
   CH₃
	—	—	1.6270 (25)	51

—C(CH₃)₂C₆H₅	136–137	—	—	60, 73, 107

—CHC₆H₅
    |
   C₂H₅
	58.4–59.6	—	—	51

—(CH₂)₄C₆H₅	20–24	136–140/0.25	—	158
—(CH₂)₉CH₃	—	183–184/1.4	1.5399 (20)	29

Substituent	mp (°C)	bp/mm	n_D (°C)	References
—CH₂— (1-naphthyl)	114–115	—	—	98
—(CH₂)₁₁CH₃	35–36	—	—	29
—CH(C₆H₅)₂	78.5–79.5	—	—	60[e], 142
—CH₂CH(C₆H₅)₂	52–55	—	—	120
—C(C₆H₅)₂—CH₃	131–132	—	—	107
—(CH₂)₁₅CH₃	55.0–55.6	—	—	174
—C(C₆H₅)₃	190–190.5	—	—	107
1,1'—CH₃	39–40.5	—	1.5900 (35)	49, 83, 88, 130
1,2 or 1,3—CH₃	—	77/4, 119/13	1.6007 (20)	91
1,1'—CH₂CH₃	—35	123–124/5.5, 87–89/0.15	1.5800–1.5807 (20), 1.5761 (25)	78, 79[e] 81, 90, 142, 153, 174
1,2 or 1,3—CH₂CH₃	—	—	1.5761–1.5850 (20)	81, 84
1,1'—(CH₂)₂CH₃	—	137–138/5	1.5603–1.5619 (20)	78, 153
1,1'—CH(CH₃)₂	—	124–125/3, 91/0.025	1.5604 (20), 1.5596 (25.5)	56, 58, 73, 90
1—CH₂CH₂CH₃, 1'—CH₂C(CH₃)₃	—	125–130/1	—	27
1,1'—(CH₂)₃CH₃	—	164–165/6	1.5511–1.5530 (20)	78, 153
1,X—(CH₂)₃CH₃	—	155–157/3.5	1.1432 (20)	79[e]
1,1'—CH₂CH(CH₃)₂	—	97/0.5	—	52, 67
1—CH₂CH(CH₃)₂	—	118–122/0.5	—	27

Table 5-3 (Contd.)
I. Ferrocene Derivatives

SUBSTITUENT	M.P.	B.P.	REFRACTIVE INDEX	LITERATURE REFERENCE
A. Alkyl (Contd.)				
1'—CH$_2$C(CH$_3$)$_3$	56–57	—	—	27
1—CH$_2$CH(CH$_3$)$_2$				
3—CH$_2$C(CH$_3$)$_3$				
1,1'—C(CH$_3$)$_3$	—	124.5–125/3	1.5581 (20)	85
		108/0.05	1.550 (21.5)	56, 58
		129/0.5	—	68, 133
1,X—C(CH$_3$)$_3$	61	—	—	68
1,1'—(CH$_2$)$_4$CH$_3$	—	125–135/0.04	1.5428 (20)	153, 155
1,1'—CH$_2$CH$_2$CH(CH$_3$)$_2$	—	128/0.3	—	70
1,1'—C(CH$_3$)$_2$	—	162–163/4	1.5602 (20)	68, 85
CH$_2$CH$_3$				
1,1'—CH$_2$C(CH$_3$)$_3$	68–69	—	—	27, 67, 71
1,3—CH$_2$C(CH$_3$)$_3$	127	—	—	27
1—CH$_2$C(CH$_3$)$_3$	—	134/2	—	27
1'—(CH$_2$)$_2$CHCH$_2$C(CH$_3$)$_3$				
CH$_3$				
1—CH$_2$C(CH$_3$)$_3$, 1'—CH$_2$C$_6$H$_{11}$	37–38	—	—	27
1—CH$_2$C(CH$_3$)$_3$, 3—CH$_2$C$_6$H$_{11}$	64–66	—	—	27
1—CH$_2$C(CH$_3$)$_3$, 1'—(CH$_2$)$_2$C$_6$H$_5$	54.0–54.5	—	—	27

Substituent	MP (°C)	BP (°C/mm)	n_D	Refs
$1—CH_2C(CH_3)_3,\ 1'—CH_2C_6H_4Cl\text{-}o$	57.7–58.5	—	—	27
$1,1'—(CH_2)_5CH_3$	—	189/1.6	1.5320 (20)	29
$1,1'—CH_2CH_2C(CH_3)_3$	62	—	—	70
$1,1'—C(CH_3)_2CH_2CH_2CH_3$	21	130/0.3	—	69
$1,1'—C(CH_2CH_3)_2CH_3$	34	—	—	69
$1,1'—C_6H_{11}$	42.5	160/0.07	—	50
$1,1'—$ (1-methylcyclohexyl, CH_3)	67	—	—	69
$1,1'—(CH_2)_7CH_3$	73	—	—	67
$1,1'—CH_2C_6H_5$	103–105	—	—	36, 78, 83, 128, 153
$1,1'—(CH_2)_7CH_3$	−16	190–193/0.15	1.5214 (25)	174
$1,1'—C(CH_2)_3CH_3CH_2CH_3$	—	Oil[e]	—	69
$1,1'—CH_2CH_2C_6H_5$	70	—	—	26
$1,1'—CH_2CH_2CHCH_2C(CH_3)_3CH_3$	—	Oil[e]	—	70
$1,1'—C(CH_3)_2C_6H_5$	133.5–134	—	—	56, 58
$1,1'—(CH_2)_9CH_3$	11.5	197–205/0.04	1.5142 (25)	174

Table 5-3 (Contd.)
I. Ferrocene Derivatives

A. Alkyl (Contd.)

SUBSTITUENT	M.P.	B.P.	REFRACTIVE INDEX	LITERATURE REFERENCE
1,1'—CH₂CH₂— (drawn 3,4-dimethylphenyl structure with CH₃, CH₃)	77	—	—	70
1,1'— (drawn cyclohexyl structure with C₆H₅)	135–136	—	—	58
1,1'—(CH₂)₁₁CH₃	30.6–30.8	—	—	174
1,1'—(CH₂)₁₂CH₃	38–39	—	—	174
1,1'—CH(C₆H₅)₂	164.5–165	—	—	73, 83, 107, 117, 142, 182
1,1'—C(C₆H₅)₂ $\mid$ CH₃	210	—	—	107
1,1'—CH(C₆H₅)CH₂C₆H₅	α, 106–107; β, 94–95	—	—	134; 134
1,1'—(CH₂)₁₅CH₃	41.2—42.4	—	—	174
1,1'—C(C₆H₅)₃	286	—	—	60ᵇ, 73, 107
—CH₂—	144–146	—	—	119, 140, 152
—CH₂—CH₂—	196–197.5	—	—	82ᵇ, 94, 96, 99, 120, 137

Structure	m.p. (°C)	b.p.		Ref.
—CH(CH$_3$)—	147–149	—	—	79^b, 96, 138
—(CH$_2$)$_3$—	87–89	—	—	158
—(CH$_2$)$_4$—	106–111	—	—	152, 157, 158
—CH$_2$CH$_2$CH(CH$_3$)—	80–82	—	—	158
—CH—(CH$_2$)$_4$—CH(CH$_3$)— (CH$_3$)	—	180–200/0.5	—	152
—(CH$_2$)$_6$—	—	—	—	152
—CHC$_6$H$_5$—	133–135	190–200/0.3	—	119, 178
—(CH$_2$)$_8$—	~40	—	—	120
—CH(C$_6$H$_5$)—CH(C$_6$H$_5$)—	α, β, 218–220; β, 276–278; α, β, 229–230; α, β, 270–271	—	—	10–12, 120
—CCH$_2$C$_6$H$_5$ (C$_6$H$_5$)	267–268	—	—	82^b, 99, 137
—CH(C$_6$H$_5$)—Fe—(C$_6$H$_5$) ferrocenyl	—	—	—	99
—CH(C$_6$H$_5$)—	194–196	—	—	59

Table 5-3 (Contd.)

I. Ferrocene Derivatives

A. Alkyl (Contd.)

SUBSTITUENT	M.P.	B.P.	REFRACTIVE INDEX	LITERATURE REFERENCE
$\begin{array}{c} H \\ \| \\ -C- \\ \| \end{array}$	313–314	—	—	104, 119
1,1'—CH$_3$, 2—CH$_2$CH$_3$	—	Oil[e]	—	135
1,1'—CH$_3$, 3—CH$_2$CH$_3$	—	Oil[e]	—	135
1,1',2 or 1,1',3—CH$_2$CH$_3$	—	—	1.5613 (20)	81
1,X,Y—CH$_2$CH$_3$[e]	—	145–153/5	—	79
1,1',2 or 1,1',3—C(CH$_3$)$_3$	—	—	—	107
1,X,Y—C(CH$_3$)$_3$	91	—	—	68, 90
1,X,Y,Z—C(CH$_3$)$_3$	—	195–200/3	—	90
1,X,Y,Z—C(CH$_3$)$_2$ $\begin{array}{c} \| \\ CH_2CH_3 \end{array}$	110	—	—	68
1,1',2,2'—CH$_2$C$_6$H$_5$	154.5–155.5	—	—	74
1,1',2,2'—CH$_2$C$_6$H$_4$CH$_3$-p	117–118	—	—	74
1,1',2,2'—CH$_2$C$_6$H$_4$F-p	142–143	—	—	74
1,1',2,2'—CH$_2$C$_6$H$_4$Cl-o	163.5–164.5	—	—	74
1,1',2,2'—CH$_2$C$_6$H$_4$Cl-p	169–171	—	—	74
1,1',2,2'—CH$_2$C$_6$H$_4$Br-o	117.5–118	—	—	74
1,1',2,2'—CH$_2$C$_6$H$_4$Br-p	207–208	—	—	74

	mp (°C)	bp	n_D	References
1,1'—C(C₆H₅)₃, X,X'—C₆H₅	174–175	—	—	73
1,1',X,Y—CH₂(C₆H₅)₂	80–130	—	—	107
1,1'—CH₃, X,Y,Z—CH₂CH₃	—	Oil[e]	—	88
1,1',X,Y,Z—C(C₆H₅)₃	>300°	—	—	107
1,2,3,4,5,1',2',3',4',5'—CH₂CH₃	210–230 (dec.)	—	—	156

B. Alkenyl

	mp (°C)	bp	n_D	References
—CH=CH₂	56	80–85/0.2	—	1, 22, 44, 66, 152, 154 / 120
—CH=CHCl	—	Oil[e]	—	158
—CH=CCl₂	55–58	—	—	158
—CH=CH— (*cis*)	195–198	—	—	120
(*trans*)	265–267			
	39–40	—	—	44[b]
—C=CH₂ with CH₃	162–164	—	—	138
—CH=CHCH₃	25	80–90/0.4	1.6310 (25)	51, 152, 154[c]
C=CH₂ with CH₂ / CH₃	77.5–78.5	—	—	51, 138
—CH₂CH=CH₂	—	93–95/1	1.5990 (20)	98
—CH₂CH₂CH=CH₂	—	128–130/1	1.5940 (20)	98
—C=CHCH₃ with CH₃	30–35	—	1.5709 (20)	152, 154
cyclopentenyl (or double bond isomer)	64–65	170–176/10	—	176, 177

161

Table 5-3 (Contd.)

I. Ferrocene Derivatives

SUBSTITUENT	M.P.	B.P.	REFRACTIVE INDEX	LITERATURE REFERENCE
B. Alkenyl (Contd.)				
—CH=CHC$_6$H$_5$	121–121.5	—	—	120, 162
—C=CH$_2$ C$_6$H$_5$	119–120	—	—	64
—CH=C(C$_6$H$_5$)$_2$	77–79	—	—	120
—C=C— C$_6$H$_5$C$_6$H$_5$ (*trans*)	278–280	—	—	120
—CH—CH=CH$_2$ OH	—	105–115/0.3	—	157
CH$_3$ —C—CH=CH$_2$ OH	—	100–110/0.2	—	152, 157
—CH—CH—CHO	90–95	—	—	157
—CHCH=CHC$_6$H$_5$ (*cis*) OH	78–80	—	—	157
—CHCH=CHC$_6$H$_5$ (*trans*) OH	56–63	—	—	157

Structure	mp	bp	Ref.
—C=CHC₆H₅ / —CN	112–114	—	45
—CH—O—CH—[a,c] / —CH=CH₂ CH=CH₂	—	—	157
—CH₂— (cyclopentadienyl)[e]	—	104/0.15	115, 119
—CH=CH—CH=CHC₆H₅	189–191	—	157
(C₆H₅-cyclopentadiene) (or double bond isomer)	102–104	—	106
—CH=CH—CH=CH—C	230 (dec.)	—	152
—CH=CH—CH=CH—CH—[c]	—	—	157
—CH=CH—CH₂—CH₂—CH=CH—[c]	—	—	154
—CH=C=CH—	—	100/10	157
—CH=C=CHC₆H₅	98–100	—	157
—CH= (cyclopentadienyl)	—	oil[e]	115, 119
—CH=C=C=C=C=CH—[a,c]	—	—	157

163

Table 5-3 (Contd.)
I. Ferrocene Derivatives

SUBSTITUENT	M.P.	B.P.	REFRACTIVE INDEX	LITERATURE REFERENCE
B. Alkenyl (Contd.)				
				32
R = —CH_3	171–173.5	—	—	
—C_2H_5	159–160	—	—	
—$CH(CH_3)_2$	165.5–167	—	—	
—$CH_2CH{=}CH_2$	166–168	—	—	
—$(CH_2)_3CH_3$	132–133.5	—	—	
—C_6H_5	194–195	—	—	
	68–69.5	—	—	32
				32

R =				
—CH₃	162–164	—	—	
—C₂H₅	148–151	—	—	
—CH(CH₃)₂	142–145	—	—	
—CH₂CH=CH₂	155–158	—	—	
—(CH₂)₃CH₃	125–127	—	—	
—C₆H₅	166–168	—	—	

	159–162	—	—	32

	194–195	—	—	172
1,1'—CH=CH₂[c]	—	—	—	154
1,1'—C=CH₂ with CH₃	58–59	—	—	56, 58
1,1'—C=CHCH₃ with CH₃	α, 39	—	1.6235 (25)	132
	β, —	Oil[c]	1.6221 (25)	132

Table 5-3 (Contd.)
I. Ferrocene Derivatives

B. Alkenyl (Contd.)

SUBSTITUENT	M.P.	B.P.	REFRACTIVE INDEX	LITERATURE REFERENCE
1,1'- [cyclopentenyl]^c	—	—	—	139
1,1'- [cyclohexenyl]	44	180/0.15	1.6215 (24)	56, 58
1,1'- [cycloheptatrienyl]^c	—	—	—	147
1,1'—CH=CH OCOCH₃	—	Oil^c	—	126
1—CH=CH₂, 2—CH₂OH	—	149–153/2	—	66
1—CH=CH₂, 2—CH₂CH₃ (optically active)	—	Oil $[\alpha]^{22}_{565} + 24°$, $[\alpha]^{22}_{589} + 7°$ (c. 2.3, ethanol)	—	159
1—CH=CH₂, 2—CH₂CN	—	156–159/1.4	—	66
1,1'—C=CHC₆H₅ / C₆H₅	α, 148–150	—	—	134
	β, 144–148	—	—	134
1,1'—C=CHC₆H₄Cl-p / C₆H₄Cl-p	α, 169–170	—	—	134
	β, 161–162	—	—	134

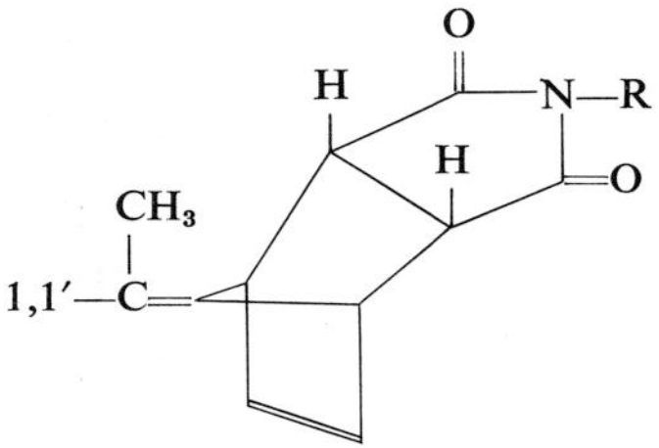

			196–200	32
			110–115	
			α, 135–137	
			β, 185	
			171–174	
			134–138	
			α, 180–182	
			β, 247	
			176–180	32
			54-55	8

R = —CH₃

—C₂H₅

—CH(CH₃)₂

—CH₂CH=CH₂

—(CH₂)₃CH₃

—C₆H₅

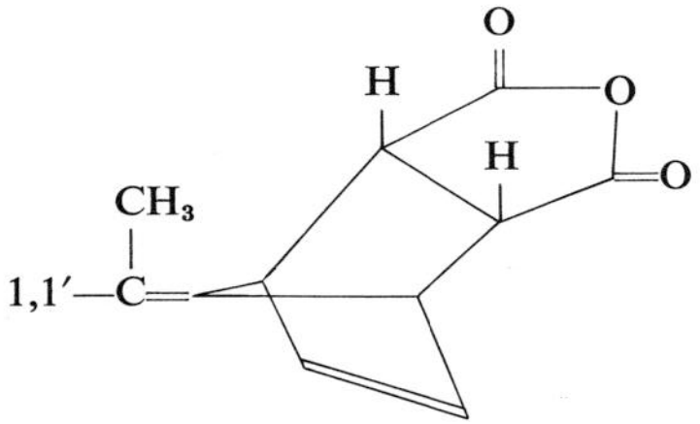

1,1'—C with CH₃

—C≡CH

167

Table 5-3 (Contd.)
I. Ferrocene Derivatives

SUBSTITUENT	M.P.	B.P.	REFRACTIVE INDEX	LITERATURE REFERENCE
C. Alkynyl				
$-C{\equiv}CCH_3$	86–88	—	—	157
$-CH_2C{\equiv}CH$	—	90–100/10	—	157
$-CH-C{\equiv}CH$, $\;CH_3$	—	100–120/10	—	157
$-C{\equiv}CC_6H_5$	121–123	—	—	120
$-CH_2C{\equiv}CC_6H_5$	79–81	—	—	120, 157
$-C{\equiv}CCH_2C_6H_5$	50–70	—	—	157
$-C{\equiv}C-$	244–246	—	—	120
$-CH_2-C{\equiv}C-CH_2-$	105–108	—	—	157
$-CH-C{\equiv}C-CH-$, $\;CH_3\;\;CH_3$	α, 150–154; β, 128–135	—	—	152
$-C{\equiv}CCO_2H$	122	—	—	8
$-CH-C{\equiv}CH$, $\;OH$	81–83	100–110/0.5	—	152
CH_3, $-CC{\equiv}CH$, OH	46–49	—	—	152
$-OH$	112–114	—	—	63

168

—CH—C≡C—C₆H₅ —OH	—	—	73–75	152
C₆H₅ —C—C≡CH —OH	—	—	89–90	63
—CH—C≡C—CO₂H^c —OH	—	—	—	152
—CH—C≡C—CHCH₃ —OH —OH	—	—	114–132	152
—CH—C≡C—CH—C₆H₅ —OH —OH	—	—	α, 127–131	152
			β, 108–112	
—CH=CHC≡CH	—	—	61–63	120
—C≡C—C≡C—C₆H₅	—	—	112–113	158
—C≡C—C≡C—	—	—	196–198	158
—CH₂—C≡C—C≡C—CH₂—	—	—	126–134	157
—CH—C≡C—C≡C—CH— —OH —OH	—	—	>200	152
CH₃ —C—C≡C—C≡C—C— —OH CH₃ —OH	—	—	90–125	152
(—CH=CHC≡C)₂	—	—	216–218	120
—C≡C—Hg—C≡C—	—	—	230–235 (dec.)	158
—CH₂—C≡C—Hg—C≡C—CH₂—	—	—	175–178	157

169

Table 5-3 (Contd.)
I. Ferrocene Derivatives

SUBSTITUENT	M.P.	B.P.	REFRACTIVE INDEX	LITERATURE REFERENCE
D. Hydroxyalkyl, Alkoxyalkyl, Oxoalkyl				
—CH_2OH	81–82	—	—	17, 35, 42, 72, 83, 109, 148, 66a
—CH_2OCH_2—	134–136	—	—	35, 46, 89, 148, 154
—CH_2OCH_3	—	106–107.5/1.5 118.5–119.5/3	1.5996–1.6003 (20)	94, 95
—$CH_2OCH_2CH_3$	—	112–113.5/2 117–118/3 68–70/0.3	1.5840–1.5855 (20)	94, 95, 103
—$CH_2OCH_2CH{=}CH_2$	—	120–121/2.5	1.5908 (20)	95
—$CH_2OCH_2CH_2CH_2CH_3$	31–32.5	105–106/2	1.5695 (20)	103
—$CH_2OC(CH_3)_3$	73.5–74	—	—	95
—$CH_2O(CH_2)_8CH_3$	22.5–23.5	—	—	95
—$CH_2O(CH_2)_9CH_3$	35–37	—	—	95
—$CH_2OCH_2C_6H_5$	88–90	—	—	94, 95
—CH_2OCH_2 (furyl)	49.5–50.5	—	—	95
—$CH_2OC_6H_5$	129–130	—	—	91

Structure	mp	bp	$[\alpha]$	Ref.
—CH₂O— (naphthalene)	121–123	—	—	91
sugar (CH₂OR, OR, OR, OR)	R = H, 135–136	—	α_D^{22} −33.7 (C, 1.0 in H₂O)	28
	R = Ac, 183–185	—	α_D^{21} −11.7 (C, 1.0 in CHCl₃)	
—CH₂OCOCH₃	74–76	—	—	103
—CH₂OCOC₆H₅	132–133	—	—	72, 103
—CH₂OCOC₆H₄NH₂-o	123–124	—	—	103
—CH₂CH₂OH	49–50	—	—	136
	32.5–33.5	—	—	65, 158
—CH₂CH₂O— (sugar)	174	—	α_D^{23} −28 (C, 0.3 in H₂O)	28
—CH₂COC₆H₅	80–82	—	—	120
—CH₂CH₂CH₂OH	—	135–145/0.03	—	148
—CH=CHCH₂OH	67–70	140–145/0.05	—	148
—CHCH₃ / OH	78.2–78.7	—	—	1, 42, 48, 64

171

Table 5-3 (Contd.)
I. Ferrocene Derivatives

D. Hydroxyalkyl, Alkoxyalkyl, Oxoalkyl (Contd.)

SUBSTITUENT	M.P.	B.P.	REFRACTIVE INDEX	LITERATURE REFERENCE
—CHCH₃ / —O—	157	—	—	64
—CHCH₃ / —CH—CH₂Cl / —O—	45–47	—	—	158
—CH—CH₂Cl / —CHCH₃	—	$50/10^{-5}$	1.5739 (25)	48
—OCH₂CH₃ / —CHCH₃	70.2–71	—	—	1, 22, 48
—OCOCH₃ / —CHCH₂Cl / —OH	76–77	—	—	158
—CHCHCl₂ / —OH	68–71	—	—	158
—CH—CH₂OH / —OH	148–152 (dec.)	—	—	158

Structure	mp (°C)	bp (°C/mm)	n_D	Ref.
—CHCH₂CH₃, —OH	—	80–09/0.4	1.6110 (20)	152
—CHCH₂CH₃—O—CHCH₂CH₃	171–171.5	—	—	64
—CHCH₂CH=CH₂, —OH	145–147	—	—	64
—CHCH(CH₃)₂, —OH	56–58	—	—	53
—CH(CH₂)₃CH₃, —OH	—	115–125/0.2	1.5940 (20)	155
—CH(CH₂)₃CH₃—O—CH(CH₂)₃CH₃	170–171	—	—	64
—(CH₂)₅CHCH₃, —OH	—	145–150/0.3	—	155
—CHC₆H₅, —OH	80.3–80.5	—	—	64, 128, 178
—CHC₆H₄OH-o, —OH	83.5–84.5	—	—	102

Table 5-3 (Contd.)
I. Ferrocene Derivatives

D. Hydroxyalkyl, Alkoxyalkyl, Oxoalkyl (Contd.)

SUBSTITUENT	M.P.	B.P.	REFRACTIVE INDEX	LITERATURE REFERENCE
—CHC$_6$H$_4$OCH$_3$-o | OCH$_3$	113–114	—	—	102
—CHC$_6$H$_5$—O—	110–112	—	—	178
—CHC$_6$H$_5$ —CHC$_6$H$_5$ | O—OCH$_3$	111–112	—	—	77, 178
—CHC$_6$H$_5$—O—	74–75	—	—	178
—CH(CH$_3$)$_2$	64	—	—	26
—CHCH$_2$C$_6$H$_5$ | OH	82–83	—	—	162
—CHCH$_2$CH$_2$CH$_2$N(CH$_3$)$_2$ | OH	81–81.5	—	—	47
—CHCH$_2$CH$_2$ (O=)	130–131	—	—	162

Structure	mp (°C)			Ref.
$-CC_6H_5$ / $-OH$ / CH_2CH_3	81–81.5	—	—	64
$-CC_6H_5$ / $-OH$ / $(CH_2)_2CH_3$	110–111	—	—	63
$-CC_6H_5$ / $-OH$ / $(CH_2)_4CH_3$	87–88	—	—	63
$-CC_6H_5$ / $-OH$ / $C(C_6H_5)_2$	65–66	—	—	63
$-OH$ / C_6H_5	136–137	—	—	7, 142
$-CC_6H_4CH_3\text{-}p$ / $-OH$	124–127	—	—	7
$-CH(CH_2)_3Si(CH_3)_3$ / $-OH$ / CH_3	−28	—	—	64
$-C(CH_2)_3Si(CH_3)_3$ / $-OH$	−41	—	—	64

Table 5-3 (Contd.)
I. Ferrocene Derivatives

D. Hydroxyalkyl, Alkoxyalkyl, Oxoalkyl (Contd.)

SUBSTITUENT	M.P.	B.P.	REFRACTIVE INDEX	LITERATURE REFERENCE
C_6H_5 $-C(CH_2)_3Si(CH_3)_3$ OH	98–99	—	—	64
$-CH-$ OH	176–177	—	—	53[c], 119, 146, 152
$-CH-$ OCH_2CH_3	122–128	—	—	152
$CH-O-CH$	244–245 (dec.)	—	—	119
CH_3 OH $-CHCH_2CH-$	109–111	—	—	119
OH $-C-$ $(CH_2)_3CH_3$	148–150	—	—	119
OH $-C-$ C_6H_5	195–197	—	—	119, 178[a]

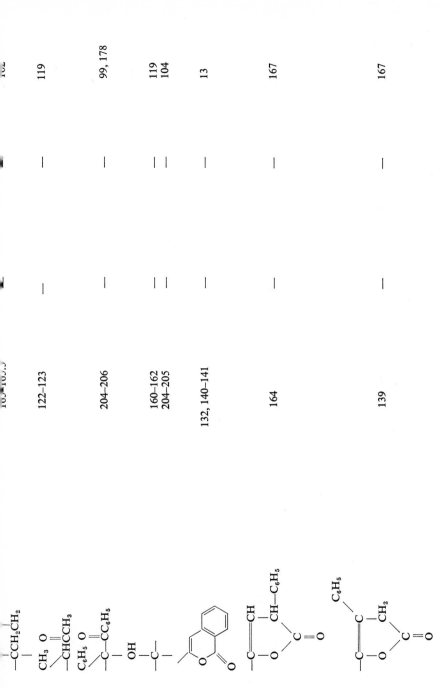

162				
119	—	—	122–123	
99, 178	—	—	204–206	
119 / 104	||	||	160–162 / 204–205	
13	—	—	132, 140–141	
167	—	—	164	
167	—	—	139	

177

Table 5-3 (Contd.)
I. Ferrocene Derivatives

SUBSTITUENT	M.P.	B.P.	REFRACTIVE INDEX	LITERATURE REFERENCE
D. Hydroxyalkyl, Alkoxyalkyl, Oxoalkyl (Contd.)				
—CH₂CH₂CCF₃ (O=)	34.5–35	—	—	141
—CHCH₂CH₂CH— / OH	134–135	—	—	152, 162
CH₂—CH₂ / —CH CH— / O (ring)	124.5–125	—	—	162
—CH(CH₂)₄CH— / OH OH	145–149	—	—	152
C₆H₅ C₆H₅ / —C—C— / OH OH	125–145 (dec.)	—	—	178
1,1'—CH₂OH	85–86 / 107–108	—	— —	83 / 115
1,1'—CHCH₃ / OH	69–71	—	—	35, 77
1,1'—C(CH₃)₂ / OH	124	—	—	132

Substituent	m.p. (°C)			Ref.
CH_3 $1,1'-CCH_2CH_3$ $-OH$	α, 100–101 β, 115–116	—	—	132
$1,1'-CHC_6H_5$ $-OH$	136–137	—	—	128
$1,1'-CHC_6H_5$ $O(CH_2)_2CH_3$	90–94	—	—	132
$1,1'-C(C_6H_5)_2$ $-OH$	179–181	—	—	83, 132, 142
$1,2-C(C_6H_5)_2$ $-OH$	195–196	—	—	7
$1,1'-C(CH_2C_6H_5)C_6H_5$ $-OH$	163–164	—	—	134
$1,1'-C(CH_2C_6H_4Cl\text{-}p)C_6H_4Cl\text{-}p$ $-OH$	212–215 (dec.)	—	—	134
$1,1'-CHCH_2C_6H_5$ $-OH$	140	—	—	26
$1,1'-CHCH_2CH_2$ $O-CO$	165 (dec.)	—	—	35
$1-CH_2CH_3,\ 2-CH_2OH$	55–57	—	—	66
$1-CH_2OH,\ 2-C(C_6H_5)_2$ OH	146	—	—	7

Table 5-3 (Contd.)
I. Ferrocene Derivatives

SUBSTITUENT	M.P.	B.P.	REFRACTIVE INDEX	LITERATURE REFERENCE
D. Hydroxyalkyl, Alkoxyalkyl, Oxoalkyl (Contd.)				
1—CH₃, 2—CHCH₃ —OH	α, 55–56 β, 54–55.2	—	—	49
1—CH₃, 2—C(C₆H₅)₂ —OH	167	—	—	7
1,1'—CH₃, 2—CHCH₃ —OH OCOCH₃	—	α, Oil[e] β, Oil[e]	—	49
1—CHCH₃, 1'—Cl	—	—	1.5806 (25)	37
E. Aminoalkyl, Amidoalkyl, Azidoalkyl				
—CH₂NH₂	30–35	90–95/0.02	—	148
—CH₂NH₂·HCl	185–190		—	148
—CHCH₃[c] NH₂	—	—	—	22
—CHCH₃·HCl NH₂	166–167	—	—	22
—CHC₆H₅ NH₂	69–71	—	—	12

Substituent	Derivative	M.p.	B.p.	n_D	Refs.
—CH₂NHC₆H₅		85–86	—	—	5
—CH₂N(CH₃)₂		—	91–92/0.45	1.5893 (25)	40, 41, 72
	Picrate	162–163 (dec.)	—	—	72
(piperidine) N—H	oxalate	212–214 (dec.)	—	—	160
—CH₂N(piperidine)		84–85.5	—	—	112
—CHCH₃ / —N(CH₃)₂		—	111/0.65	1.5883 (25)	42
—CH₂N⁺(CH₃)₃	I⁻	220 (dec.)	—	—	35, 40, 41, 72, 110, 112, 66b
	Picrate	175 (dec.)	—	—	109
—CH₂N⁺(CH₃)₂ / CH₂CH₃	Br⁻	160–163 (dec.)	—	—	95
CH₂CH₃	I⁻	185–188 (dec.)	—	—	109
—CH₂N⁺(CH₃)₂ / CH₂CH₂CH₃	Br⁻	167–170 (dec.)	—	—	109
CH₂CH₂CH₃	I⁻	180.5–181 (dec.)	—	—	109
CH₂N⁺(CH₃)₂ / CH₂CH=CH₂	Br⁻	179–181 (dec.)	—	—	109
CH₂CH=CH₂	I⁻	183.5–186 (dec.)	—	—	109
	Picrate	128–130.5 (dec.)	—	—	109
CH₂N⁺(C₂H₅)₂ / CH₃	I⁻	159–162 (dec.)	—	—	91

181

Table 5-3 (Contd.)

I. Ferrocene Derivatives

E. Aminoalkyl, Amidoalkyl, Azidoalkyl (Contd.)

Substituent	M.P.	B.P.	Refractive index	Literature reference
$-CH_2\overset{+}{N}(CH_3)_2CH_2CH_2CH_2CH_3$ Br^-	134.5–136.5 (dec.)	—	—	109
$-CH_2\overset{+}{N}(CH_3)_2CH_2CH_2CH_2CH_3$ I^-	155.5–157 (dec.)	—	—	109
$-CH_2NHCH_2CH_2OH$	81–84	—	—	148
$-CH_3\overset{+}{N}(CH_3)_2CH_2CH_2CH_2CH_3$ I^-	—	—	—	109
$-CH_2\overset{+}{N}(CH_3)_2CH_2Ph$ Cl^-	188.5–189.5 (dec.)	—	—	109
$-CH_2\overset{+}{N}(CH_3)_2CH_2Ph$ I^-	180–182 (dec.)	—	—	109
$-CH_2\overset{+}{N}(CH_3)_2CH_2COOC_2H_5$ Cl^-	141–143 (dec.)	—	—	109
$-CH_2\overset{+}{N}(CH_3)_2CH_2COC_6H_5$ Br^-	138–140 (dec.)	—	—	109
$-CH_2\overset{+}{N}(CH_3)_2CH_2-$ (pyridinium) Br^-	214–215.5 (dec.)	—	—	109
$-CH_2NH-$ 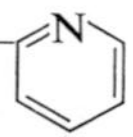 (pyridyl)	138–140	—	—	5
$-CH_2NHCH_2CH_2N(CH_3)_2 \cdot 2HCl$	203–205	—	—	5

		M.P.	B.P.		References
$-CH_2NHCH_2CO_2C_2H_5$		—	130–140/0.02	—	148
$-CH_2NHCH_2CO_2C_2H_5 \cdot HCl$		149–151 (dec.)	—	—	148
$-CH_2NHCONHCH_2C_6H_5$		129–131	—	—	148
$-CH_2NHCONH$		130–132	—	—	148
$C_6H_5CHCO_2C_2H_5$ / $-CH_2NHCONH$		139–141	—	—	148
$C_6H_5CHCO_2H$ / $-CH_2NC_6H_5$		140–141	—	—	5
$COCH_2Cl$ / $-CHC_6H_5$		184–186	—	—	12
$NHCOC_6H_5$ / $-CH_2NC_6H_5$		71–73	—	—	5
(piperidine) $COCH_2N$		—	—	—	148
$-CH_2{-}N{=}C{=}O$		—	110–120/0.1	—	—
$-CH_2CH_2NH_2$		—	118–120/0.5	—	65, 114
$-CH_2CH_2NH_2 \cdot HBr$		198–200 (dec.)	—	—	75
$-CH_2CH_2NHCH_3$		—	96–98/0.1	—	114
	Picrate	182–183	—	—	114
$-CH_2CH_2N(CH_3)_2$		—	103–104/0.35	1.5805 (25)	40, 41, 44
	Picrate	180–183 (dec.)	—	—	44, 114
$[-CH_2CH_2N(CH_3)_3]_2CH_2$	Picrate	181	—	—	114
$-CH_2CH_2\overset{+}{N}(CH_3)_3$	I⁻	248–250 (dec.)	—	—	44, 65, 114
	Picrate	150–152	—	—	44, 65
$-CH_2CH_2NHCHO$		69–70	—	—	114
$-CH_2CH_2NHCOCH_3$		117–118	—	—	113, 114

Table 5-3 (Contd.)

I. Ferrocene Derivatives

E. Aminoalkyl, Amidoalkyl, Azidoalkyl (Contd.)

SUBSTITUENT	M.P.	B.P.	REFRACTIVE INDEX	LITERATURE REFERENCE
—CHCH₃ / —N₃	—	Oil^c	1.6110–1.6116 (20)	8, 21, 22
—CHC₆H₅ / —N₃	49–50	—	1.6432 (25)	10, 12, 20
1,1'—CHCH₃·HCl / —NH₂	180 (dec.)	—	—	125, 127
1,1'—(CH₂)₄NH₂	137–138	—	—	35
1,1'—CHCH₃ / —N(CH₃)₂	—	120/1	—	59
1,1'—CH₂N(CH₃)₂^e	150 (dec.)	—	—	59
Picrate	—	—	—	115
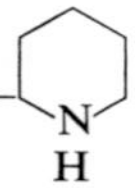 1,1'—CH₂ [piperidine] — dioxalate	219–222 (dec.)	—	—	160
1,1'—CH₂N⁺(CH₃)₃ I⁻	260 (dec.)	—	—	115
Picrate	228 (dec.)	—	—	59
1—CH₃, 2 or 3—CH₂N(CH₃)₂	—	115–118/1, 138–140/5	1.5812 (20)	91
1—CH₃, 2 or 3—CH₂N⁺(CH₃)₃ I⁻	185 (dec.)	—	—	91

Compound	mp (°C)	bp (°C/mm)	n_D	Ref.
1—CH₂CH₃, 2—CH₂N(CH₃)₂ Picrate	162–162.5	Oil^c	—	66 / 66
1—CH₂CH₃, 2—CH₂N(CH₃)₂⁺ I⁻	172–175	—	—	66
1,1'—CH₂N(CH₃)₂, 2 or 3—CH₃	—	130–131.5/1	1.5622 (20)	91
1,1'—SCH₃, 2—CH₂N(CH₃)₂	—	—	—	57 (only NMR Spectral data given)
1,1'—SCH₃, 3—CH₂N(CH₃)₂	—	—	—	57 (only NMR Spectral data given)

F. *Haloalkyl*

Compound	mp (°C)	bp (°C/mm)	n_D	Ref.
—CHCH₃ / —Cl	66–68	—	—	8
—CH₂CH₂Cl	52–54	—	—	158
—CHCH₃ / —Br	48–50	—	—	8
—CH₂CHCl₂	81–82	—	—	158
—CH—CH₂ / —Br Br	63–64	—	—	8

G. *Alkylcarboxylic Acids, Esters, Amides, and Nitriles. Amino Acids.*

Compound	mp (°C)	bp (°C/mm)	n_D	Ref.
—CH₂CO₂H	154–156	—	—	35, 41, 65, 112, 136
—CH₂CN	81–83	—	—	41, 65, 112, 66c
—CH₂CN (morpholine amide)	148–149	—	—	35

Table 5-3 (Contd.)
I. Ferrocene Derivatives

G. *Alkylcarboxylic Acids, Esters, Amides, and Nitriles. Amino Acids (Contd.)*

SUBSTITUENT	M.P.	B.P.	REFRACTIVE INDEX	REFERENCE LITERATURE
—CH₂CN (morpholine, S)	128.5–129	—	—	35, 136
—(CH₂)₂CO₂H	119–120	—	—	43, 112, 136 141, 142, 148 166
—(CH₂)₂CO₂C₂H₅	25–26	—	—	142
—(CH₂)₃CO₂H	117–118	—	—	87, 136, 166
—(CH₂)₃CO₂CH₃	—	168–170/4	—	166
—(CH₂)₃CO₂C₂H₅	40–42	158/1	—	166
—(CH₂)₄CO₂H	109–110	—	—	136
—(CH₂)₅CO₂H	91.5–92.5	—	—	136
—CH₂CH(CO₂H)₂	133–134 (dec.)	—	—	43
—CH₂CH(CO₂C₂H₅)₂[c]	—	—	—	43
—CH₂ (cyclohexane, HO₂C)	120	—	—	26
—CH₂CHCH₂CO₂H | C₆H₅	118	—	—	167

Compound				Refs

—CH₂CHCH₂CO₂CH₃
    |
    C₆H₅
	51	—	—	167

—CH₂CH₂CHCO₂H
        |
        C₆H₅
	131	—	—	167

—CH₂CH₂CHCO₂CH₃
        |
        C₆H₅
	75	—	—	167

—CH₂C₆H₄CO₂H-o	173–174	—	—	87
—CH₂CH₂C₆H₄CO₂H-o	138	—	—	13
—CH₂C₆H₄CH₂CO₂H-o	112–114	—	—	13
—CH₂CHCO₂H	321–333	—	—	43, 112, 148

—CH₂—CHCO₂H
    |
    NH₂
	180–185	—	—	148

—CH₂(CO₂H)₂
    |
    NHCHO
	160–161	—	—	112

—CH₂C(CO₂C₂H₅)₂
    |
    NHCHO
	90–91	175–185/0.05	—	112, 148

—CH₂CCO₂C₂H₅
    |
    CN
    |
    NHCOCH₃
	172–178	—	—	43

—CH₂CHCO₂H
    |
    NHCOC₆H₁₁
	222–223	—	—	112

Table 5-3 (Contd.)

I. Ferrocene Derivatives

SUBSTITUENT	M.P.	B.P.	REFRACTIVE INDEX	LITERATURE REFERENCE
G. Alkylcarboxylic Acids, Esters, Amides, and Nitriles. Amino Acids (Contd.)				
—CH₂CHCO₂H NHCOC₆H₅	185–187	—	—	148
—CH=CCO₂H NHCOC₆H₅	218–219	—	—	14, 16, 112, 148
1,1'—CH₂CO₂H	140–143	—	—	136
1,1'—CH₂CO₂CH₃	—	Oil[c]	—	136
1,1'—CH₂CN (morpholine) 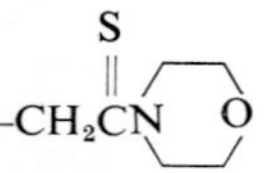	200 (dec.)	—	—	136
1,1'—(CH₂)₂CO₂H	142–145	—	—	150, 151
1,1'—(CH₂)₂CO₂C₂H₅	—	190–210/0.5	—	150, 151
1,1'—(CH₂)₃CO₂H	110–113	—	—	80, 141, 142, 151
1,1'—(CH₂)₃CO₂CH₃	16.5–17.5	200–210/0.2, 148/10⁻⁴	—	80, 150, 151
1,1'—(CH₂)₄CO₂H	151–155	—	—	151
1,1'—(CH₂)₄CO₂CH₃	—	210–215/0.3	—	151
1—(CH₂)₃CO₂H, 1'—(CH₂)₄CO₂H	84–86	—	—	150, 151
1—CH₂CH₃, 2—CH₂CO₂H	124–125	—	—	66
1—CH₂CH₃, 2—CH₂CN	—	Oil[c]	—	66

—CH₂Li[d]	—	—	—	94
—CH₂SCN	—	—	59–61	91
—CH₂SCH₂—	—	—	107–108 (dec.)	103
—CH₂SSCH₂—	—	—	125–127 (dec.)	103
—CH₂Si(CH₃)₃	—	—	46.5–47.5	94
—CH₂SO₃Na	—	—	>200°	91
—CH₂$\overset{+}{P}$(C₆H₅)₃ I⁻	—	—	254–256	120
—CHCOC₆H₅ I⁻	—	—	176–179	120
$\overset{+}{P}$(C₆H₅)₃ / =CCOC₆H₅	—	—	193–196	120
=P(C₆H₅)₃ / —CHCO— I⁻ / $\overset{+}{P}$(C₆H₅)₃	—	—	200–203	120
—CCO— / =P(C₆H₅)₃	—	—	201–203	120
1,1'—CH₂— (ferrocene)	—	—	166–168	119
—CH₂P(C₆H₅)₂	—	—	85–87	120
—CH₂$\overset{+}{P}$(C₆H₅)₂ I⁻ / CH₃	—	—	201–202	120
—CH₂— (thiophene)	—	—	60–62	155

189

Table 5-3 (Contd.)
I. Ferrocene Derivatives

SUBSTITUENT	M.P.	B.P.	REFRACTIVE INDEX	LITERATURE REFERENCE
H. Miscellaneous Derivatives (Contd.)				
1,1'—CH₂— (thienyl)	61–63	—	—	155
—CH₂SO₂—	175–180 (dec.)	—	—	122
—CH(OH)— (thienyl)	70–72	—	—	155
1,1'—CH(OH)— (thienyl)	100–105	—	—	155
—CH₂— (thienyl—CH₂CH₃)	—	115–120/0.001	—	155
1-(CH₂)₄CH₃, 1'—CH₂— (thienyl)	—	180–190/0.4	—	155
(isoxazole)	110–112	—	—	157
(pyrazole)	148–152	—	—	157

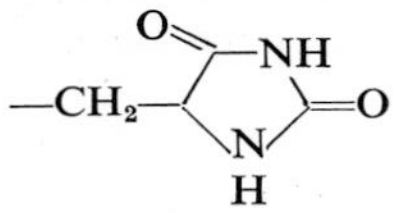

148

148

115

59

22
22, 48

22, 48

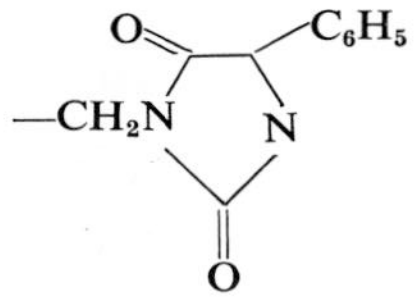

—

—

—

—

— —

—

—

—

Red oil[c]

—

II. Ruthenocene Derivatives

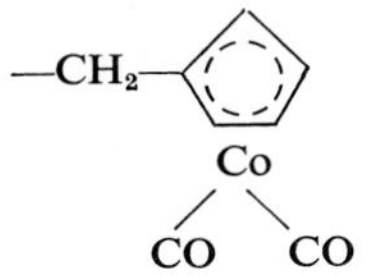

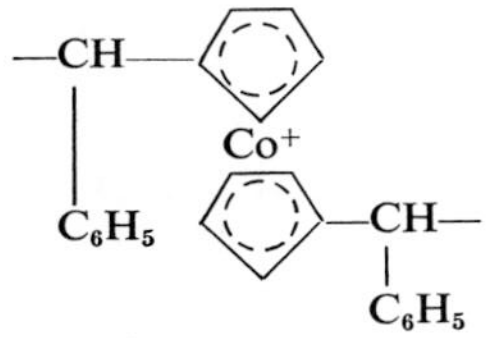

—
—

—

217–219

>300°

—

—[c]

51–52
64–64.2

64–64.5

ClO_4^-

—NH, O, N, H, CH₂ (hydantoin structure)

C_6H_5 / N, O, N, CH₂, O (phenyl hydantoin structure)

benzyl—Co(CO)₃ structure

Co⁺ with —CH—C_6H_5 and —CH—C_6H_5 substituents

—CH=CH₂
—CHCH₃, —OH

—CHCH₃, OCOCH₃

191

Table 5-3 (Contd.)
I. Ruthenocene Derivatives

SUBSTITUENT	M.P.	B.P.	REFRACTIVE INDEX	LITERATURE REFERENCE
—CHC$_6$H$_5$ / OH	105.6–106.2	—	—	19, 20
—CHOCH— / C$_6$H$_5$ C$_6$H$_5$	158.6–159.2	—	—	20
—CHC$_6$H$_5$ / N$_3$	48.5–50.0	—	—	19
III. Osmocene Derivatives				
—CH=CH$_2$	59–59.5	—	—	22
—CHCH$_3$ / OH	75.0–75.3	—	—	22, 48
—CHCH$_3$ / OCOCH$_3$	65.5–76.0	—	—	22, 48
—CHC$_6$H$_5$ / OH	115.7–116.0	—	—	20
IV. Nickelocene Derivatives				
1,1'—CH(CH$_3$)$_2$	—	128/0.3	—	59
1,1'—C(CH$_3$)$_2$C$_6$H$_5$	109–110	—	—	59

a Structure uncertain.
b Structure given is incorrect.
c No data given.

REFERENCES

1. Arimoto, F. S., and A. C. Haven, *J. Am. Chem. Soc.*, **77**, 6295 (1955).
2. Baddeley, G., *Quart. Rev.*, **8**, 355 (1954).
3. Baggett, H. N., A. B. Foster, A. H. Haines, and M. Stacey, *J. Chem. Soc.*, 3528 (1960).
4. Baltzly, R., *J. Am. Chem. Soc.*, **65**, 1984 (1943).
5. Barben, I. K., *J. Chem. Soc.*, 1827 (1961).
6. Beckwith, A. L. J., and R. J. Leydon, *Tetrahedron Letters*, **6**, 385 (1963).
7. Benkeser, R. A., W. P. Fitzgerald, and M. S. Meltzer, *J. Org. Chem.*, **26**, 2569 (1961).
8. Benkeser, R. A., and W. P. Fitzgerald, *J. Org. Chem.*, **26**, 4179 (1961).
8a. Benkeser, R. A., and J. L. Bach, *J. Am. Chem. Soc.*, **86**, 890 (1964).
9. Benson, R. E., and R. V. Lindsay, *J. Am. Chem. Soc.*, **79**, 5471 (1957).
10. Berger, A., J. Kleinberg, and W. E. MeEwen, *Chem. & Ind.* (*London*), 204 (1960).
11. Berger, A., J. Kleinberg, and W. E. McEwen, *Chem. & Ind.* (*London*), 1245 (1960).
12. Berger, A., W. E. McEwen, and J. Kleinberg, *J. Am. Chem. Soc.*, **83**, 2274 (1961).
13. Boichard, J., and M. Delepine, *Compt. Rend.*, **253**, 2702 (1961).
14. Broadhead, G. D., J. M. Osgerby, and P. L. Pauson, *Chem. & Ind.* (*London*), 209 (1957).
15. Boyer, J. H., and F. C. Canter, *Chem. Rev.*, **54**, 26 (1954).
16. Broadhead, G. D., J. M. Osgerby, and P. L. Pauson, *Chem. & Ind.* (*London*), 209 (1957).
17. Broadhead, G. D., J. M. Osgerby, and P. L. Pauson, *J. Chem. Soc.*, 650 (1958).
18. Brown, B. R., and A. M. S. White, *J. Chem. Soc.*, 3755 (1957).
19. Bublitz, D. E., J. Kleinberg, and W. E. McEwen, *Chem. & Ind.* (*London*), 936 (1960).
20. Bublitz, D. E., W. E. McEwen, and J. Kleinberg, *J. Am. Chem. Soc.*, **84**, 1845 (1962).
21. Buell, G. R., W. E. McEwen, and J. Kleinberg, *Tetrahedron Letters*, No. 5, 16 (1959).
22. Buell, G. R., W. E. McEwen, and J. Kleinberg, *J. Am. Chem. Soc.*, **84**, 40 (1962).
23. Bunton, C. A., and A. Konasiewicz, *J. Chem. Soc.*, 1354 (1955).
24. Cais, M., and M. Feldkimel, *Tetrahedron Letters*, 444 (1961).
25. Cottes, S. G., and H. Rosenberg, *Chem. & Ind.* (*London*), 860 (1963).
26. Dabard, R., and B. Gautheron, *Compt. Rend.*, **254**, 2014 (1962).
27. Day, L. A., Brit. Pat. 864,198 (March 29, 1961); *C. A.*, **55**, 17647 (1961).
28. DeBelder, A. N., E. J. Bourne, and J. B. Piedham, *J. Chem. Soc.*, 4464 (1961).
29. DeYoung, E. L., *J. Org. Chem.*, **26**, 1312 (1961).
30. Drefahl, G., G. Plötner, and I. Winnefeld, *Ber.*, **95**, 2788 (1962).
31. Furdik, M., S. Toma, and J. Suchy, *Chem. Zvesti*, **15**, 547 (1961).
32. Furdik, M., S. Toma, and J. Suchy, *Chem. Zvesti*, **16**, 719 (1962).
33. Goldberg, S. I., *J. Am. Chem. Soc.*, **84**, 3022 (1962).
34. Gough, S. T. D., and S. Trippett, *J. Chem. Soc.*, 2333 (1962).
35. Graham, P. J., R. V. Lindsey, G. W. Parshal, M. L. Peterson, and G. M. Whitman *J. Am. Chem. Soc.*, **79**, 3416 (1957).
36. Hallam, B. F., and P. L. Pauson, *J. Chem. Soc.*, 3030 (1956).
37. Hall, D. W., and J. H. Richards, *J. Org. Chem.*, **28**, 1549 (1963).
38. Hartung, W. H., and F. S. Crossley, *J. Am. Chem. Soc.*, **56**, 158 (1934).

39. Hartung, W. H., and R. Simonoff in *Organic Reactions*, Vol. VII, Wiley, New York, 1953, p. 263.
40. Hauser, C. R., and J. K. Lindsay, *J. Org. Chem.*, **21**, 382 (1956).
41. Hauser, C. R., J. K. Lindsay, D. Lednicer, and C. E. Cain, *J. Org. Chem.*, **22**, 717 (1957).
42. Hauser, C. R., and J. K. Lindsay, *J. Org. Chem.*, **22**, 906 (1957).
43. Hauser, C. R., and J. K. Lindsay, *J. Org. Chem.*, **22**, 1246 (1957).
44. Hauser, C. R., J. K. Lindsay, and D. Lednicer, *J. Org. Chem.*, **23**, 358 (1958).
45. Hauser, C. R., and C. E. Cain, *J. Org. Chem.*, **23**, 2006 (1958).
46. Hauser, C. R., and C. E. Cain, *J. Org. Chem.*, **23**, 2007 (1958).
47. Hauser, C. R., R. L. Pruett, and T. A. Mashburn, *J. Org. Chem.*, **26**, 1800 (1961).
48. Hill, E. A., and J. H. Richards, *J. Am. Chem. Soc.*, **83**, 3840 (1961).
49. Hill, E. A., and J. H. Richards, *J. Am. Chem. Soc.*, **83**, 4216 (1961).
50. Hill, E. A., *J. Org. Chem.*, **28**, 3586 (1963).
51. Hoh, G. L. K., W. E. McEwen, and J. Kleinberg, *J. Am. Chem. Soc.*, **83**, 3949 (1961).
52. Jones, W. G. M., T. Leigh, and J. L. Madinaveita, Brit. Pat. 841,710 (July 20, 1960); *C. A.*, **55**, 25173 (1961).
53. Jutz, C., *Tetrahedron Letters*, No. 21, 1 (1959).
54. Jutz, C., private communication.
55. Kantor, S. W., and C. R. Hauser, *J. Am. Chem. Soc.*, **73**, 4122 (1951).
56. Knox, G. R., and P. L. Pauson, *Proc. Chem. Soc.*, 289 (1958).
57. Knox, G. R., P. L. Pauson, and G. V. D. Tiers, *Chem. & Ind.(London)*, 1046(1959).
58. Knox, G. R., and P. L. Pauson, *J. Chem. Soc.*, 4610 (1961).
59. Knox, G. R., J. D. Munro, P. L. Pauson, G. H. Smith, and W. E. Watts, *J. Chem. Soc.*, 4619 (1961).
60. Koestler, R. C., and W. F. Little, *Chem. & Ind. (London)*, 1589 (1958).
61. Kolesnikov, G. S., V. V. Korshak, and T. V. Smirnova, *Doklady Akad. Nauk SSSR*, **126**, 307 (1959).
62. Kozikowski, J., R. E. Maginn, and M. S. Klove, *J. Am. Chem. Soc.*, **81**, 2995 (1959).
63. Kuan-Li, Wu, E. B. Sokolova, I. E. Chlenov, and A. D. Petrov, *Doklady Akad. Nauk SSSR*, **137**, 111 (1961).
64. Kuan-Li, Wu, E. B. Sokolova, L. A. Leites, and A. D. Petrov, *Izvestia Akad. Nauk SSSR, Otdel. Khim. Nauk*, 887 (1962).
65. Lednicer, D., J. K. Lindsay, and C. R. Hauser, *J. Org. Chem.*, **23**, 653 (1958).
66. Lednicer, D., and C. R. Hauser, *J. Org. Chem.*, **24**, 43 (1959).
66a. Lednicer, D., T. A. Mashburn, and C. R. Hauser, *Organic Syntheses*, Wiley, N.Y., 1960, vol. 40, p. 52.
66b. Lednicer, D. and C. R. Hauser, *Organic Syntheses*, Wiley, N.Y., 1960, vol. 40, p. 31.
66c. Lednicer, D. and C. R. Hauser, *Organic Syntheses*, Wiley, N.Y., 1960, vol. 40, p. 45.
67. Leigh, T., Brit. Pat. 819,108 (August 26, 1959); *C. A.*, **54**, 7732 (1960).
68. Leigh, T., Brit. Pat. 828,965 (Feb. 24, 1960); *C. A.*, **54**, 15402 (1960).
69. Leigh, T., Brit. Pat. 869,058 (May, 25, 1961); *C. A.*, **56**, 3516 (1962).
70. Leigh, T., Brit. Pat. 869,504 (May 31, 1961); *C. A.*, **55**, 24790 (1961).
71. Leigh, T., Brit. Pat. 870,949 (June 21, 1961); *C. A.*, **56**, 3517 (1962).
72. Lindsay, J. K., and C. R. Hauser, *J. Org. Chem.*, **22**, 355 (1957).
73. Little, W. F., and R. C. Koestler, *J. Am. Chem. Soc.*, **26**, 3247 (1961).

74. Little, W. F., and R. C. Koestler, *J. Org. Chem.*, **26**, 3245 (1961).
75. Loev, B., and M. Flores, *J. Org. Chem.*, **26**, 3595 (1961).
76. Luttringhaus, A., and W. Kulick, *Angew. Chem.*, **70**, 438 (1958).
77. Mashburn, T. A., and C. R. Hasuer, *J. Org. Chem.*, **26**, 1671 (1961).
78. Nesmeyanov, A. N., and N. A. Vol'kenau, *Doklady Akad. Nauk SSSR*, **107**, 262 (1956).
79. Nesmeyanov, A. N., and N. S. Kochetkova, *Doklady Akad. Nauk SSSR*, **109**, 543 (1956).
80. Nesmeyanov, A. N. et al., *Doklady Akad. Nauk SSSR*, **111**, 368 (1956).
81. Nesmeyanov, A. N., and N. A. Vol'kenau, *Doklady Akad. Nauk SSSR*, **111**, 605 (1956).
82. Nesmeyanov, A. N., and I. I. Kritskaya, *Izvestia Akad. Nauk SSSR, Otdel. Khim. Nauk*, 253 (1956).
83. Nesmeyanov, A. N., E. G. Perevalova and Z. A. Bienoravichute, *Doklady Akad. Nauk SSSR*, **112**, 439 (1957).
84. Nesmeyanov, A. N., and N. S. Kochetkova, *Doklady Akad. Nauk SSSR*, **114**, 800 (1957).
85. Nesmeyanov, A. N., and N. S. Kochetkova, *Doklady Akad. Nauk SSSR*, **117**, 92 (1957).
86. Nesmeyanov, A. N., L. A. Kazitsina, B. V. Lokshin, and I. I. Kritskaya, *Doklady Akad. Nauk SSSR*, **117**, 433 (1957).
87. Nesmeyanov, A. N., N. A. Vol'kenau, and V. D. Vilchenskaya, *Doklady Akad. Nauk SSSR*, **118**, 512 (1958).
88. Nesmeyanov, A. N., E. G. Perevalova et al., *Doklady Akad. Nauk SSSR*, **120**, 1263 (1958).
89. Nesmeyanov, A. N., E. G. Perevalova et al., *Doklady Akad. Nauk SSSR*, **121**, 117 (1958).
90. Nesmeyanov, A. N., and N. S. Kochetkova, *Izvestia Akad. Nauk SSSR, Otdel. Khim. Nauk*, 242 (1958).
91. Nesmeyanov, A. N., E. G. Perevalova, L. S. Shiloutzeva, and Yu A. Ustynyuk, *Doklady Akad. Nauk SSSR*, **124**, 331 (1959).
92. Nesmeyanov, A. N., and N. S. Kochetkova, *Doklady Akad. Nauk SSSR*, **126**, 307 (1959).
93. Nesmeyanov, A. N., V. A. Sazonova, V. N. Drozd, and L. A. Nikonova, *Doklady Akad. Nauk SSSR*, **133**, 126 (1960).
94. Nesmeyanov, A. N., E. G. Perevalova, and Yu A. Ustynyuk, *Doklady Akad. Nauk SSSR*, **133**, 1105 (1960).
95. Nesmeyanov, A. N. et al., *Izvestia Akad. Nauk SSSR, Otdel. Khim. Nauk*, 554 (1960).
96. Nesmeyanov, A. N., N. S. Kochetkova, and R. B. Materikova, *Doklady Akad. Nauk SSSR*, **136**, 1096 (1961).
97. Nesmeyanov, A. N. et al., *Doklady Akad. Nauk SSSR*, **139**, 888 (1961).
98. Nesmeyanov, A. N., E. G. Perevalova, and L. S. Shilovtseva, *Izvestia Akad. Nauk SSSR, Otdel. Khim. Nauk*, 1982 (1961).
99. Nesmeyanov, A. N., and I. I. Kritskaya, *Izvestia Akad. Nauk SSSR, Otdel. Khim. Nauk*, 352 (1962).
100. Nesmeyanov, A. N., E. G. Perevalova, and L. S. Shilovtseva, *Izvestia Akad. Nauk SSSR, Otdel. Khim. Nauk*, 1767 (1962).
101. Nesmeyanov, A. N., I. I. Kritskaya, and T. V. Antipina, *Izvestia Akad. Nauk SSSR, Otdel. Khim. Nauk*, 1777 (1962).

102. Nesmeyanov, A. N. et al., *Izvestia Akad. Nauk SSSR, Otdel. Khim. Nauk,* 1990 (1962).
103. Nesmeyanov, A. N., E. G. Perevalova, L. S. Shilovtseva, and V. D. Tyurin, *Izvestia Akad. Nauk SSSR,* 1997 (1962).
104. Nesmeyanov, A. N., E. G. Perevalova, L. P. Yur'eva, and L. I. Denisovich, *Izvestia Akad. Nauk SSSR, Otdel. Khim. Nauk,* 2241 (1962).
105. Nesmeyanov, A. N., N. S. Kochetkova, P. V. Petrovskii, and E. I. Fedin, *Doklady Akad. Nauk SSSR,* **152,** 875 (1963).
106. Nesmeyanov, A. N. et al., *Izvestia Akad. Nauk SSSR, Otdel. Khim. Nauk,* 667 (1963).
107. Neuse, E. W., and D. S. Trifan, *J. Am. Chem. Soc.,* **84,** 1850 (1962).
108. Nystrom, R. F., and C. R. A. Berger, *J. Am. Chem. Soc.,* **80,** 2896 (1958).
109. Perevalova, E. G., Yu. A. Ustynyuk, and A. N. Nesmeyanov, *Izvestia Akad. Nauk SSSR, Ordel. Khim. Nauk,* 1036 (1963).
110. Perevalova, E. G., *Izvestia Akad. Nauk SSSR, Otdel. Khim. Nauk,* 1045 (1963).
111. Pruett, R. L., and E. L. Morehouse, Ger. Pat. 1,052,401 (March 12, 1959); *C. A.,* **55,** 18770 (1961).
112. Osgerby, J. M., and P. L. Pauson, *J. Chem. Soc.,* 656 (1958).
113. Osgerby, J. M., and P. L. Pauson, *Chem. & Ind. (London),* 196 (1958).
114. Osgerby, J. M., and P. L. Pauson, *J. Chem. Soc.,* 4600 (1961).
115. Osgerby, J. M., and P. L. Pauson, *J. Chem. Soc.,* 4604 (1961).
116. Paushkin, Y. M. et al., *Neftkhimiya,* **3,** 280 (1963).
117. Pauson, P. L., *J. Am. Chem. Soc.,* **76,** 2187 (1954).
118. Pauson, P. L., *Quarterly Reviews,* No. 4 (1955), p. 391.
119. Pauson, P. L., and W. E. Watts, *J. Chem. Soc.,* 3880 (1962).
120. Pauson, P. L., and W. E. Watts, *J. Chem. Soc.,* 2990 (1963).
121. Pauson, P. L., and W. E. Watts, unpublished results.
122. Perevalova, E. G., O. A. Nesmeyanova, and I. G. Lukyanova, *Doklady Akad. Nauk SSSR,* **132,** 853 (1960).
123. Plesske, K., and J. H. Richards, unpublished results.
124. Plesske, K., U. Shah, and J. H. Richards, unpublished results.
125. Pruett, R. L., Ger. Pat. 1,098, 713 (November 12, 1959); *C. A.,* **55,** 17648 (1961).
126. Pruett, R. L., U.S. Pat. 2,947,769 (August 2, 1960); *C. A.,* **55,** 565 (1961).
127. Pruett, R. L., Brit. Pat. 845, 499 (August 24, 1960); *C. A.,* **55,** 9427 (1961).
128. Rausch, M. D., M. Vogel, and H. Rosenberg, *J. Org. Chem.,* **22,** 903 (1957).
129. Rausch, M. D., and L. E. Coleman, *J. Org. Chem.,* **23,** 107 (1958).
130. Reynolds, L. T., and G. Wilkinson, *J. Inorg. and Nucl. Chem.,* **9,** 86 (1959).
131. Richards, J. H., and E. A. Hill, *J. Am. Chem. Soc.,* **81,** 3484 (1959).
132. Riemschneider, R., and D. Helm, *Ber.,* **89,** 155 (1956).
133. Riemschneider, R., and R. Nehring, *Monatsh.,* **90,** 568 (1959).
134. Riemschneider, R., and D. Helm, *Ann.,* **646,** 10 (1961).
135. Rinehart, K. L., K. L. Motz, and S. Moon, *J. Am. Chem. Soc.,* **79,** 2749 (1957).
136. Rinehart, K. L., R. J. Curby, and P. E. Sokol, *J. Am. Chem. Soc.,* **79,** 3420 (1957).
137. Rinehart, K. L., C. J. Michejda, and P. A. Kittle, *J. Am. Chem. Soc.,* **81,** 3162 (1959).
137a. Rinehart, K. L., C. J. Michejda, and P. A. Kittle, *Angew. Chem.,* **72,** 38 (1960).
138. Rinehart, K. L., P. A. Kittle, and A. F. Ellis, *J. Am. Chem. Soc.,* **82,** 2082 (1960).
139. Rinehart, K. L. et al., *J. Am. Chem. Soc.,* **82,** 4111 (1960).
140. Rinehart, K. L., A. F. Ellis, C. J. Michejda, and P. A. Kittle, *J. Am. Chem. Soc.,* **82** 4112 (1960).

141. Rinehart, K. L., R. J. Curby, D. H. Gustafson, K. G. Harrison, R. E. Bozak, and D. E. Bublitz, *J. Am. Chem. Soc.*, **84**, 3263 (1962).
142. Rosenblum, M., Thesis, Harvard University, 1953.
143. Rosenblum, M., and R. B. Woodward, *J. Am. Chem. Soc.*, **80**, 5443 (1958).
144. Rosenblum, M., A. K. Banerjee, N. Danieli, R. W. Fish, and V. Schlatter, *J. Am. Chem. Soc.*, **85**, 316 (1963).
145. Rosenblum, M., and R. W. Fish, unpublished results.
146. Schaaf, R. L., *J. Org. Chem.*, **27**, 107 (1962).
147. Schenck, G. O. et al., *Angew. Chem.*, **74**, 510 (1962).
148. Schlögl, K., *Monatsh. Chem.*, **88**, 601 (1957).
149. Schlögl, K., and H. Seiler, *Tetrahedron Letters*, No. 7, 4 (1960).
150. Schlögl, K., and H. Seiler, *Angew. Chem.*, **72**, 38 (1960).
151. Schlögl, K., and H. Seiler, *Monatsh. Chem.*, **91**, 79 (1960).
152. Schlögl, K., and A. Mohar, *Monatsh. Chem.*, **92**, 219 (1961).
153. Schlögl, K., A. Mohar, and M. Peterlik, *Monatsch. Chem.*, **92**, 921 (1961).
154. Schlögl, K., and A. Mohar, *Naturwiss.*, **9**, 376 (1961).
155. Schlögl, K., and H. Pelousek, *Ann.*, **651**, 1 (1962).
156. Schlögl, K., and M. Peterlik, *Tetrahedron Letters*, **13**, 573 (1962).
157. Schlögl, K., and A. Mohar, *Monatsh. Chem.*, **93**, 861 (1962).
158. Schlögl, K., and H. Egger, *Monatsh. Chem.*, **94**, 376 (1963).
159. Schlögl, K., and M. Fried, *Tetrahedron Letters*, **22**, 1473 (1963).
160. Schlögl, K., and M. Fried, *Monatsch. Chem.*, **94**, 537 (1963).
161. Struchkov, Yu T., *Zh. Obshch. Khim.*, **27**, 2039 (1952).
162. Sugiyama, N., H. Suzuki, Y. Shioura, and T. Teitei, *Bull. Chem. Soc. Japan*, **35**, 767 (1962).
163. Sweeney, W. M., U.S. Pat. 3,035,075 (May 15, 1962).
164. Taylor, R., *Chem. & Ind.* (*London*), 1684 (1962).
165. Thomas, C. A., *Anhydrous Aluminum Chloride in Organic Chemistry*, Reinhold, New York, 1941, pp. 110, 815.
166. Thompson, J. B., *Chem. & Ind.* (*London*), 1122 (1959).
167. Tirouflet, J., R. Dabard, and B. Gatheron, *Compt. Rend.*, **256**, 1315 (1963).
168. Trifan, D. S., and L. Nicholas, *J. Am. Chem. Soc.*, **79**, 2746 (1957).
169. Trifan, D. S., J. L. Weinmann, and L. P. Kuhn, *J. Am. Chem. Soc.*, **79**, 6566 (1957).
170. Trifan, D. S., and R. Bacskai, *Tetrahedron Letters*, **13**, 1 (1960).
171. Trifan, D. S., and R. Bacskai, *J. Am. Chem. Soc.*, **82**, 5010 (1960).
172. Ushenko, I. K., K. D. Zhikhareva, and R. Z. Rodova, *Zh. Obshch. Khim.*, **33**, 798 (1963).
173. Utyanskaya, E. Z., *Zh. Fiz. Khim.*, **35**, 2611 (1961).
174. Vogel, M., M. D. Rausch, and H. Rosenberg, *J. Org. Chem.*, **22**, 1016 (1957).
175. Walling, C., *Free Radicals in Solution*, Wiley, New York, 1957, p. 402.
176. Weinmayr, V., *J. Am. Chem. Soc.*, **77**, 3009 (1955).
177. Weinmayr, V., U.S. Pat. 2,831,879 (April 22, 1958); *C. A.*, **52**, 16367 (1958).
178. Weliky, N., and E. S. Gould, *J. Am. Chem. Soc.*, **79**, 2742 (1957).
179. West, R. et al., *J. Am. Chem. Soc.*, **84**, 3221 (1962).
180. Westman, L., and K. L. Rinehart, *Acta Chim. Scand.*, **16**, 1199 (1962).
181. Wilds, A. L. in *Organic Reactions*, Vol. II, Wiley, New York, 1944, p. 178.
182. Woodward, R. B., and E. Csendes, unpublished results, quoted by P. L. Pauson, reference 117.

6 Arylmetallocenes—radical substitution reactions

With the exception of a single brief reference to a substance believed to be phenylruthenocene (39), all of the arylmetallocenes recorded thus far in the literature are derived from ferrocene. These are listed in Table 6-5 (pages 219–232). There is no reason to believe that the corresponding derivatives of ruthenocene and osmocene are not preparable, but apparently little effort has been directed to this end.

METHODS OF SYNTHESIS

From substituted cyclopentadienes

In 1954 Pauson reported the preparation of a number of phenylferrocenes from phenylcyclopentadienyl Grignard and lithium reagents by an adaptation of the method he had employed for the synthesis of ferrocene itself (35). The method was shown to be applicable to the synthesis of highly substituted derivatives such as 1,2,4,1′,2′,4′-hexaphenylferrocene (1) and, by employing a mixture of cyclopentadienides, to the synthesis of unsymmetrical derivatives as well. The preparation of phenylferrocene (2) is illustrative of this latter procedure. Although 1,2,3-triphenyl- and 1,2,3,4-tetraphenylcyclopentadiene failed to give any ferrocene derivative with the Grignard reagent, Weinmayr (57) was able to convert the latter compound to octaphenylferrocene (3) by generating the cyclopentadienide with sodamide in liquid ammonia.

Those methods in which iron carbonyl is employed in the synthesis of ferrocene have been successfully adopted for the preparation of arylferrocenes. Hallam and Pauson (8) have described the preparation of 1,3,1′,3′-tetraphenylferrocene (4) by heating iron carbonyl in the presence of

198

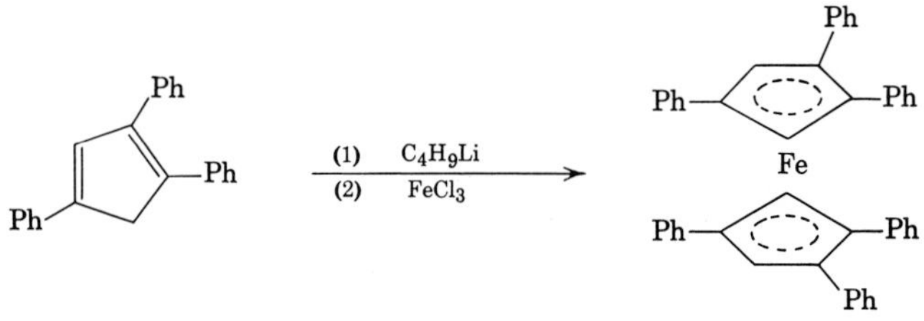
Ph
Ph
Ph
(1) C4H9Li
(2) FeCl3
Ph
Ph
Ph
Fe
Ph
Ph
Ph

(1)

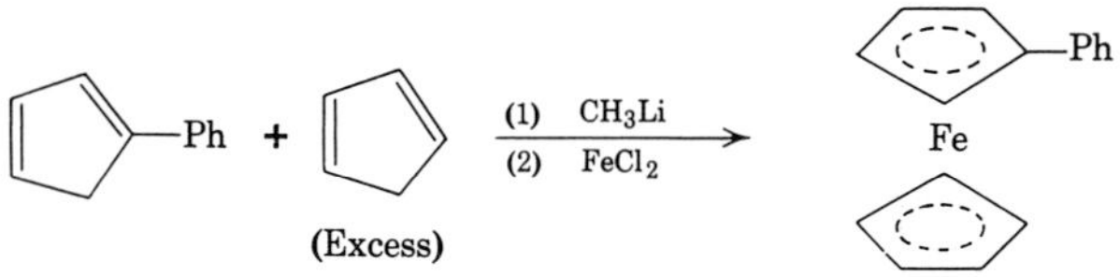
Ph
+
(Excess)
(1) CH3Li
(2) FeCl2
Ph
Fe

(2)

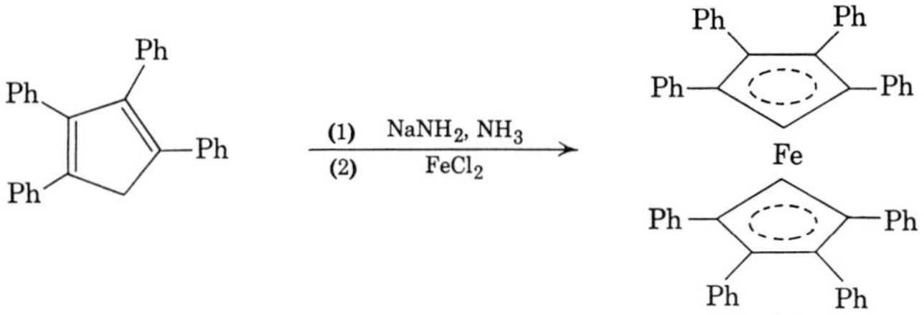
Ph
Ph
Ph
Ph
(1) NaNH2, NH3
(2) FeCl2
Ph
Ph
Ph
Ph
Fe
Ph
Ph
Ph
Ph

(3)

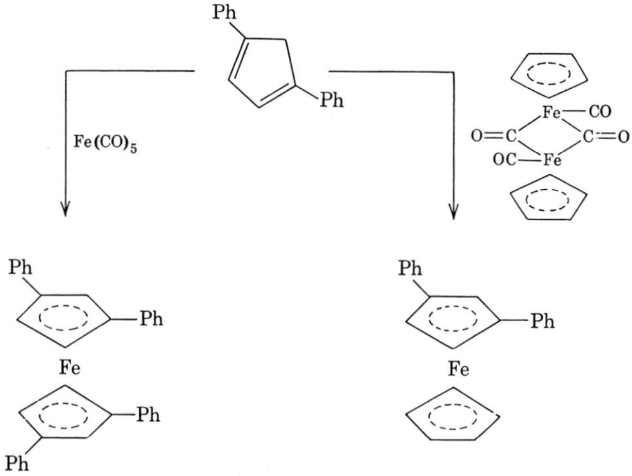
Ph
Ph
Fe(CO)5
Fe
CO
O=C
C=O
OC
Fe
Ph
Ph
Fe
Ph
Ph
Ph
Ph
Fe

(4) (5)

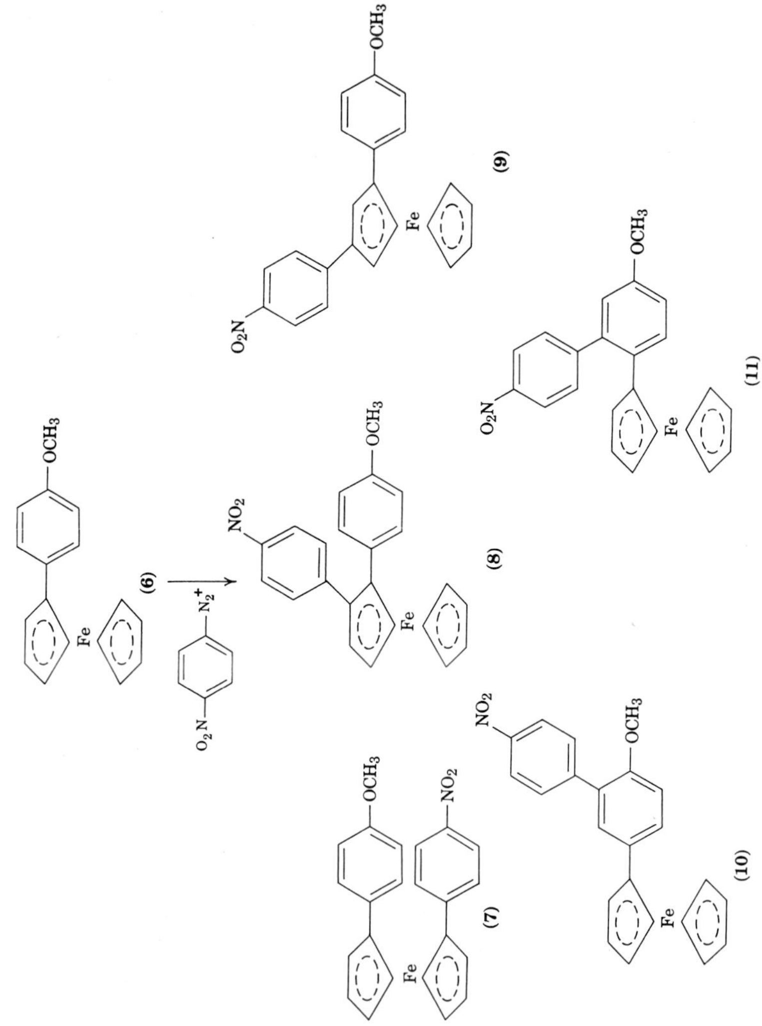
OCH3
Fe
(6)
O2N
N2+
NO2
(8)
(9)
(7)
(10)
(11)

1,3-diphenylcyclopentadiene. The structurally related disubstituted derivative (5) was similarly prepared by heating the diene in the presence of biscyclopentadienyldiiron tetracarbonyl.

Although these general synthetic procedures are now infrequently employed, owing to the discovery of the more direct arylation reactions, they are still of considerable value for the rational synthesis of poly-arylferrocenes (48).

Reaction of ferrocene with aryldiazonium salts

General Aspects. The reaction of ferrocene with aryldiazonium salts constitutes the most convenient and generally applicable procedure for the synthesis of arylferrocenes. These reactions may be carried out either in aqueous acetic acid or acetone solutions (4, 38, 48, 53, 56), in a biphasic water-ether mixture (21, 22, 25), or in chlorohydrocarbon solvents (14). Under these conditions the products are primarily monoarylferrocenes.

$$C_{10}H_{10}Fe + ArN_2^+ \rightarrow C_{10}H_9ArFe + C_{10}H_{10-n}Ar_nFe + N_2 + H^+$$

An alternative procedure, which appears to give somewhat better yields of more highly arylated products, consists in treating an aqueous ferricenium salt solution, containing a small amount of ferrocene, with an aryldiazonium salt. As we shall see, the mechanisms of these apparently disparate reactions are almost certainly identical.

Although the diarylferrocenes formed in the arylation reactions are principally the 1,1' isomers, there is little doubt that the 1,2 and 1,3 isomers are also generated, ofttimes in considerable amount (48). However, the formation of these isomers has not been commonly noted since their isolation requires somewhat more painstaking chromatographic separation procedures than have generally been applied. In addition to these substances, biarylferrocenes have also been isolated (36, 48), and these are generally accompanied by varying amounts of other side reaction products, evidently derived by radical processes, such as biphenyls, the deaminated aromatic amine and azo compounds (22, 48). The arylation of *p*-methoxyphenylferrocene (6) with *p*-nitrophenyldiazonium sulfate provides an example of a reaction from which all five isomeric diaryl- and biphenylyl type ferrocenes (7 to 11) have been isolated (48).

Little, Nielsen, and Williams (15) have recently described the preparation of derivatives such as 12 to 14 by treatment of ferrocene with bisdiazonium salts derived from *m*-phenylenediamine, benzidine, and 1,8-diaminonaphthalene respectively.

Mechanism of the Arylation Reaction. The initial step in the arylation reaction appears to be an electron-transfer reaction between ferrocene and

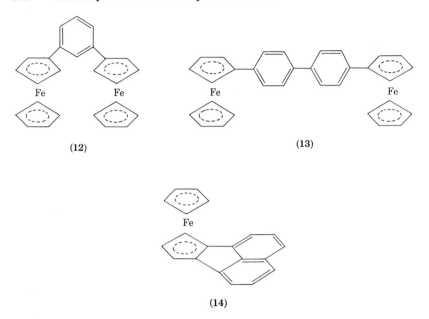

the diazonium salt, leading to the formation of a ferricenium cation and an arylazo radical (equation 1). Such an electron-transfer process is, of course, a commonly encountered aspect of the chemistry of the metallocenes. Moreover, the presence of the oxidized metallocene at the conclusion of these reactions has been demonstrated in a number of instances. There seems little doubt also that aryl radicals, derived by loss of nitrogen from the arylazo radicals, are likewise formed in these reactions. The isolation of biaryls and the deaminated aromatic amine speaks convincingly for the presence of such species (22, 48).

$$Fe + ArN_2^+ \longrightarrow Fe^+ + ArN_2 \cdot \qquad (1)$$

Little (11, 14) and Beckwith (1) have suggested that ring substitution occurs by initial coupling of the ferricenium ion, which is also a radical, with an aryl radical (equation 2). The resulting cation complex (15), which is structurally indistinguishable from the intermediate postulated in electrophilic substitutions (Chapter 4), may then similarly rearrange to the

$$\text{Fe} + + \text{Ar} \cdot \longrightarrow + \text{Fe} - \text{Ar} \tag{2}$$

$$(15)$$

$$+ \text{Fe} - \text{Ar} \longrightarrow \underset{\text{Fe}}{\overset{\text{H}}{+}}\text{Ar} \xrightarrow{-\text{H}^+} \underset{\text{Fe}}{} - \text{Ar} \tag{3}$$

$$(15) \qquad\qquad (16)$$

endocyclic sigma complex (16) and lose a proton to give the observed product (equation 3).*

Pauson's observation (36) that arylferrocenes are not formed by treatment of ferricenium salt solutions with aryldiazonium salts, except in the presence of small amounts of ferrocene is, of course, readily accounted for by this reaction sequence, since the neutral metallocene is required to initiate decomposition of the diazonium salt.

Arylation of Substituted Ferrocenes. The phenylation of methyl- and ethylferrocene has been carried out and, not unexpectedly, found to give mixtures of mono- and polyphenylalkylferrocenes (38). Only from methylferrocene was a pure substance isolated, and this was identified as 1-methyl-1'-phenylferrocene.

* While there seems little doubt that aryl radicals are formed in these reactions, some question has been raised as to whether these species are inevitably responsible for the formation of arylferrocenes in the reaction of ferrocene with diazonium salts. It has been suggested (48) that the arylferrocenes arise instead through decomposition of a ferrocene-diazonium salt complex (17) in which loss of nitrogen takes place concurrently with ring substitution by the aryl radical. However, in view of the fact that

$$+ \text{Fe} \rightarrow \text{N}_2\text{Ar}$$

$$(17)$$

the ferricenium ion has been shown to be susceptible to radical attack (page 204), such a reaction path does not appear necessary, although the ratio of mono- to diarylferrocenes obtained by Weinmayr (57) in the reaction of ferricenium solutions with a series of diazonium salts seems better in accord with it (48).

Ferrocene derivatives bearing electron withdrawing substituents are not readily arylated. Acetylferrocene, carbomethoxyferrocene, and 1,1'-dicarbomethoxyferrocene afford low yields of monoarylated products on treatment with p-nitrophenyldiazonium salts (38), while diacetyl-, dipropionyl-, dibutyryl-, and dibenzoylferrocene (18) give only arylazo-fulvenes (19) (3, 26, 28, 38).* These latter substances probably arise by coupling of the diazonium salt with an acylcyclopentadiene, which is formed by decomposition of the initially generated acylferricenium ion. The azo compounds derived from the reaction of diacetylferrocene with either phenyl- or p-nitrophenyldiazonium salts have been shown to be identical with those obtained by treatment of acetylcyclopentadiene enol acetate (20) with the corresponding diazonium salts (28).

$(R = CH_3, C_2H_5, C_3H_7, C_6H_5)$

Radical Substitution of the Ferricenium Cation. More direct evidence for the reaction of the ferricenium cation with free radicals has recently been provided by Beckwith and Leydon (1), who observed the formation of 2-cyano-2-ferrocenylpropane (22) with azobisisobutyronitrile was decomposed in aqueous ethanol in the presence of the cation.

* These substances were first formulated as 1,2,3-oxadiazine derivatives (21 or its double bond isomers) by Nesmeyanov (28), but were later shown by Bozak and Rinehart (3) to have the structure 19.

(21)

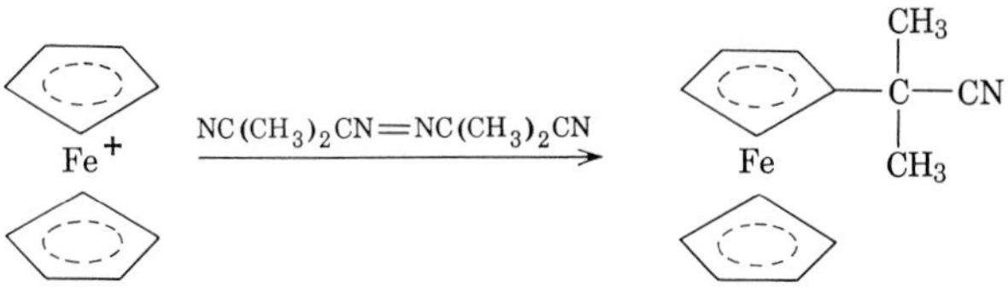

$$\text{Fe}^+ \xrightarrow{\text{NC(CH}_3)_2\text{CN}=\text{NC(CH}_3)_2\text{CN}} \text{Fe}-\overset{\overset{\text{CH}_3}{|}}{\underset{\underset{\text{CH}_3}{|}}{C}}-\text{CN}$$

(22)

These authors have also reported the formation of benzylferrocene (23), in what is described as moderate yields, when toluene solutions of *t*-butyl perbenzoate were heated in the presence of ferrocene. The following reaction mechanism (equations 4, 5, 6), which is closely analogous to that set forth by Kochi (9, 10) for the copper salt catalyzed reactions of peresters, was suggested (1).

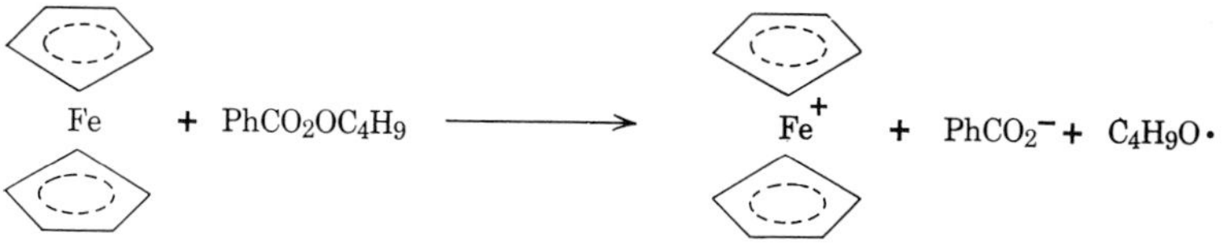

$$\text{Fe} + \text{PhCO}_2\text{OC}_4\text{H}_9 \longrightarrow \text{Fe}^+ + \text{PhCO}_2^- + \text{C}_4\text{H}_9\text{O}\cdot \quad (4)$$

$$\text{C}_6\text{H}_5\text{CH}_3 + \text{C}_4\text{H}_9\text{O}\cdot \longrightarrow \text{C}_6\text{H}_5\text{CH}_2\cdot + \text{C}_4\text{H}_9\text{OH} \quad (5)$$

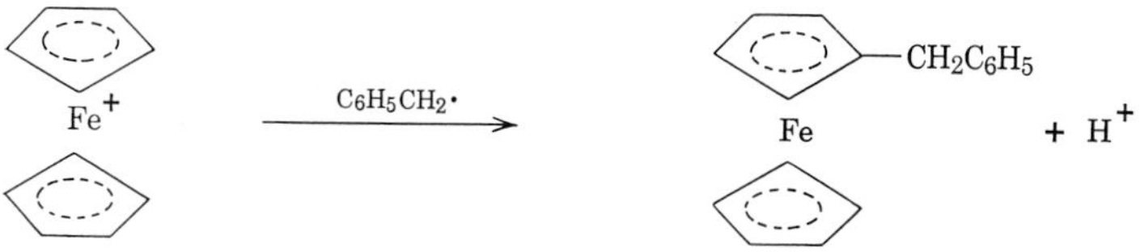

$$\text{Fe}^+ \xrightarrow{\text{C}_6\text{H}_5\text{CH}_2\cdot} \text{Fe}-\text{CH}_2\text{C}_6\text{H}_5 + \text{H}^+ \quad (6)$$

(23)

Further examples of the radical mode of substitution of ferrocene through the ferricenium ion have recently been provided by Little, Lynn, and Williams (14) in a study of the arylation reaction in halohydrocarbon solvents. When *o*-alkylbenzenediazonium salts, such as *o*-toluenediazonium, 2,6-dimethylbenzenediazonium, and mesitylenediazonium tetrafluoroborate, were allowed to react with ferrocene in methylene chloride solution, ferrocene aldehyde (24) was formed in low yield. When these reactions were carried out in chloroform, carbon tetrachloride, or bromotrichloromethane, ferrocenecarboxylic acid was formed. and, in ethylidene chloride, small amounts of acetylferrocene were isolated. None of the expected arylferrocenes were obtained from these reactions.*

* Only with *o*-toluenediazonium tetrafluoroborate in ethylene chloride was the normal product, *o*-tolylferrocene, isolated (64% yield) in addition to acetylferrocene (5% yield).

The formation of acylferrocenes and carboxylic acids can readily be accommodated in terms of the sequence exemplified by equations 7, 8, and 9 for the reaction in methylene chloride.

$$Fe + ArN_2^+ \longrightarrow Fe^+ + Ar\cdot + N_2 \qquad (7)$$

$$Ar\cdot + CH_2Cl_2 \longrightarrow ArH + CHCl_2\cdot \qquad (8)$$

$$Fe^+ \xrightarrow[-H^+]{\cdot CHCl_2} Fe{-}CHCl_2 \xrightarrow{H_2O} Fe{-}CHO \qquad (9)$$

$$(24)$$

The introduction of an electronegative group at the 4 or 6 positions of these o-alkylbenzenediazonium salts exerts a pronounced effect on the course of the reaction. For example, the diazonium salts derived from 2-methyl-6-nitroaniline and 2-methyl-4-nitroaniline gave only arylferrocenes, while with those prepared from 2,6-dimethyl-4-nitroaniline, and 2,4-dimethyl-6-nitroaniline as well as from o-iodoaniline and o-amino-biphenyl, the arylferrocenes are accompanied by small amounts of aldehyde. Thus a combination of steric and electronic factors affects a sensitive balance between aryl radical coupling with the ferricenium cation or hydrogen abstraction from the solvent. Such apparent selectivity is exceptional for aryl radicals, since these are generally regarded to be rather reactive species, but it may be that the observed selectivity is due to reversibility of the coupling reaction (equation 2). In this circumstance, bulky *ortho* substituents might be expected to retard rearrangement of the cation (**15**), while electron withdrawing substituents might suppress reversion to the radical fragments.

Nesmeyanov and co-workers (29, 32) have recently effected a direct cyanation of ferrocene and several of its derivatives by treatment with hydrogen cyanide and ferric chloride in tetrahydrofuran. Since ferrocene is rapidly oxidized to the cation and cyanide is transformed to cyanogen by ferric chloride, it seems likely that the mechanism of the cyanation

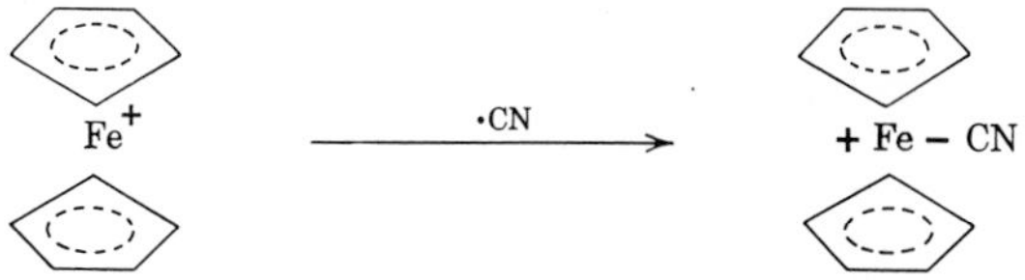

$$+ Fe - CN \qquad (10)$$

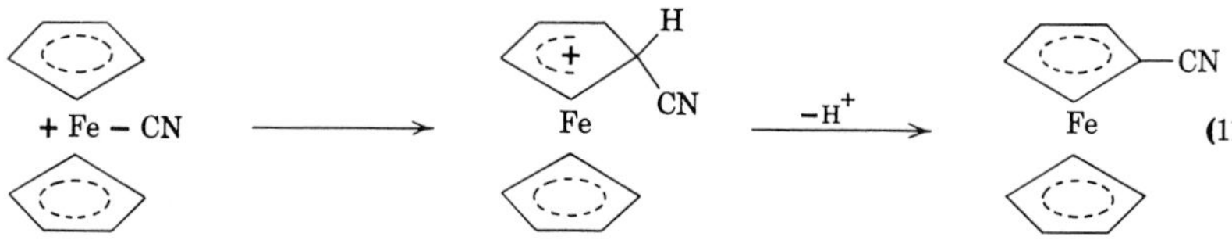

(25)

$$(11)$$

(25)   (26)

reaction (equations 10 and 11) is essentially identical with that of the arylation reaction.*

It is important to note that for both of these reactions the mechanistic distinction between radical and cationic substitution of the metallocene vanishes. We might therefore expect that the pattern of substitution for these processes in substituted ferrocenes should be identical, and largely conditioned by the relative stabilities of the isomeric σ-complexes comparable to **26**. The evidence for this conclusion, based on the results of several arylation reactions, is by no means conclusive.† However, cyanation of cyano-, acetyl-, nitro-, bromo-, and p-nitrophenylferrocene as well as ferrocenyl phenyl sulfone was found to give the 1,1′ isomers preponderantly and generally in good yield, in excellent accord with expectation and the results of Friedel-Crafts acetylation reactions (32). The fact that cyanoferrocene was found to be considerably less reactive than ferrocene in the cyanation reaction is likewise consonant with the reaction mechanism proposed.

* It was earlier suggested (49) that the radical (**27**), formed by addition of cyanide to a ferricenium ion, might be involved in the cyanation reaction rather than **25**. However, such an intermediate is improbable on energetic grounds since the odd electron would probably occupy a strongly antibonding molecular orbital as in the isoelectronic cobaltocene.

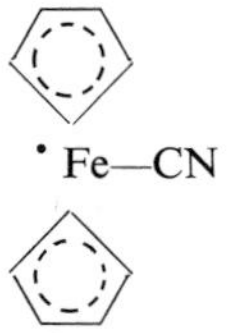

(27)

† See pages 203–204.

Radical Substitution of Ferrocene.   By contrast with the ferricenium ion, ferrocene does not appear to be particularly susceptible to attack by free radicals.   It does not react with phenyl radicals generated from phenylmagnesium bromide and cobaltous chloride (4), by treatment of benzenediazonium zincichloride with zinc powder (1), or by decomposition of phenylazotriphenylmethane in cyclohexane (4) acetic acid or trifluoroacetic acid solutions (48, 51).*   Neither does it react with 2-cyanopropyl radicals generated by decomposition of azoisobutyronitrile (1).

Although phenylferrocene is formed when *N*-nitrosoacetanilide is decomposed in cyclohexane solutions in the presence of ferrocene (4), these reactions probably involve phenyldiazonium acetate, formed by heterolytic dissociation of the intermediate phenylazoacetate (48).

The resistance of ferrocene to radical substitution is noteworthy, and suggests that either direct radical addition to the rings or indirect addition through initial attack on the metal atom is energetically prohibited. The latter mode of substitution would appear to be improbable on theoretical grounds, since the radical so generated is isoelectronic with cobaltocene and the odd electron would be required to occupy a strongly antibonding orbital.

Arylferrocenes by decomposition of diferrocenylmercury

The thermal decomposition of diaryl- or dialkylmercury compounds, which is known to give organic radicals and mercury (5), has been put to use by Rausch (40, 41) in the synthesis of phenylferrocene and of *o*- , *m*- , and *p*-biphenylferrocenes, by mixed radical coupling. The presence of silver powder is required in these reactions, and some ferrocene and diferrocenyl are also formed by hydrogen abstraction and dimerization of ferrocenyl radicals.

Use of ferrocenyllithium

Nesmeyanov, Sazonova, and Gerasimenko (33) as well as Schlögl and Fried (53) have recently reported the synthesis of mono- and 1,1'-di-α-pyridyl- as well as 2-quinolylferrocene by treatment of pyridine or

* Extensive decomposition takes place when ferrocene is heated in benzene solution in the presence of benzoyl peroxide (4, 34), but no well-defined organic products are formed.

quinoline with mono- and diferrocenyllithium. These syntheses, which are based on the analogous reactions of alkyl- and aryllithiums with pyridine (6), have also been extended by the latter authors to the preparation of the isomeric α-pyridyl-methylferrocenes (**29** to **31**) by treatment of the mixture of methylferrocenyllithium isomers with pyridine. The relative yields of isomers formed in this latter reaction was found to be in the order 1,1′ > 1,3 ≫ 1,2.

SUBSTITUTION OF ARYLFERROCENES*

Chloromercuration

The chloromercuration of arylferrocenes has not been widely examined. Although *p*-nitrophenylferrocene resists Friedel-Crafts acetylation, Nesmeyanov and co-workers (26) report that it can be chloromercurated. Oddly enough, although the conversion in this reaction is, as might be expected, low, the product is reported to be a bischloromercury derivative. The positions of the chloromercury groups were not established, but it is possible that at least one of these groups is on the benzene ring.

Sulfonation

Sulfonation of phenylferrocene with dioxane-sulfur trioxide is reported to give only phenylferrocene-1′-sulfonic acid, which was isolated in unspecified yield as the lead salt (30).

* Acylation of arylferrocenes has been treated in Chapter 4, page 74, and aminomethylation in Chapter 5, page 142.

Nitration

Nesmeyanov and co-workers (30) have carried out the nitration of phenylferrocene employing ethyl nitrate and aluminum chloride as nitrating agent. Whereas ferrocene itself is rapidly oxidized and suffers extensive decomposition even under the mildest of nitrating conditions, phenylferrocene was found to be somewhat more resistant. However, ring substitution was not observed and the sole product, formed in low yield, was p-nitrophenylferrocene.

PHYSICAL PROPERTIES OF ARYLFERROCENES

Ionization constants

The ionization constants for a series of ferrocenyl substituted benzoic acids, phenols and anilines, which have been reported by Nesmeyanov (23, 27), are given in Table 6-1. The pronounced electron donor capacity of the ferrocenyl substituent is apparent from these data, from which σ_p

Table 6-1
Ionization Constants of Ferrocenyl Substituted Acids and Bases

COMPOUND	K_A	REFERENCE
A. Benzoic Acids[a]		
Benzoic acid	8.1×10^{-8}	27
p-Ferrocenylbenzoic acid	3.7×10^{-8}	27
o-Ferrocenylbenzoic acid	6.05×10^{-8}	27
B. Phenols[b]		
Phenol	4.7×10^{-12}	23
p-Ferrocenylphenol	1.6×10^{-12}	23
p-Phenylphenol	0.91×10^{-11}	23
C. Anilines[b]		
	K_B	
Aniline	7.2×10^{-11}	23
p-Ferrocenylaniline	2.2×10^{-10}	23
m-Ferrocenylaniline	1.4×10^{-10}	23

[a] Determined in 70% dioxane at 20° C.
[b] Determined in 80% ethanol at 20° C.

and σ_m constants of -0.17 and -0.07 may be calculated for this group from the recent compilation of ρ values given by Wells (58). These may be compared with σ_p and σ_m constant values of $+0.06$ and -0.01, respectively, for the phenyl group (18). A comparison of published pK_a values for ferrocenoic and benzoic acids (2, 12, 42, 44) leads to a σ constant of -0.23 for the ferrocenyl group.

The basicities of several m- and p-ferrocenylazobenzenes, prepared by condensation of aminophenylferrocenes with substituted nitrosobenzenes (11), have been determined by Little, Berry, and Kannan (13). Both the meta and para derivatives were found to be significantly weaker bases than their unsubstituted analogs, and it has been suggested that the metallocene nucleus is protonated (on the metal atom) prior to protonation of the azo group. Values of $+0.291$ and $+0.286$ were calculated for the substituent constants, σ_p and σ_m, respectively, for the protonated metallocene group.

The ultraviolet and visible absorption spectra of these substances have also been studied (11). The p-ferrocenylazobenzenes exhibit a pronounced bathochromic shift of absorption near 350 and 450 mμ, compared with their m-isomers, reflecting the more extended conjugation in these substances.

Dipole moments

Dipole moments of 2.06 and 3.12 D have been determined for mono- and 1,1'-bis-p-chlorophenylferrocene, respectively (43, 55). The dipole moment of the disubstituted arylferrocene is about 0.2 D greater than that calculated for a free rotating ferrocene model and may possibly reflect some stabilization of conformations in which the benzene rings are partially or fully eclipsed. However, the calculated figure for the free rotating model may well be within the limits of experimental error.

Infrared spectra

Aside from the aromatic absorptions between 6 and 7 μ, monoaryl- and 1,1'-diarylferrocenes exhibit a medium intensity band near 11.25 μ, which is quite characteristic of these substances, and may be associated with a C—H bending mode on the ferrocene ring. By contrast, the homoannularly substituted diaryl derivatives do not exhibit absorption at 11.25 μ, but instead the 1,2 isomers have a medium intensity peak near 10.85 μ, while the 1,3 derivatives are characterized by doublet absorption at 11.05 and 11.15 μ (45, 48).

Table 6-2

Ultraviolet Absorption Bands of Arylferrocenes

SUBSTITUENT	ABSORPTION BANDS AND MOLAR EXTINCTIONS[a]					REFERENCE
Phenyl	238 (17,600)	278 (10,600)	310[b]	447 (330)		16, 49, 57
1,1'-Diphenyl	239 (24,700)	281 (16,500)	335[b]	453 (569)		16, 49, 57
1,2-Diphenyl	238 (21,800)	263 (11,800)[c]	320 (1780)[c]	446 (297)		49
1,3-Diphenyl	248 (28,200)	275 (14,300)[c]	355 (2620)[c]	465 (498)		49
p-Chlorophenyl	243 (18,150)	281 (13,800)	315[b]	450 (346)		49, 57
1,1'-p-Chlorophenyl	346 (27,900)	280 (17,300)	335[b]	457 (772)		51, 57
p-Methoxyphenyl	243 (18,000)	282 (14,500)	—	454 (307)		22, 49
1,1'-p-Methoxyphenyl	244 (25,000)	279 (20,400)	340[b]	454 (536)		49
1,2-p-Methoxyphenyl	247 (25,100)	275 (15,000)[c]	330[b]	450 (307)		49
1,3-p-Methoxyphenyl	255 (37,300)	300[b]	340[b]	465 (488)		49
5,4'-Dimethoxy-2-biphenylyl	237 (27,500)	284 (16,500)	d	d		49
p-Acetylphenyl	266 (9850)	304 (16,280)	376 (2290)	466 (1130)		49
1,1'-p-Acetylphenyl	286 (30,000)	308 (19,000)[b]	390 (4220)	465 (2000)[b]		49
1,2-p-Acetylphenyl	264 (21,600)	291 (25,500)	363 (3440)	460 (1540)		49
1,3-p-Acetylphenyl	300 (31,000)		407 (7520)	480 (2630)[c]		49
p-Nitrophenyl	228 (16,500)	280[b]	329 (12,700)	404 (2500)	507 (2800)	16, 22, 49, 57
1,1'-p-Nitrophenyl	224 (18,800)	290[b]	317 (22,200)	460 (4700)		22, 51
m-Nitrophenyl[e,f]	—	No clearly defined maxima				25

Compound						Reference
p-Aminophenyl[e,f]	248	287	—	445		25
p-Acetamidophenyl[e,f]	255	290	—	438		25
p-Benzamidophenyl[e,f]	—	281	—	427		25
p-Benzalaminophenyl[e,f]	247	290	—	460		25
p-Hydroxyphenyl	242 (15,900)	280 (12,800)	345 (294)[b]	446 (294)		25, 54, 57
p-Carbethoxyphenyl	—	—	362 (3100)	456 (1180)		16
Tris-p-biphenylyl	—	273 (35,000)	363 (5840)[c]	—		56
α-Naphthyl	225 (50,000)	279 (6450)	302 (7400)	356 (1500)	446 (330)	15
1,2-Perinaphthyl	229 (43,600)	290 (13,200)	321 (6800)	420 (1600)	485 (1800)	15
1-p-Methoxyphenyl-1'-p-nitrophenyl	230 (17,000)[c]	284 (14,600)	325 (8980)	410 (1820)[c]	520 (1760)	49
1-p-Methoxyphenyl-2-p-nitrophenyl	240 (22,000)	280 (12,600)	310[b]	400 (2040)[c]	495 (1740)	49
1-p-Methoxyphenyl-3-p-nitrophenyl	245 (19,000)	290 (18,300)	350 (10,600)[b]	405 (4000)[b]	510 (2820)	49
5-Methoxy-4'-nitro-2-biphenylyl	215 (36,700)	280 (20,540)	340[b]	440 (710)		50
2-Methoxy-4'-nitro-5-biphenyl	245 (18,900)	286 (24,800)	340[b]	440 (745)		50

a Unless otherwise noted, all spectra were determined in 95% ethanol solution.
b Peak appears as an inflection and its extinction coefficient and position cannot be accurately determined.
c Peak appears as a broad shoulder and its position is uncertain.
d No data available.
e Taken in methylene chloride solution.
f Only absorption curve and λ_{max} were given.

Ultraviolet absorption spectra

Arylferrocenes generally exhibit four absorption peaks in their ultra-violet spectra. Two of these lie between 220 and 330 mμ and are of high intensity (ε, 10,000 to 20,000), while two others of much lower intensity (ε, 3000 to 4000) are to be found in the region of 335 to 460 mμ. Very similar short wavelength peaks are said to be present in the spectrum of ferrocene itself, but appear to be largely obscured by high intensity end absorption (54). The two short wavelength bands are probably associated with electronic transitions from levels in which metal orbitals make significant contributions to bonding or antibonding levels largely localized on the cyclopentadienyl rings. The two long wavelength bands are most reasonably attributed to metal *d-d* type transitions, but some mixing of ring orbitals in the unfilled level must be assumed in order to account for the moderate bathochromic shifts of these bands when electron withdrawing groups are substituted on the phenyl ring.

Spectral data for a series of arylferrocenes are given in Table 6-2. Included are data for several isomeric diarylferrocenes which illustrate several further general points of interest. With the exception of the *p*-acetylphenylferrocenes, the spectrum of each of the heteroannularly disubstituted arylferrocenes closely resembles that of the corresponding monoaryl derivative, suggesting little effective conjugation between the rings (16, 49). Even the spectrum of the diarylferrocene (32), in which cross conjugation of the substituent groups might be expected to be most favored, can be very closely reproduced by summing the spectra of the component monoarylferrocenes (33 and 34) (49). By contrast, resonance interactions between the substituents in 1,3 diarylferrocenes are clearly

(32)

(33)

(34)

evident from a comparison of their spectra with that of the related 1,1′ isomers. Steric crowding in the 1,2 isomers, which prevents both benzene rings from being simultaneously coplanar with the cyclopentadienyl ring, is reflected in the hypsochromic shift and relatively low absorption coefficient of the band near 280 mμ in the spectra of these substances.

Nuclear magnetic resonance spectra

The n.m.r. spectra of arylferrocenes are, in general, straightforwardly interpretable on the basis of first-order spin-splitting approximations, and constitute a valuable source of structural information (50). Moreover, the inherent rigidity of the metallocene nucleus makes these derivatives particularly well suited for the examination of diamagnetic anisotropies.

Table 6-3

N.M.R. Absorption of Monoarylferrocenes

R	CHEMICAL SHIFTS $(\tau)^{\text{a}}$		
	$C_{2,5}$	$C_{3,4}$	$C_{1'-5'}$
—NO$_2$	5.25 t	5.52 t	5.95 s
—COCH$_3$	5.30 t	5.61 t	5.96 s
—H	5.38 t	5.72 t	5.97 s
—Cl	5.44 t	5.71 t	5.99 s
—OCH$_3$	5.45 t	5.76 t	5.98 s

[a] Determined in CDCl$_3$, at a concentration of approximately 60 mg./cc., at 60 mc.; s, singlet and t, triplet.

In general, the aryl substituent deshields both the protons of $C_{2,5}$ and $C_{3,4}$ of the substituted ring, but the effect is more pronounced for protons at $C_{2,5}$. Adjacent and cross-ring coupling constants ($J_{2,3}$ and $J_{2,4}$, respectively) are very nearly equal and considerably smaller than the chemical shift difference between the two pairs of protons, so that these appear as unsymmetrical triplets corresponding to an A_2X_2 set. Data for several *p*-substituted phenylferrocenes are given in Table 6-3. As can be seen from the table, the chemical shift of protons in the unsubstituted cyclopentadienyl ring does not vary significantly, and is quite close to that observed in ferrocene (5.96 τ). A much greater variation in chemical shifts is evident for protons in the substituted ring. In fact, the chemical shifts for each of these pairs of protons show a fairly good correlation with the Hammett σ constant for the p-substituents in the aryl group.

Spectral data for several isomeric diarylferrocenes are recorded in Table 6-4. The structures of the homoannularly substituted derivatives are

Table 6-4

N.M.R. Absorption of Diarylferrocenes

			CHEMICAL SHIFTS $(\tau)^{a}$				
R	R'	Isomer	C_2	C_3	C_4	C_5	$C_{1'-5'}$
H	H	1,1'	5.55 t	5.80 t	5.80 t	5.55 t	—
		1,2	—	5.45 d	5.63 t	5.45 d	5.90 s
		1,3	4.85 t	—	5.15 d	5.15 d	6.08 s
OCH_3	OCH_3	1,1'	5.60 t	5.83 t	5.83 t	5.60 t	—
		1,2	—	5.55 d	5.72 t	5.55 d	5.95 s
		1,3	4.98 t	—	5.30 d	5.30 d	6.10 s
$COCH_3$	$COCH_3$	1,1'	5.45 t	5.68 t	5.68 t	5.45 t	—
		1,2	—	5.35 d	5.51 t	5.35 d	5.89 s
		1,3	4.72 t	—	5.03 d	5.03 d	6.07 s
OCH_3	NO_2	1,1'	5.60 t	5.78 t	5.78 t	5.60 t	— C_{2-5}
			5.40 t	5.52 t	5.52 t	5.40 t	— $C_{2'-5'}$
		1,2	—	5.52 d	5.55 t	5.41 d	5.89 s
		1,3	4.90 t	—	5.15 d	5.15 t	6.10 s
Br	Br	1,1'	5.56 t	5.78 t	5.78 t	5.56 t	—

^{a} Determined in $CDCl_3$, at a concentration of approximately 60 mg./cc., at 60 mc.; s, singlet, d, doublet, and t, triplet.

uniquely defined by the positions, relative intensities, and splitting patterns of protons in the substituted cyclopentadienyl ring. In the 1,2-diarylferrocenes, the equivalent protons at $C_{3,5}$ give rise to the expected lower field doublet, while the single proton at C_4 appears as a triplet. This pattern is precisely reversed in the 1,3 derivatives.

Although aryl ring-current effects on the chemical shift of protons in the unsubstituted ring of monoarylferrocenes are not discernible, these effects are evident in the homoannularly substituted diaryl derivatives. In the 1,3 derivatives the aryl groups can be coplanar and consequently exert a maximum shielding effect on the protons in the unsubstituted cyclopentadienyl ring. Steric hindrance precludes such an arrangement in the 1,2 derivatives, and these protons are instead slightly deshielded by the aryl substituents.*

The biphenyl derivatives (**35** and **36**) are of particular interest in this context since the mutual anisotropy effects of the aryl rings and the metallocene nucleus is detectable in these substances. In the *o*-biphenylyl derivative, models indicate that the *p*-nitrophenyl ring rides over the top of the cyclopentadienyl ring as shown in **37**. In these conformations the $C_{2,5}$ protons and, to a lesser extent, the $C_{3,4}$ protons of this ring are in the shielding volume associated with the *p*-nitrophenyl ring, and their shift to higher field is readily apparent by a comparison of the chemical shifts of these protons in **35** and **36** (τ values for all protons are indicated in the figures). The region above the cyclopentadienyl ring is apparently also shielding so that protons in the *ortho* and *meta* positions of the

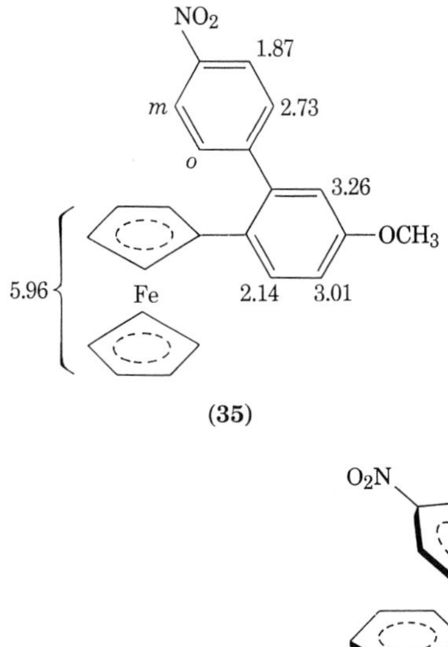

(35)

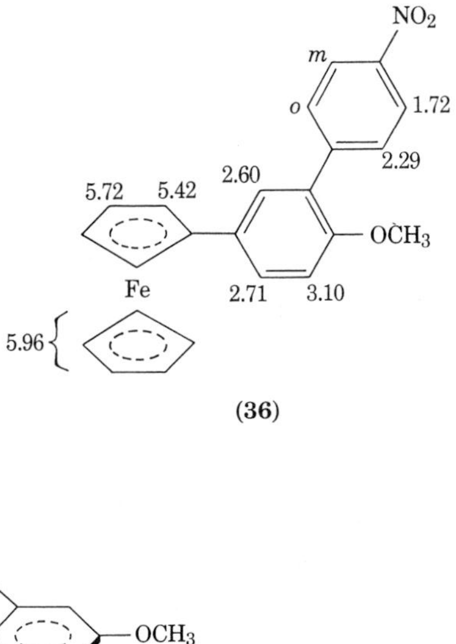

(36)

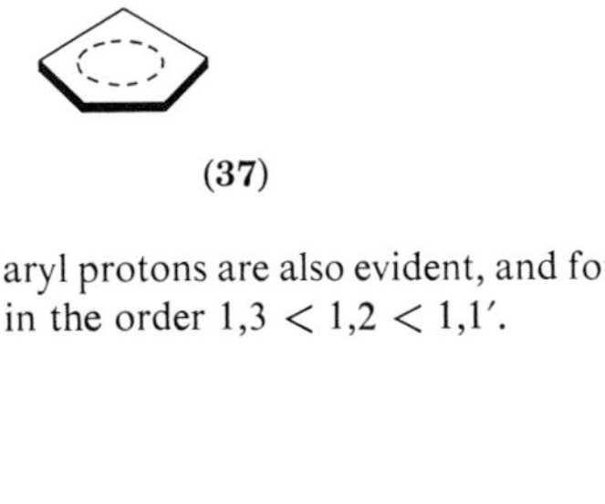

(37)

* Mutual shielding effects of aryl protons are also evident, and for both *o* and *m* protons in diarylferrocenes increases in the order 1,3 < 1,2 < 1,1'.

p-nitrophenyl group in **35** are similarly shifted to higher field. By contrast, the single *ortho* proton in the *p*-methoxyphenyl ring of **35**, which is constrained to a region between the two cyclopentadienyl rings, is evidently highly deshielded. These observations define a molecular diamagnetic anisotropy which is in accord with the relative principal susceptibilities recently determined by Mulay and Fox (19, 20).

PREFACE TO TABLE 6-5

Organization

Aryl derivatives are listed in the following order: phenylferrocenes; derivatives in which the phenyl ring is substituted by alkyl, acyl, carboxy, nitrogen, oxygen and halogen; mixed aryl derivatives; biphenyl, phenylene, naphthyl and heteroaromatic derivatives; aryl derivatives of alkyl, acyl and carboxyferrocenes.

Mono-, di- and polyarylferrocenes with identical aryl substituents are grouped together.

Melting points

In general the highest melting point reported in the literature is given, except where there appears to be agreement from several independent sources on a lower value. In cases where substantial differences occur in the literature, both values are recorded.

Refractive indices

Where two or more values of the index of refraction at the same temperature are reported, the upper and lower values are given. The temperature at which the refractive index was determined is given in parentheses.

Footnotes

[a] From substituted cyclopentadiene.
[b] From diazonium salt reaction.
[c] From diferrocenylmercury.
[d] By electrophilic substitution of an arylferrocene.
[e] By chemical transformation of an arylferrocene.
[f] By substitution of an arylferricenium salt.
[g] Probably a mixture of isomers.
[h] No structure given.
[i] From ferrocenyllithium.

Table 6-5
Arylferrocenes

SUBSTITUENT	M.P.	B.P. AND INDEX OF REFRACTION	METHOD OF SYNTHESIS	LITERATURE REFERENCE
$-C_6H_5$	114–115	—	a	35, 57
			b	4, 46, 48, 57
			c	40, 41
$1,1'-C_6H_5$	156–157	—	a	35
			b	4, 46, 48, 57
$1,2-C_6H_5$	109–110	—	b	48
$1,3-C_6H_5$	107	—	a	8
$1,1',X-C_6H_5$	116–118	—	b	4
$1,3,1',3'-C_6H_5$	220–222	—	a	8, 35
Penta-$C_6H_5{}^h$	240–245	—	b	22
$1,2,4,1',2',4'-C_6H_5$	227–228	—	a	35
$1,2,3,4,1',2',3',4'-C_6H_5$	322	—	a	57
$-C_6H_4CH_3\text{-}o$	51–52	—	b	4, 15
$-C_6H_4CH_3\text{-}p$	139–140	—	b	22, 38
$1,1'-C_6H_4CH_3\text{-}p$	168–169	—	b	38
$-C_6H_4CH_2CH_2CHCO_2H\text{-}p$ $\quad\quad\|$ $\quad\quad NH_2$	>300	—	e	52
$-C_6H_4CH_2CH_2CHCO_2H\text{-}p$ $\quad\quad\|$ $\quad\quad NHCHO$	190–194 (dec.)	—	e	52

Table 6-5 (Contd.)
Arylferrocenes

SUBSTITUENT	M.P.	B.P. AND INDEX OF REFRACTION	METHOD OF SYNTHESIS	LITERATURE REFERENCE
$-C_6H_4CH_2C(CO_2C_2H_5)-p$ NHCHO	165–164	—	b	52
$-C_6H_4CH_2OH-o$	65–66	—	b	15
$-C_6H_4C(OH)-Ph_2$	129–131	—	e	15
$-C_6H_4CF_3-m$	97.5–98	—	b	15
$-C_6H_4COCH_3-p$	176–178	—	b	46, 48
$1,1'-C_6H_4COCH_3-p$	243–245 (dec.)	—	b	46, 48
$1,2-C_6H_4COCH_3-p$	146–147	—	b	48
$1,3-C_6H_4COCH_3-p$	202–204	—	b	48
$-C_6H_4CO_2H-o$	128–129	—	b	4, 15, 24, 27
$-C_6H_4CO_2CH_3-o$	74–75	—	b	15, 24
$1,1'-C_6H_4CO_2H-o$	195	—	b	57
$-C_6H_4CO_2H-m$	166–169	—	b	15
$-C_6H_4CO_2CH_3-m$	70–71	—	b	15

—C$_6$H$_4$CO$_2$C$_2$H$_5$-m	82–83	—	b	15
—C$_6$H$_4$CO$_2$CH(C$_6$H$_5$)$_2$-m	150.5–151.5	—	b	15
—C$_6$H$_4$CO$_2$H-p	253–257 (dec.)	—	b	24, 27
—C$_6$H$_4$CO$_2$CH$_3$-p	124–125	—	e	15
—C$_6$H$_4$CO$_2$C$_2$H$_5$-p	88–90	—	b	24
—C$_6$H$_4$CO$_2$CH(C$_6$H$_5$)$_2$-p	132.5–133	—	b	15
—C$_6$H$_4$CN-p	145–146	—	b	15
—C$_6$H$_4$NH$_2$-m	117–118	—	e	11, 25
—C$_6$H$_4$N=CHC$_6$H$_5$-m	145–146	—	e	25
—C$_6$H$_4$NHCOC$_6$H$_5$-m	207.0–209.5	—	e	11
—C$_6$H$_4$NH$_2$-p	159–160.5	—	e	11, 25
—C$_6$H$_4$NH$_2$·HCl-p	165–170 (dec.)	—	e	25
—C$_6$H$_4$N=CHC$_6$H$_5$-p	151–152.5	—	e	25
—C$_6$H$_4$N=CHC$_6$H$_5$-p·HCl	173–180 (dec.)	—	e	25
—C$_6$H$_4$NHCOCH$_3$-p	300–302 (dec.)	—	e	25
—C$_6$H$_4$NHCOC$_6$H$_5$-p	222–223	—	e	25
—NHSO$_2$⟨⟩NHCOCH$_3$·⟨CH$_3$,CH$_3$⟩	189.5–191 (dec.)	—	e	25
1,1′—C$_6$H$_4$NH$_2$-p	203–206	—	e	26
1,1′—C$_6$H$_4$N=CHC$_6$H$_5$-p	222–223	—	e	26

Table 6-5 (Contd.)
Arylferrocenes

SUBSTITUENT	M.P.	B.P. AND INDEX OF REFRACTION	METHOD OF SYNTHESIS	LITERATURE REFERENCE
N=N (phenylazo)	109.8–111.8	—	e	11
N=N	122.8–123.8	—	b, e	11
N=N (CH_3)	180.8–181.8	—	e	11
N=N (CF_3)	116.5–118	—	e	11
N=N (OCH_3)	182–184	—	e	13
N=N (NO_2)	166–168	—	e	11

(4-NO_2-phenyl)–N=N–(phenyl)	260 (dec.)	—	e	11
(3-Cl-phenyl)–N=N–(phenyl)	66.0–68.5	—	e	11
(4-Cl-phenyl)–N=N–(phenyl)	118–119	—	e	11
(2-Cl-phenyl)–N=N–(phenyl)	134.0–135.5	—	e	11
(3-Cl-phenyl)–N=N–(phenyl)	134–136	—	e	11
(4-Cl-phenyl)–N=N–(phenyl)	217.5–218.7	—	e	11
(4-Br-phenyl)–N=N–(phenyl)	117–119	—	e	11

Table 6-5 (Contd.)
Arylferrocenes

SUBSTITUENT	M.P.	B.P. AND INDEX OF REFRACTION	METHOD OF SYNTHESIS	LITERATURE REFERENCE
(C$_6$H$_4$ azo compound, para-Br)	216.5–218	—	e	11
(C$_6$H$_4$ azo compound, meta-I)	153–155	—	e	11
(C$_6$H$_4$ azo compound, para-I)	196–197.5	—	e	11
—C$_6$H$_4$NO$_2$-o	112–114	—	b	4
—C$_6$H$_4$NO$_2$-m	84–85	—	b	25
—C$_6$H$_4$NO$_2$-p	169–170	—	b	4, 21, 22, 57
			d	30
1,1'—C$_6$H$_4$NO$_2$-p	> 300 (dec.)	—	b	21, 22, 57
(dimethyl-nitro substituted C$_6$H$_2$: CH$_3$, CH$_3$, O$_2$N)	68–69.5	—	b	15

CH$_3$, CH$_3$, NO$_2$ (trimethyl-nitro arene)	160–161	—	b	15
CH$_3$, NO$_2$ (methyl-nitro arene)	127–129	—	b	15
CH$_3$, NO$_2$ (methyl-nitro arene)	101–102	—	b	15
CH$_3$, NO$_2$ (methyl-nitro arene)	129–131	—	b	15
—C$_6$H$_4$OCH$_3$-o	44–45	—	b	15
—C$_6$H$_4$OC$_2$H$_5$-o	72–73	—	b	15
—C$_6$H$_4$OH-p	165	—	b	4, 25, 56
—C$_6$H$_4$OCH$_3$-p	112–114	—	b	4, 22, 48

Table 6-5 (Contd.)

Arylferrocenes

SUBSTITUENT	M.P.	B.P. AND INDEX OF REFRACTION	METHOD OF SYNTHESIS	LITERATURE REFERENCE
1,1'—C$_6$H$_4$OCH$_3$-p	172–174	—	e	25
1,2—C$_6$H$_4$OCH$_3$-p	119–121	—	b	4, 48
—	129.5–130.5	—	a, b	48
1,X 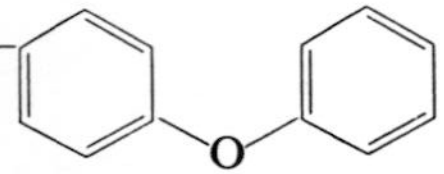		Oil^g	—	7
—C$_6$H$_4$F-o	105.5–107	—	b	15
—C$_6$H$_4$Cl-o	55–56	—	b	15
—C$_6$H$_4$Cl-m	77–78	—	b	4
1,1'—C$_6$H$_4$Cl-m	183–184	—	b	4
—C$_6$H$_4$Cl-p	122	—	b	57
1,1'—C$_6$H$_4$Cl-p	192	—	b	57
—C$_6$H$_4$Br-o	79–80	—	b	15
—C$_6$H$_4$Br-m	85–86	—	b	15
—C$_6$H$_4$Br-p	125	—	b	15, 17
1,1'—C$_6$H$_4$Br-p	197–197.5	—	d	26
—C$_6$H$_4$I-o	59–60	—	b	15

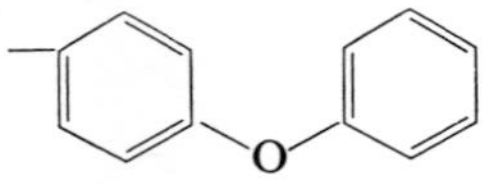

—$C_6H_4SO_3Ba$	—	—	b	4
1—C_6H_5, 1'—$C_6H_4COCH_3$-p	151–152	—	d	46
1—$C_6H_4OCH_3$-p, 1'—$C_6H_4NO_2$-p	214–216	—	b	49
1—$C_6H_4OCH_3$-p, 2—$C_6H_4NO_2$-p	146–148	—	b	49
1—$C_6H_4OCH_3$-p, 3—$C_6H_4NO_2$-p	193–195	—	b	49
1—$C_6H_4OCH_3$-p, 1,X—$C_6H_4NO_2$-p	165.5–167.5	—	b	49
	133–134	—	b	15, 41, 48
	102.5–103	—	b	41, 48
	164–165	—	b	37, 41, 48
	189–191	—	b, e	15
	>300 (dec.)	—	b, e	15
1,2	158–160	—	b	15

Table 6-5 (Contd.)
Arylferrocenes

SUBSTITUENT	M.P.	B.P. AND INDEX OF REFRACTION	METHOD OF SYNTHESIS	LITERATURE REFERENCE
1,1'-X	135–140	—	b	57
OMe	154–155	—	b	48
NO_2	158–159 (double m.p.) 178–180	—	b	49
NO_2	210–212	—	b	49
CO_2H	220	—	b	57

Structure	mp		b/i	Refs.
CO$_2$H (1,1',X)	300 (dec.)	—	b	57
(1,1')	92–93	—	i	33, 53
(1,1')	179–180	—	i	33, 53
	57–59	—	b	53
(1,1')	141–144	—	b	53
	139–141	—	i	53
(1,1')	209–211	—	i	53

Table 6-5 (Contd.)
Arylferrocenes

SUBSTITUENT	M.P.	B.P. AND INDEX OF REFRACTION	METHOD OF SYNTHESIS	LITERATURE REFERENCE
(benzothiazol-2-yl, CH_3)	154–155	—	b	56
(benzothiazol-2-yl, CH_3) 1,1′	240	—	b	56
(benzothiazol-2-yl, CH_3)	185	—	b	56
(benzothiazol-2-yl, CH_3) 1,1′	261	—	b	56
(benzothiazolium dye, CH_2CH_3 / CH_2CH_3) Iodide	252 (dec.)	—	e	57
Bromide	245 (dec.)	—	e	57

Structure (pentamethine cyanine of benzothiazolium):

CH_2CH_3—N⁺(benzothiazole ring, S)—CH=CH—CH=CH—CH—(benzothiazole ring, S)—N—CH_2CH_3

Substituents	Iodide / Bromide, m.p. or b.p. (°C)	n_D / density	Footnote	Refs.
1—C_6H_5, 1'—CH_3	Iodide 265 (dec.); Bromide 257 (dec.)	—	e, e	57, 57
1—C_6H_5, 1'—CH_2CH_3	88–89	—	b	30, 38
1—C_6H_5, 1'—$CH_2N(CH_3)_2$	—	1.6470(20)[g]	b	38
1—C_6H_5, 1'—$CH_2N(CH_3)_3I^-$	150–160/3	(1.6315)[g]	d	30
1—C_6H_5, 2 or 3—$CH_2N(CH_3)_3I^-$	90–95	—	d, e	30, 31
1—C_6H_5, 2 or 3—$CH_2N(CH_3)_3I^-$	167–170	—	d, e	31
1,1'—C_6H_5, 3—CH_2CH_3	143–145	—	d, e	31
1—C_6H_5, 2 or 3—CN	88–90	—	e	47
1—C_6H_5, 2 or 3—$CONH_2$	155.5–156.5 (dec.)	[g]	f	32
1—C_6H_5, 2 or 3—$CONH_2$	—	—	e	32
1—$C_6H_4CH_3$-p, 1'—$CH_2N(CH_3)_3I^-$	95–99	—	d, e	31
1—$C_6H_4CH_3$-p, 2 or 3—$CH_2N(CH_3)_3I^-$	172–175	—	d, e	31
1—$C_6H_4NO_2$-p, 1'—CN	134–135	—	f	32
X—$C_6H_4NO_2$-p, 1,1'—CO_2CH_3	140–141	—	b	38
X—$C_6H_4NO_2$-p, 1,1'—CO_2CH_3	163–165	—	b	38
1—$C_6H_4NO_2$-p, 2 or 3—CO_2CH_3	151–153	—	b	38

Table 6-5 (Contd.)
Arylferrocenes

SUBSTITUENT	M.P.	B.P. AND INDEX OF REFRACTION	METHOD OF SYNTHESIS	LITERATURE REFERENCE
1—$C_6H_4NO_2$, 1'—$COCH_3$	122–123	—	b	38
1—$C_6H_4NO_2$-p, 2 or 3—$COCH_3$	158–160	—	b	38
1'—CH_3	37–38	—	i	53
2—CH_3	Oil	—	i	53
3—CH_3	Oil	100–105/0.06	i	53

_a — the pyridine ring structure is shown at the 1-position.

a From substituted cyclopentadiene.
b From diazonium salt reaction.
c From diferrocenylmercury.
d By electrophilic substitution of an arylferrocene.
e By chemical transformation of an arylferrocene.
f By substitution of an arylferricenium salt.
g Probably a mixture of isomers.
h No structure given.
i From ferrocenyllithium.

REFERENCES

1. Beckwith, A. L. J., and R. J. Leydon, *Tetrahedron Letters*, **6**, 385 (1963).
2. Benkeser, R. A., D. Goggin, and G. Schroll, *J. Am. Chem. Soc.*, **76**, 4025 (1954).
3. Bozak, R. E., and K. L. Rinehart, *J. Am. Chem. Soc.*, **84**, 1589 (1962).
4. Broadhead, G. D., and P. L. Pauson, *J. Chem. Soc.*, 367 (1955).
5. For leading references, see G. E. Coates, *Organo-Metallic Compounds*, Methuen and Co., Ltd., London, Second Edition, 1960, p. 81, and reference 41.
6. Evans, J. C. W., and C. F. H. Allen, *Org. Syntheses*, Coll. Vol. 2, 517 (1943).
7. Goldberg, S. I., *J. Org. Chem.*, **25**, 482 (1960).
8. Hallam, B. F., and P. L. Pauson, *J. Chem. Soc.*, 3030 (1956).
9. Kochi, J. K., *Tetrahedron Letters*, **18**, 483 (1962).
10. Kochi, J. K., *J. Am. Chem. Soc.*, **84**, 774 (1962).
11. Little, W. F., and A. K. Clark, *J. Org. Chem.*, **25**, 1979 (1960).
12. Little, W. F., and R. Eisenthal, *J. Org. Chem.*, **26**, 3609 (1961).
13. Little, W. F., R. A. Berry, and P. Kannan, *J. Am. Chem. Soc.*, **84**, 2525 (1962).
14. Little, W. F., K. N. Lynn, and R. Williams, *J. Am. Chem. Soc.*, **85**, 3055 (1963).
15. Little, W. F., B. Nielsen, and R. Williams, *Chem. & Ind.* (*London*), 195 (1964).
16. Lundquist, R. T., and M. Cais, *J. Org. Chem.*, **27**, 1167 (1962).
17. Mason, J. G., and M. Rosenblum, *J. Am. Chem. Soc.*, **82**, 4206 (1960).
18. McDaniel, D. H., and H. C. Brown, *J. Org. Chem.*, **23**, 420 (1958).
19. Mulay, L. N., and Sr. Mary Eleanor Fox, *J. Am. Chem. Soc.*, **84**, 1308 (1962).
20. Mulay, L. N., and M. E. Fox, *J. Chem. Phys.*, **38**, 760 (1963).
21. Nesmeyanov, A. N., E. G. Perevalova, R. V. Golovnya, and O. A. Nesmeyanov, *Doklady Akad. Nauk SSSR*, **97**, 459 (1954).
22. Nesmeyanov, A. N., E. G. Perevalova, and R. V. Golovnya, *Doklady Akad. Nauk SSSR*, **99**, 539 (1954).
23. Nesmeyanov, A. N., E. G. Perevalova, and R. V. Golovnya, *Doklady Akad. Nauk SSSR*, **103**, 81 (1955).
24. Nesmeyanov, A. N., Referatenband XIV Internationaler Kongress für Reine und Angewandte Chemie, Zürich, 1955, p. 193.
25. Nesmeyanov, A. N., E. G. Perevalova, R. V. Golovnya, and L. S. Shilovtseva, *Doklady Akad. Nauk SSSR*, **102**, 535 (1955).
26. Nesmeyanov, A. N., E. G. Perevalova, R. V. Golovnya, N. A. Simukova, and O. V. Starovsky, *Izvest. Akad. Nauk SSSR, Otdel. Khim. Nauk*, 638 (1957).
27. Nesmeyanov, A. N., *Proc. Royal Soc.*, **246A**, 495 (1958).
28. Nesmeyanov, A. N., et al., *Doklady Akad. Nauk SSSR*, **133**, 851 (1960).
29. Nesmeyanov, A. N., and E. G. Perevalova et al., *Ber.*, **93**, 2729 (1960).
30. Nesmeyanov, A. N., et al., *Doklady Akad. Nauk SSSR*, **139**, 888 (1961).
31. Nesmeyanov, A. N., E. G. Perevalova, and L. S. Shilovtseva, *Izvest. Akad. Nauk SSSR, Otdel. Khim. Nauk*, 1767 (1962).
32. Nesmeyanov, A. N., E. G. Perevalova, L. P. Yur'eva, and K. I. Grandberg, *Izvest. Akad. Nauk SSSR, Otdel. Khim. Nauk*, 1772 (1962).
33. Nesmeyanov, A. N., V. A. Sazonova, and V. A. Gerasimenko, *Doklady Akad. Nauk SSSR*, **147**, 634 (1962).
34. Pausacker, K. N., *Australian J. Chem.*, **11**, 509 (1958).
35. Pauson, P. L., *J. Am. Chem. Soc.*, **76**, 2187 (1954).
36. Pauson, P. L., *Quart. Rev.*, No. 4 (1955), p. 391.
37. Pauson, P. L., private communication.

38. Perevalova, E. G., N. A. Simukova, T. V. Nikitina, P. D. Reshetov, and A. N. Nesmeyanov, *Izvest. Akad. Nauk SSSR, Otdel. Khim. Nauk*, **77** (1961).
39. Rausch, M. D., E. O. Fischer, and H. Grubert, *J. Am. Chem. Soc.*, **82**, 76 (1960).
40. Rausch, M. D., *J. Am. Chem. Soc.*, **82**, 2080 (1960).
41. Rausch, M. D., *Inorg. Chem.*, **1**, 414 (1962).
42. Rinehart, K. L., K. L. Motz, and S. Moon, *J. Am. Chem. Soc.*, **79**, 2749 (1952).
43. Rogers, M., private communication.
44. Rosenblum, M., Thesis, Harvard University, 1953.
45. Rosenblum, M., *Chem. & Ind. (London)*, 953 (1958).
46. Rosenblum, M., *J. Am. Chem. Soc.*, **81**, 4530 (1959).
47. Rosenblum, M., and W. G. Howells, *J. Am. Chem. Soc.*, **184**, 1167 (1962).
48. Rosenblum, M., W. G. Howells, A. K. Banerjee, and C. Bennett, *J. Am. Chem. Soc.*, **84**, 2726 (1962).
49. Rosenblum, M., J. O. Santer, and W. G. Howells, *J. Am. Chem. Soc.*, **85**, 1450 (1963).
50. Rosenblum, M., and R. W. Fish, unpublished results.
51. Rosenblum, M., and W. G. Howells, unpublished observations.
52. Schlögl, K., *Monatsch.*, **88**, 601 (1957).
53. Schlögl, K., and M. Fried, *Monatsch.*, **94**, 537 (1963).
54. Scott, D. R., and R. S. Becker, *J. Chem. Phys.*, **35**, 516 (1962).
55. Semenov, D. A., and J. D. Roberts, *J. Am. Chem. Soc.*, **79**, 2741 (1957).
56. Ushenko, I. K., K. D. Zhikhareva, and F. Z. Rodova, *Zh. Obshch. Khim.*, **33**, 798 (1963).
57. Weinmayr, V., *J. Am. Chem. Soc.*, **77**, 3012 (1955).
58. Wells, P. R., *Chem. Rev.*, **63**, 171 (1963).

Index